CUT HERE

THE RED BOOK OF UNITED STATES COINS

— *1964* —

A GUIDE BOOK
of
UNITED STATES COINS

17th Revised Edition

Fully Illustrated
Catalog and Price List — 1616 to Date

By R. S. YEOMAN

Including . . .

A BRIEF HISTORY OF AMERICAN COINAGE
EARLY AMERICAN COINS AND TOKENS
EARLY MINT ISSUES • REGULAR MINT ISSUES
PRIVATE, STATE AND TERRITORIAL GOLD
SILVER AND GOLD COMMEMORATIVE ISSUES
PROOFS

WEHMAN BROS.
PUBLISHERS
158 MAIN STREET
HACKENSACK, N. J.

Copyright © MCMLXIII by
WHITMAN PUBLISHING COMPANY
RACINE, WISCONSIN
Printed in U.S.A. by Western Printing and Lithographing Company

9051

CONDITION OF COINS

FAIR. Coin has sufficient design and letters to be easily identified. Excessive wear.

G. or **GOOD.** All of design, every feature and legend must be plain and date clear.

V. G. or **VERY GOOD.** Features all clear and bold. Better than good, but not quite fine.

F. or **FINE.** Obviously a circulated coin but little wear. Mint lustre gone. All letters in LIBERTY and mottoes clear.

V. FINE or **VERY FINE.** Shows enough wear on high spots to be noticable. Still retains enough lustre to be desirable.

EX. FINE or **EXTREMELY FINE.** Slightly circulated with some lustre but faint evidence of wear.

UNC. or **UNCIRCULATED.** New. Regular mint striking, but never placed in circulation. Older pieces may be tarnished or "toned."

PF. or **PROOF.** Coins with mirror-like surface, specially struck at Philadelphia only, for coin collectors. Also sandblast and matte proof. See Page 60.

Coins from Branch mints having a mirror-like surface are not proofs but are first strikings of new dies.

IMPORTANT: Coins in any condition with defects, such as those which are bent, corroded, scratched, holed, nicked, stained, oxidized, mutilated, or have other imperfections are worth less than if free of these defects.

THE SPANISH MILLED DOLLAR
The Coin of Our Nation's Founders

The Spanish milled dollar valued at eight reales, otherwise known as the "pillar dollar" and "piece of eight," has been given a place in romantic fiction unequalled by any other coin.

This time-honored piece, along with its fractional parts, such as two reales and four reales, was the chief coin of the American Colonists and was the forerunner of our own silver dollar and its fractional divisions, such as the quarter-dollar and half-dollar.

THE PURPOSE OF THIS BOOK

Coin values listed in the Guide Book are averaged from data supplied by contributors several months before publication. The coin market is so active in some categories that values can easily change during this period. Prices are shown as a guide and are not intended to serve as a price-list for any dealer's stock.

Prices rise because: 1. The trend of our economy is inflationary. 2. The number of collectors is increasing rapidly, while coin supplies remain stationary. 3. Dealers can procure their stock of coins only from collectors or other dealers, who expect a profit over and above what they originally paid.

Prices decline because: 1. Speculators buy and sell in large quantities, drawing in thousands of unwary persons looking for quick profits. When the average collector stops buying, the prices drop. 2. Hoards of coins suddenly are released from estates of deceased collectors or Federal Reserve vaults (as in the case of silver dollars) and the like. Such conditions usually adjust themselves within months or a few years.

Those who edit, contribute to, and publish this book, advocate the collecting of coins for pleasure and educational benefits. A secondary consideration is that of investment, the profits from which are realized over the long term based on intelligent purchases of the best grades of coins.

Neither the publishers, nor the editor, deal in coins; therefore, the prices shown are not offers to sell but are included only as general information.

We thank all contributors to this edition.

R. S. YEOMAN

The Handbook of United States Coins, containing average prices dealers will pay for certain specified coins, is obtainable at hobby dealers for $1.00.

QUANTITIES OF COINS STRUCK

Collectors are cautioned that mint reports are not always reliable for estimating the rarity of coins. In the early years of the mint, dies of previous years were often used until they became worn or broken.

It should also be emphasized that quantities reported, particularly for gold and silver, cover the number of coins struck and have no reference to the quantity reaching actual circulation. Many issues were deposited in the treasury as backing for paper currency and were later melted. There are other similar examples.

The rarity of gold pieces struck before 1834, particularly half eagles, can be traced to the fact that the gold content was reduced in 1834, making previous issues greater in value than their face, causing extensive melting and reminting.

The quantities reported by the mint of three dollar gold pieces from 1873 to 1877 and half cents from 1832 to 1836 are subject to doubt.

Mint quantities are shown adjacent to each date throughout the book.

PROOF TOTALS ARE SHOWN IN PARENTHESES

CONTRIBUTORS TO THE SEVENTEENTH EDITION

KENNETH E. BRESSETT, Co-ordinating Editor

A. E. Bebee	A. M. Kagin	James Ruddy
M. H. Bolender	Paul Kagin	Dick Rudolf
Q. David Bowers	Abe Kosoff	F. K. Saab
Dan Brown	Abner Kreisberg	Earl Schill
Hy Brown	Ken Lee	J. R. Shapiro
Malcolm O. E. Chell-Frost	A. I. Martin	Norm Shultz
Alan Cohen	Ralph Mefford	Leonard Stark
Jerry Cohen	Bill Mertes	Maurice Storck
B. M. Douglas	Franklyn H. Miller	Don Thompson
Ben Dreiske	Ken Nichols	R. E. Wallace
Darvin France	Al Overton	Tom Warfield
Charles French	Earl Parker	Frank Washburn
Bernard Gimelson	Richard Picker	Harold Whiteneck
Garland Hughes	Elmer Ray	Leo Young

Credit is due:
Herbert Bergen, Harry X Boosel (1873), William L. Clark, Alan D. Craig, George Fuld, Gen. M. S. Newton, Hubert L. Polzer, Richard Rogers, Max M. Schwartz, Neil Shafer and Arlie Slabaugh for special data and service in connection with this book.

Those now deceased, but whose contributions have been a part of this book since early editions, include:
David M. Bullowa, Charles E. Green, Richard D. Kenney, Stuart Mosher, Lewis M. Reagan, Herbert E. Rowold, Walter Thompson and Farran Zerbe.

Brief guides to grading are placed before each major coin type in this book. For those readers who desire more detailed descriptions of all coin grades, we recommend A GUIDE TO THE GRADING OF UNITED STATES COINS by Martin R. Brown and John W. Dunn.

ACKNOWLEDGMENT

Selected listings and related material in this edition are from THE STANDARD CATALOGUE OF UNITED STATES COINS and are reproduced with permission of FORD NUMISMATIC PUBLICATIONS, New York, N.Y. For additional data and comparative pricing information see the 18th (last edition) of THE STANDARD CATALOGUE (1957).

AN INTRODUCTION TO UNITED STATES COINS

Money of the Early Americans

The story of American money, which occupies a period of about three centuries, began when the early settlers in New England carried on their fur trade with the Indians through the use of wampum, which had been fashioned from mussel shells in the form of "beads." Beaver skins, wampum, and in Virginia, tobacco, soon became the common accepted media of exchange for all other available commodities. The immigrants, in fact, had little use for coined money at first, but when traders arrived from foreign lands, coins were usually demanded in payment for goods. Any foreign coins were usually accepted, such as French louis, English guineas, German thalers, Dutch ducats, and various Spanish coins, including doubloons and particularly the Spanish milled dollar, or piece of eight. The coin last mentioned remained as a standard money unit throughout the entire colonial period. Even after the Revolutionary War, the Spanish dollar and its fractional parts continued to circulate in this country with official sanction until 1857. One real equaled $12\frac{1}{2}$ cents and was known as a "bit." A quarter of the dollar thus became known as "two bits," a term still in common use.

England consistently ignored the plight of the Colonists and made no effort to provide gold or silver coins, or a small-change currency for them. Although coins known as "Hogge Money" were provided for the Sommer Islands, now known as the Bermudas, about the year 1616, the first coins minted in America were minted by John Hull in the Massachusetts Bay Colony. The General Court of the colony granted him authority to begin coinage. Starting in 1652 the Boston mint provided the famous N.E., pine tree, and similar shillings, with their fractional parts, for the hardpressed colonists. Other colonies tried similar projects but failed.

As time went on coins and tokens of many types were introduced and employed by the colonists in their daily course of business. Lord Baltimore in Maryland was responsible for a series of silver pieces, which were probably struck in England in 1659. Mark Newby introduced a piece known as St. Patrick's Halfpence into the province of New Jersey in 1682. Coins dated 1722 to 1724, known as Rosa Americana and Hibernia coppers, were produced by William Wood in England and were widely circulated in America. The Carolina and New England Elephant tokens were current in the years following 1694. There were also a few issues of uncertain date and origin, such as the New Yorke Token and the New England Stiver which circulated among the Dutch settlers and were probably sent over from Holland.

Enterprising American individuals were responsible for some of the copper pieces which circulated during the eighteenth century. The Gloucester Token, about which little is known, was one of these. John Higley of Granby, Connecticut, made an interesting series of three pence pieces during the period from 1737 to 1739. J. Chalmers, a goldsmith in Annapolis, Maryland, issued silver shillings, sixpence, and three pence pieces in 1783. In 1787 Ephraim Brasher, a New York goldsmith, struck a gold piece of the value of a doubloon (about $16.00). Standish Barry of Baltimore, Maryland, made a curious silver token three pence in 1790.

Still other tokens, struck in England, reached our shores in Revolutionary times and were for the most part speculative ventures. These much-needed, small-denomination coppers were readily circulated because of the great scarcity of fractional coins. Included in this category were the Nova Constellatio coppers and the Bar cent.

During the period of confederation following the War of Independence, still more English tokens were added to the great variety of coins and tokens employed in the new nation. In 1787 the Nova Eboracs, known as New York Coppers, the Georgius Triumpho, the Auctori Plebis, and later the Kentucky, Myddelton and Franklin Press tokens were introduced.

Another interesting series, important because of their close association with our first president, comprises those tokens bearing the portrait of Washington. They circulated during and after the Confederation.

Coinage of the States

The Articles of Confederation, adopted July 9, 1778, provided that Congress should have the sole right to regulate the alloy and value of coin struck by their own authority or by that of the respective states.

Each state, therefore, had the right to coin money, but Congress served as a regulating authority. New Hampshire was the first state to consider coinage, but few if any coins were placed in circulation. The only specimens known bear the date 1776.

Vermont, Connecticut, and New Jersey, granted coining privileges to companies or individuals. Massachusetts erected its own mint in which copper coins were produced. A number of interesting varieties of these state issues, most of which were struck in fairly large quantities, can still be easily acquired, and form the basis for many present day collections of early American coins.

The Beginnings of United States Coinage

Throughout the Colonial years, Americans had become accustomed to the use of the Spanish dollar and its fractional parts, the real, the medio (half-real), etc. It was only natural, therefore, that when a national coinage was under consideration that the dollar was mentioned most frequently. In earlier years currency statutes in many of the colonies had given first consideration to the Spanish dollar. Connecticut, Massachusetts, and Virginia, particularly, passed laws making Spanish coins a legal tender. The first issue of Continental paper money May 10, 1775, offers further evidence that the dollar was to be our basic money unit, for it provided that the notes should be payable in "Spanish Milled dollars or the value thereof in gold or silver."

The Assistant Financier of the Confederation, Gouverneur Morris, proposed a decimal coinage ratio, and his plan was incorporated in a report presented by Robert Morris, Superintendent of Finance, to the Congress, January 15, 1782. Plans for a mint were advanced, and a uniform national currency to relieve the confused money conditions was outlined. Morris's unit, 1/1440 of a dollar, was calculated to agree without a fraction with all the different valuations of the Spanish milled dollar in the various States. Although a government mint was approved February 21, 1782, no immediate action was taken. During 1784 Thomas Jefferson, then a member of the House of Representatives, brought in a report concerning the plan, and expressed disagreement with Morris' complicated money unit. He advocated the simple dollar unit because he believed the dollar was already as familiar and convenient a unit of value as the British pound. He favored the decimal system and remarked that, "The most easy ratio of multiplication and division is that of ten. President George Washington referred to it as 'a measure, which in my opinion, has become indispensibly necessary.' "

The Grand Committee in May 1785 recommended a gold five-dollar piece; a dollar of silver with fractional coins, of the same metal, in denominations of half, quarter, tenth, and twentieth parts of a dollar; and copper pieces valued at one-hundredth and one two-hundredth of a dollar.

In 1783 Robert Morris submitted a series of pattern pieces in silver, which were designed by Dudley to carry out the decimal idea for United

States money. These are known as the Nova Constellatio Patterns and consist of the "Mark" or 1,000 units, the "Quint" or 500 units, and the "Bit" or 100 units. The unit was to be a quarter grain of silver. This was not the first attempt at a dollar coin, for the Continental currency piece of dollar size, dated 1776, had been struck in such metals as brass, pewter, and silver. The variety in silver probably saw limited service as a dollar.

Congress gave formal approval to the basic dollar unit and decimal coinage ratio in its resolution of July 6, 1785, but other more pressing matters delayed further action. Not until the Constitutional Convention had placed the country on firm ground and the new nation had elected George Washington as President, did the congress again turn attention to the subject of currency, a mint, and a coinage system.

The Massachusetts cents and half-cents struck in 1787 and 1788, were the first official coins to bear a stated value in terms of decimal parts of the dollar unit in this country. The cent represented a hundredth part of a Spanish dollar.

The first federally authorized coin was the Fugio Cent, sometimes called the Franklin Cent, as he was supposed to have supplied the design and composed the legends. This piece, similar in design to the Continental Currency dollar of 1776, was privately struck in 1787 by contract with the Government.

Alexander Hamilton, then Secretary of the Treasury, reported his views on monetary matters January 21, 1791. He concurred in all essentials with the decimal subdivisions and multiples of the dollar contained in the earlier resolutions, and urged the use of both gold and silver in our standard money.

Congress passed a resolution March 3, 1791, that a mint be established, and authorized the President to engage artists and procure machinery for the making of coins. No immediate steps were taken, but when Washington delivered his third annual address, he recommended immediate establishment of a mint.

On April 2, 1792, a bill was finally passed providing "that the money of account of the United States should be expressed in dollars or units, dismes or tenths, cents or hundredths, and milles or thousandths; a disme being the tenth part of a dollar, a cent the hundredth part of a dollar, a mille the thousandth part of a dollar . . ."

Denominations specified in the act were as follows:

	Value of	Grains Pure	Grains Standard
Gold Eagle	$10.00	247 - 4/8	270
Gold Half Eagle	5.00	123 - 6/8	135
Gold Quarter Eagle	2.50	61 - 7/8	67 - 4/8
Silver Dollar	1.00	371 - 4/16	416
Silver Half-Dollar	.50	185 - 10/16	208
Silver Quarter-Dollar	.25	92 - 13/16	104
Silver Disme (dime)	.10	37 - 2/16	41 - 3/5
Silver Half-Disme	.05	18 - 9/16	20 - 4/5
Copper Cent	.01	11 pennyweights	
Copper Half-Cent	.005	5½ pennyweights	

The word "pure" meant unalloyed metal; "standard" meant, in the case of gold, 11/12 fine or 11 parts pure metal to one part alloy, which was mixed with the pure metal to improve the wearing qualities of the coins.

The law also provided for free coinage of gold and silver coins at the fixed ratio of 15 to one, and a token coinage of copper cents and half-cents. Under the free coinage provision no charge was to be made for converting gold or silver bullion into coins "weight for weight." At the depositor's option, however, he could demand an immediate exchange of coins for his bullion, for which privilege a deduction of one-half of one per cent was to be imposed.

Washington appointed David Rittenhouse, a well-known philosopher and scientist, as the first Director of the Mint. A mint building was started nearly four months after the passage of the Act of April 2, 1792. It was located on Seventh Street near Arch in Philadelphia.

The first coin struck at the new mint was the half-disme. Several hundred of these pieces were produced during the month of October 1792 before the mint was completed. Washington supplied some of his own private plate to the value of about one hundred dollars for these first mint coins. Dismes also were probably struck at this time or a short while later. The portrait on these pieces is presumed to be modeled by Martha Washington.

Copper for cents and half-cents was covered in the Act of May 8, 1792 when the purchase of not over 150 tons was authorized. On September 11, 1792, six pounds of old copper were purchased, this being the first purchase of copper for coinage, which was probably used for the striking of patterns.

Planchets with upset rims for cents and half-cents were purchased from Boulton of Birmingham, England from 1798 to 1838.

Several pattern coins were prepared in 1792 before regular mint operations commenced. These included the silver center cent by Voigt, a smaller piece than that of regular issue. The small plug of silver, worth about three-quarters of a cent, was evidently intended to bring the intrinsic value of the coin up to the value of one cent and permit production of a coin of more convenient size. Alexander Hamilton had mentioned a year before that the proposed "intrinsic value" cent would be too large, and suggested that the amount of copper could be reduced and a trace of silver added. This pattern cent with a silver center may have been designed to conform to this recommendation.

The cents by Robert Birch are equally interesting. These patterns are identified by their legends which read "LIBERTY PARENT OF SCIENCE AND INDUSTRY" and "TO BE ESTEEMED BE USEFUL." The cent with an eagle on the reverse side belongs among the early patterns devised before regular issues were struck.

The first depositor of silver was the bank of Maryland, which sent $80,715.73 ½ in French coins to the mint July 18, 1794. Moses Brown, a Boston merchant, deposited the first gold in the form of ingots, February 12, 1795, amounting to $2,276.22, receiving silver coin in payment. The first coins transferred to the Treasurer consisted of 11,178 cents on March 1, 1793. The first return of coined silver was made on October 15, 1794, and the first gold coins were delivered July 31, 1795, 744 half-eagles.

File marks on early U. S. Coins are a mint process of weight adjustment.

Regular Mint Issues

Cents and half-cents exclusively were coined during the year 1793, and by 1799 approximately $50,000 in these coins had been placed in circulation. This amount proved insufficient for the requirements of commerce, and small denomination coins of the states and of foreign countries continued in use during the first few years of the nineteenth century.

One of the most serious problems confronting the commercial interests during the early years was the failure of the government to provide a sufficient volume of circulating coins. The fault, contrary to popular opinion at the time, did not lie with any lack of effort on the part of the mint. Other circumstances tended to interfere with the expected steady flow of new coinage into the channels of trade.

Free circulation of United States gold and silver coins was greatly hindered by speculators. The silver dollars, for example, were easily exchanged for worn Spanish dollars of reduced weight and value, which meant the export of most of the new dollars as fast as they were minted, and a complete loss to American trade channels.

Gold coins failed to circulate for similar reasons. The ratio of 15 to 1 between gold and silver was close to the world ratio when Hamilton recommended it, but by 1799 the ratio in European commercial centers had reached 15¾ to 1. At this rate the undervalued gold coins tended to flow out of the country, or were reduced for bullion. After 1800, therefore, United States gold coins were rarely seen in general circulation. As no remedy could be found, coinage of the Eagle and the silver dollar was suspended by President Jefferson in 1804 and 1806 respectively. It is generally conceded that the silver dollar was discontinued in 1804, although the last coins minted for the period were dated 1803.

Lacking gold coins and silver dollars, the half-dollar became the desirable coin for large transactions, bank reserves, and foreign payments. Until 1830, in fact, half-dollars circulated very little as they were mainly transferred from bank to bank. This will account for the relatively good supply of half-dollars of this period which are still available to collectors in better than average condition. A senate committee of 1830 reported that United States silver coins were considered as so much bullion and were accordingly "lost to the community as coins."

There was only a negligible coinage of quarters, dimes, and half-dimes from 1794 to 1834. It has been estimated that there was less than one piece for each person in the country in the year 1830. This period has been described as one of nondescript currency, made up of banknotes, underweight foreign gold coins, foreign silver coins of many varieties, and domestic fractional silver coins. Notes of "wildcat banks" flooded the country before 1830 and were much more common than silver coins.

On June 28, 1834, a new law was passed reducing the weight of standard gold, which had the effect of placing our money on a gold standard. Trade and finance were greatly benefited by this act, which also proved a boon to the gold mines of Georgia and North Carolina. Branch mints in Dahlonega, Georgia, and Charlotte, North Carolina, were established two or three years later to handle the newly-mined gold at the source. The Templeton Ried and Bechtler issues of private gold coins were struck in this area.

The law of January 18, 1837, completely revised and standardized the mint and coinage laws. Legal standards, mint charges, legal tender, mint procedure, tolerance in coin weights, accounting methods, a bullion fund, standardization of gold and silver coins to 900 thousandths fine, and other desirable regulations were covered by the new legislation. Results of importance to the collector were the changes in type for the various coin denominations and the resumption of coinage of the Eagle and silver dollar shortly thereafter.

The political and financial elements underwent a crisis at about this time. The familiar "Jackson Tokens" and fractional notes of banks and commercial establishments completely eclipsed the circulation of metallic currency. This was the era of "shinplasters."

The California gold discovery in 1848 was responsible for an interesting series of private, state, and territorial gold issues in the Western states, culminating in the establishment of a branch mint at San Francisco in 1854.

Two new regular gold issues were adopted in 1849. In that year the double Eagle and gold dollar joined our American family of coins. The California gold fields greatly influenced the world gold market making the exportation of silver profitable. For example, the silver in two half-dollars was worth $1.03½ in gold. The newly introduced gold dollars soon took over the burden and hastened the disappearance of silver coins from trade channels. This was the situation when the new three-cent postage rate brought about the bill authorizing the coinage of the silver three-cent piece in 1851. This was our country's first subsidiary coin, for its value was intrinsically 86% of its face value, an expedient designed to prevent its withdrawal from circulation.

The three-dollar gold piece was authorized by the act of February 21, 1853. Never a popular or necessary coin, it nevertheless was issued regularly until 1889.

On February 21, 1853, fractional silver coins were made subsidiary resulting from the fact that the weight of all silver pieces, excepting the dollar, was reduced. As the coins were now worth less than their face value free coinage of silver was prohibited, and the mint was authorized to purchase its silver requirements on its own account using the bullion fund of the mint, and, according to law, "the profit of said coinage shall be, . . . transferred to the account of the treasury of the United States."

Arrows were placed at the date on all silver coins except three-cent pieces and dollars, and on the quarters and half-dollars rays were added on the reverse side to denote the change of weight. In 1854 the rays were removed, and in 1856 the arrows disappeared. Production of silver coins in large quantities during this period greatly relieved the demands on gold dollars and three-cent pieces. Consequently for the first time in our nation's history there was a sufficient supply of fractional coins in general circulation.

The law of 1857 was designed primarily to reform the copper coinage. No matter how interesting and valuable the large cents and half-cents may have become in the eyes of the modern collector, they were very unpopular with the people and cost the mint too much to produce.

The new law abolished the half-cent piece, and reduced the size and changed the design of the cent. The new eagle or white cent contained 88% copper and 12% nickel. Several hundred were stamped from dies bearing the date 1856, a quantity considered by many to be too large for a pattern issue. Yet, no authority for the issue existed before 1857. Other important effects of the law were the retirement of the Spanish silver coins from circulation, and dispersal of the new cents in such excessive quantities as to create a nuisance to business houses, particularly in the eastern cities. The Indian head device replaced the Eagle in 1859, and in 1864 the weight of the cent was further reduced and its composition changed to a proportion of 95% copper and 5% tin and zinc. This bronze composition has been standard for our cent except for the year 1943. In 1962 the alloy was changed to 95% copper and 5% zinc.

Both Jefferson and Hamilton had contended in their day that the currency of money of small value benefits society. The history of our cent and its daily use proves the soundness of this principle.

Abundance turned to scarcity following the outbreak of the Civil War. Anticipation of a scarcity and depreciation of the paper money was sufficient to induce hoarding. The large volume of greenbacks in circulation caused a premium on gold, and subsidiary silver as a result of the sudden depreciation quickly vanished in the North. Resort was soon made to postage stamps for small change. All types of fractional notes were put out at this time by municipalities and the Government. "Postage currency" became widely used, and in 1863 a great variety of tokens appeared to help fill the vacuum. Like the tokens of 1837 they were of two general classes, tradesman's coins and imitations of legal cents. The latter were usually produced at a profit, many of which were political or patriotic in character, with slogans typical of the times.

The Law of 1864, which effected changes in the cent, provided also for the new bronze two-cent piece. The act, moreover, provided legal tender status for these two coins up to ten times their value. The two-cent piece was the first coin to bear the motto IN GOD WE TRUST. The new coin was readily accepted by the people but proved an unnecessary denomination, going out of fashion and being discontinued only nine years later.

Secretary Chase had issued a great many currency notes of three-cent denomination early in 1865. The nickel interests seized upon this circumstance to fight for a new three-cent coin for redemption of the paper money. A law was quickly passed and signed by the president as of March 3, 1865, providing for a three-cent coin of 75-25 copper-nickel composition. Our country now possessed two types of three-cent pieces. The nickel three-cent piece was struck continuously until 1889; the three-cent silver until 1873.

The new copper-nickel alloy ratio was selected for the five-cent coin, adopted May 16, 1866, to be thereafter known as a "nickel." Again the people had a coin value available in two forms. The silver half-dime, like the three-cent piece, was retired from service in 1873.

The Carson City Mint was established in 1870 as a convenient depository for the miners in that area and operated until 1893.

The Law of March 3, 1871, was a redemption measure and was passed to provide a means for the disposal to the United States Treasury of millions of minor coins, which had accumulated in the hands of postmasters, newsdealers, and others. Small-denomination coins as a result of this new law were placed on an equal footing and could be redeemed when presented in lots of twenty dollars.

There was a general revision of the coinage laws in 1873. Several years of study and debate preceded the final enactment. The legislative history of the bill occupies hundreds of pages of the Congressional Globe, and the result was considered by many a clumsy attempt and a failure. The law has sometimes been referred to as the "Crime of '73." One consequence of the bill, which achieved final enactment February 12, 1873, was the elimination of the silver dollar. In its stead the Trade dollar of greater weight was provided for use in commerce with the Orient in competition with the Mexican dollar. The legal tender provision, which unintentionally gave the trade dollar currency within our borders, was repealed the following year.

The charge for converting standard gold bullion into coin was reduced by the act to one-fifth of one per cent. The same rate was imposed on silver bullion for coining trade dollars only.

It may be a surprise to some collectors to learn that the silver dollar had not circulated to any great extent in the United States after 1803. The coin had been turned out steadily since 1840, but for various reasons such as exportation, melting, and holding in bank vaults, the dollar was virtually an unknown coin. The Law of 1873 in effect demonetized silver and committed our country to a gold standard. The silver mining interests came' to realize what had occurred a little later, and the ensuing quarter century of political and monetary history was filled with their voluble protests. There was a constant bitter struggle for the return to bimetallism.

From an economic point of view the inadequate supply of gold was responsible for a gradual decline in prices throughout the world. This brought about a gradual business depression in our country, particularly in the South and Middle-West. Private silver interests influenced great sections of the West for bimetallism as a remedy for the failing price level. Authorities have concluded that a world-wide adoption of bimetallism would have improved economic conditions, but the United States alone proceeding to place their money on a double standard at the old 16 to 1 ratio would have led only to a worse situation.

Of particular importance to collectors, however, were those features of the Law of 1873 which affected the status and physical properties of the individual coins. The weight of the half-dollar, quarter, and dime, was slightly changed and arrows were placed at the date for the ensuing two years to indicate the difference in weight. Silver three-cent pieces, half-dimes, and two-cent pieces were abolished by the act, and the manufacture of minor coins was restricted to the Mint at Philadelphia.

The next coinage legislation was that of March 3, 1875, which authorized the twenty-cent piece. This denomination was purely an experiment, and the coin was short-lived, for the general public complained about its similarity in design and size to the quarter-dollar. The last twenty-cent pieces were struck in 1878, and all were proofs. No logical reason for this coin's existence has ever been advanced.

The Bland-Allison Act of February 28, 1878, gave the Secretary authority to purchase two to four million dollars worth of silver bullion each month to be coined into silver dollars. The coin, never popular, was produced in minimum quantities. This was not a bimetallic law, nor was it a free coinage act. Strictly speaking it was a subsidiary coinage law, called by some "a wretched compromise."

The North and East so disliked the silver dollar that they found their way back to the Treasury, mostly through tax payments. Secretary Manning transferred ownership to the people and removed them from Treasury holdings by the simple expedient of issuing silver certificates in small bills to effect a wide circulation.

The Bland-Allison Act was repealed in 1890 and the Sherman Act took its place. Under this new law 4,500,000 ounces of silver per month could be paid for with Treasury Notes that were to be legal tender, and redeemable in gold or silver dollars coined from the bullion purchased. Important in this case was the fact that the notes were constantly being redeemed for gold which was mainly exported. The measure was actually a government subsidy for the silver miners and as such it was marked for failure, and was hastily repealed. The Bland-Allison Act and the Sherman Act gave a total of 570 million silver dollars to our monetary stocks.

The "Gold Standard Act" of 1900 gave our country a single standard, but re-affirmed the fiction that the silver dollar is a standard coin. It still enjoys unlimited, legal tender, but is as much a subsidiary coin, practically speaking, as the dime, for its value in terms of standard gold, even before the gold surrender executive order, was far below its face value.

The lapse in coinage after 1904 and until 1921 was due to lack of bullion. Legislation authorizing further metal supplies for silver dollars was not forthcoming until 1918 when the Pittman Act provided silver for the new dollars.

The new type dollar issued from 1921 to 1935 was a commemorative peace coin, which might easily have been a half-dollar. The peace dollar, in fact, was issued without congressional sanction, under the terms of the Pittman Act, which referred to the bullion and in no way affected the design.

Before the first world war the value of gold was equal to the value of gold coined into money. In order to encourage a steady flow of gold to the mints the government (with the exception of the period 1853-1873) had adopted a policy of gratuitous coinage. The cost of converting gold into coin had generally been considered an expense chargeable to the government.

In practice the mint made fine bars for commercial use or mint bars for coinage at its discretion. The bars in later years were stored in vaults and gold or silver certificates issued in place of the coins.

On March 6, 1933 an order was issued by the President prohibiting banks from paying out gold and gold certificates without permission, and gold currency was thus kept for reserve purposes. Gold imports and newly mined domestic gold must now be sold to the government. Gold may not be hoarded, and there is no free domestic gold market. The coinage of all denominations above 50 cents was suspended after 1935.

No important legislation has been placed on the books governing the coinage system since the redemption law of 1879. Our Federal Reserve System has withstood all strains of war and economic disturbances. The rate of issue of the one, five, and ten cent pieces has been greatly accelerated during the twentieth century. Cents particularly are in greater demand because of "odd sum" prices, sales taxes, etc.

By the Law of September 26, 1890, changes in designs of United States coins cannot be made oftener than once every twenty-five years. Since that date, there have been design changes in all denominations and there have been many gold and silver commemorative issues. These factors are largely responsible for the ever increasing interest in coin collecting.

COINS AND TOKENS OF THE
ENGLISH-AMERICAN COLONIES

★ Star Throughout Colonial Section Indicates That Facsimiles Exist.

Copies of certain early American issues were made to provide facsimiles of rare issues that would otherwise be unobtainable. A star has been placed adjacent to such early American coins or tokens, together with the fabricator's name for which corresponding copies are known.

The specimens illustrated are the genuine specimens.

SOMMER ISLANDS (Bermuda)

This coinage, the first struck for the English-American colonies, was issued about 1616. The coins were known as "Hogge Money" or "Hoggies."

The pieces were made of brass or a similar substance lightly silvered, in four denominations; shilling, sixpence, threepence and twopence, represented by Roman numerals. The hog is the main device and appears on the obverse side of each. SOMMER ISLANDS is inscribed within beaded circles. The reverse shows a full-rigged galleon with the flag of St. George on each of four masts.

The islands were named, during this early period, for Sir George Somers who was shipwrecked there in 1609 while enroute to the Virginia Plantation. Shakespeare's "The Tempest" was supposedly based on this incident.

The Bermuda Islands, as they are known today, were named for Juan Bermudez who is believed to have stopped there in 1515. A few hogs which he carried for delivery to the West Indies were left behind. When Somers and his party arrived many years later, the islands were over-run with the beasts, and they served as a welcome source of food for the members of the expedition.

	Good	Fine
Shilling	$210.00	$450.00
Sixpence, Large Portholes	175.00	375.00
Sixpence, Small Portholes	V. Rare	
Threepence	V. Rare	
Twopence	210.00	450.00

Shilling   ★Dickeson

Sixpence   Large Portholes   Small Portholes

Threepence   Twopence

MASSACHUSETTS
New England

The earliest medium of exchange in the New England settlements was wampum The General Court of Massachusetts in 1637 ordered "that wampampege should passe at 6 a penny for any sume under 12 d." Wampum consisted of shells of various colors ground to the size of a grain of corn. A hole was drilled through each piece so they could be strung on leather thongs for convenience, and adornment.

Corn, pelts and bullets were frequently offered in lieu of coins, which were almost non-existent. Currency brought over from England, Holland and other countries tended to flow back across the Atlantic for much needed supplies. The colonists thus thrown on their own resources, dealt with the friendly Indians in kind. In 1661 the law authorizing wampum as legal tender was repealed.

Agitation for a standard coinage reached its height in 1651. England, with a civil war between the Puritans and Royalists on her hands, ignored the colonists, who took matters into their own hands in 1652.

The General Court in 1652 ordered the first metallic currency in the English Americas (The Spaniards had established a mint in Mexico City in 1535), the silver N.E. shillings, and fractional denominations. Silver bullion was procured principally from the West Indies. Joseph Jenks made the die for the first impression at Iron Works (Saugus, Massachusetts) just outside of Boston where the mint was located. John Hull was appointed mint-master; his assistant was Robert Sanderson (or Saunderson). Mint-master Hull received one shilling threepence for every twenty shillings coined as his compensation. This fee was adjusted several times during his term as mint-master.

Note: Early American coins in select condition (V. Fine, Ex. Fine, etc.) are much higher priced as these coins are scarce in these higher grades.

NE Shilling (1652)   ★Wyatt

NE Sixpence (1652)   ★Wyatt   NE Threepence (1652)

	Good	Fine
NE Shilling	$300.00	$700.00
NE Sixpence	———	———
NE Threepence (2 known)	———	———

WILLOW TREE PIECES

The simplicity of the design on the N.E. coins invited counterfeiting and clipping of the edges. Therefore, they were soon replaced by the Willow, Oak and Pine Tree Series.

The "tree" coins were minted about thirty years without change of date; Charles II disapproved of the issues, and mintages dated 1652 could not be easily proven to be unauthorized.

The coinage was abandoned in 1682; a proposal to renew coinage in 1686 was rejected by the General Court.

Willow Tree Shilling (1653-1660)

Willow Tree Sixpence (1653-1660)   Willow Tree Threepence (1653-1660)

	Good	Fine
Willow Tree Shilling	$325.00	$800.00
Willow Tree Sixpence	600.00	———
Willow Tree Threepence (3 known)	———	———

OAK TREE PIECES

Oak Tree Shilling (1660-1667) ★ Wyatt   Oak Tree Sixpence (1660-1667)
Various Die Varieties

Oak Tree Shilling	62.50	125.00
Oak Tree Sixpence	75.00	150.00

OAK TREE PIECES

★ Wyatt

Oak Tree Threepence (1660-1667)

Good $65.00   Fine $110.00

Oak Tree Twopence (1662)

Good $50.00   Fine $100.00

PINE TREE PIECES
Various Die Varieties

★Tatham

Pine Tree Shilling — Large Planchet (1667-1674)

The first pine tree coins were stamped on wide thin planchets. The later issues were narrower and thicker in imitation of English coins.

Pine Tree Shilling — Small Planchet (1675-1682)

Pine Tree Sixpence ★Wyatt   Pine Tree Threepence ★Wyatt

	Good	Fine
Pine Tree Shilling, Large Planchet	$70.00	$150.00
Pine Tree Shilling, Small Planchet	60.00	125.00
Pine Tree Sixpence	50.00	100.00
Pine Tree Threepence	50.00	100.00

GOOD SAMARITAN SHILLING

Although this piece was formerly thought to be a pattern for the 1652 shillings, recent findings show that the known specimens are all fabrications. Three different varieties are known. The most common type was made by Thomas Wyatt, about 1856. The variety pictured here is somewhat older and is probably unique.

Good Samaritan Shilling (Unique)..................... ———

MARYLAND

In 1658 Cecil the second Lord Baltimore and "Lord Proprietor of Maryland" began an issue of coinage. These pieces were made in England.

There were four denominations, shillings, sixpence, fourpence (groat) in silver, and the small copper penny (denarium). The silver coins show the bust of Cecil Calvert (Lord Baltimore) on the obverse, and the Baltimore family arms with the values in Roman numeral form and the legend **CRESCITE ET MULTIPLICAMINI** (Increase and be multiplied) on the reverse. The obverse of the penny is similar, but the reverse has a ducal coronet with two pennants and the inscription **DENARIUM, TERRAE-MARIAE** (Penny, Maryland). Numerous die varieties and patterns exist in this series.

Lord Baltimore Shilling

Fourpence
(Groat)

Sixpence   Penny (denarium)   ★Idler

	Good	Fine
Shilling...	$140.00	$300.00
Sixpence...	125.00	200.00
Fourpence...	190.00	350.00
Penny (Copper) (Ex. Rare)........................	———	———

ST. PATRICK OR MARK NEWBY HALFPENCE
NEW JERSEY

Mark Newby, who came from Dublin, Ireland, in November 1681, brought some halfpence pieces believed by Nelson to have been struck in Dublin in 1678. These were called St. Patrick Halfpence.

The coin received wide currency in the New Jersey Province, having been authorized to pass as legal tender by the general assembly in May 1682.

Many of these have a brass insert at the crown so that when the coin was struck it would appear as though it were a golden crown.

There was also a smaller piece known as a farthing. These copper pieces exist in many die varieties. The obverses show a crowned king kneeling playing a harp. The legend FLOREAT REX (May the King prosper) is separated by a crown. The reverse side of the halfpence shows St. Patrick with a crozier in his left and a trefoil in his right hand, surrounded by people. At his left is a shield. The legend is ECCE GREX (Behold the flock).

The farthing reverse shows St. Patrick driving away reptiles and serpents, as he holds a Metropolitan cross in his left hand. The legend reads QUIESCAT PLEBS (May the people be at ease). Numerous die variations exist.

St. Patrick
Halfpence

St. Patrick
Farthing

	Good	Fine
St. Patrick Halfpence	$30.00	$ 70.00
St. Patrick Farthing, with Brass Plug on Obv	20.00	45.00
St. Patrick Farthing without Brass Plug	20.00	45.00
St. Patrick Farthing, Silver	125.00	225.00

COINAGE OF WILLIAM WOOD
ROSA AMERICANA AND HIBERNIA COINS

William Wood, an Englishman, obtained a patent from George I to make copper tokens for Ireland and the American Colonies.

The first pieces struck were undated; others bear the dates 1722, 1723, 1724 and 1733. The Rosa Americana pieces were issued in three denominations, twopence, penny and halfpennies, and were intended for America. This type had a full-blown rose on the reverse with the words ROSA AMERICANA UTILE DULCI (American Rose — the useful with the pleasant).

The obverse, common to both Rosa Americana and Hibernia pieces, shows the head of George I and the legend GEORGIUS D:G: MAG: BRI: FRA: ET. HIB: REX. (George, by the Grace of God, King of Great Britain, France and Ireland). Rosa Americana tokens were not well received by the American Colonists.

ROSA AMERICANA

	Good	Fine	Ex. F.
Twopence (No Date)	$15.00	$50.00	$100.00
Twopence (No Date) Motto without Label (3 known)	——	——	——

	Good	Fine	Ex. F.
1722 Twopence, Period after REX	15.00	50.00	100.00
1722 Twopence, No Period after REX	15.00	50.00	100.00

	Good	Fine	Ex. F.
1722 Penny UTILE DULCI	15.00	40.00	75.00
1722 Penny VTILE DVLCI	10.00	30.00	55.00

	Good	Fine	Ex. F.
1722 Halfpenny D. G. REX ROSA AMERI. UTILE DULCI	20.00	50.00	90.00
1722 Halfpenny DEI GRATIA REX UTILE DULCI	15.00	30.00	45.00
1722 Halfpenny VTILE DVLCI	——	——	——

ROSA AMERICANA

	Good	Fine	Ex. F.
1723 Twopence	$15.00	$35.00	$75.00

| 1723 Penny | 12.50 | 30.00 | 70.00 |

| 1723 Halfpenny | 12.50 | 27.50 | 65.00 |
| 1723 Halfpenny Uncrowned Rose | 25.00 | 52.50 | 90.00 |

| 1724 Twopence (Pattern) | —— | —— | —— |

ROSA AMERICANA

	Fine	Ex. Fine
1724 Penny...	——	——
1724 Penny (Undated) ROSA: SINE: SPINA. (3 known)..	——	——

★A. S. Robinson

	Fine	Ex. Fine
1733 Twopence (Pattern) Proof........................	——	——

The 1733 twopence is a pattern piece and bears the bust of George II facing to the left. Issued by the successors to the coinage patent, since William Wood had died in 1730.

HIBERNIA OR WOOD'S COINAGE

The type intended for Ireland had a seated figure with a harp on the reverse side and the word HIBERNIA. Denominations struck were halfpenny and farthing with dates 1722, 1723 and 1724. Hibernia coins were unpopular in Ireland, so most of them were sent to the American Colonies.

First Type   Second Type

	Good	Fine	Ex. F.
1722 Halfpenny, First Type, Harp at Left	$ 6.50	$16.00	$27.50
1722 Halfpenny, Second Type, Harp at Right	8.00	25.00	35.00
1723 Halfpenny.................................	5.00	12.50	25.00
1723 over 22 Halfpenny..........................	12.50	32.50	60.00

HIBERNIA COINS

1723 Hibernia Farthing   1724 Hibernia Halfpenny

	Good	Fine	Ex. F.
1723 Hibernia Farthing	$ 7.50	$17.50	$30.00
1724 Hibernia Halfpenny	8.00	20.00	32.50
1724 Hibernia Farthing	8.50	22.50	37.50

COINAGE OF THE STATES

NEW HAMPSHIRE

New Hampshire was the first of the states to consider the subject of coinage following the declaration of independence.

William Moulton was empowered to make a limited quantity of coins of pure copper authorized by the State House of Representatives March 13, 1776. Although patterns were prepared, it is generally believed that they were not approved. Little of the proposed coinage was ever actually circulated.

★Betts   ★ Copley

	V. Good
1776 New Hampshire Halfpenny	———
1776 New Hampshire Halfpenny WM in Center (3 known)	———
1776 New Hampshire Halfpenny, Engraved Type (Unique)	———

[22]

VERMONT

Reuben Harmon, Jr., of Rupert, Vermont, was granted permission to coin copper pieces on June 15, 1785. The well-known Vermont cents were first produced in that year.

Harmon's mint was located in the northeast corner of Rupert near a stream known as Millbrook. Col. William Cooley, a New York goldsmith, made the dies.

	Good	Fine		Good	Fine
1785 Cent IMMUNE COLUMBIA....	$200.00	$400.00	1786 Cent Baby Head......	$ 20.00	$ 65.00
1785 Cent VERMONTS....	25.00	55.00	1786 Cent Bust Left.......	25.00	72.50
1785 Cent VERMONTIS...	25.00	65.00	1787 Cent Bust Left.......	175.00	———
1786 Cent VERMON-TENSIUM......	17.50	55.00	1787 Cent (Several Varieties)........	10.00	25.00

VERMONT

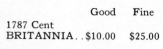

	Good	Fine
1787 Cent BRITANNIA	$10.00	$25.00

	Good	Fine
1788 Cent (Several varieties)	$10.00	$ 22.50
1788 Cent VERMON AUOTORI	——	——
1788 Cent *ET LIB* *INDE	30.00	100.00

	Good	Fine
1788 Cent GEORGIVS III REX	$17.50	$40.00

NEW YORK

There are no records to show that coinage was authorized for New York following the Revolutionary War. The only coinage laws passed were those regulating coins already in use.

A firm composed of ten individuals became associated in 1787 for the purpose of striking copper coins, at Newburgh. The establishment was called a "Manufactory of hardware," but the operations there were conducted in secret and looked upon as illegal.

Members of the firm included Reuben Harmon, Jr., who operated the mint at Rupert, Vermont; James F. Atlee, a die engraver and others.

The articles of agreement offer an interesting sidelight on the trade in tokens of that day. Reuben Harmon and William Cooley were listed as co-partners "in such trades and merchandizing and in the coinage of copper for the state of Vermont, Connecticut and New York, for their most benefit advantage and profit."

Perhaps many of the pieces now classified as Connecticut coins, the Vermon Auctori with the Britannia reverse and the counterfeit George III halfpence were products of this "hardware manufactory."

The Nova Eborac (New York) issues are supposed to have been struck in England as a speculative venture.

Cents attributed to New York during the period of 1786 and 1787 include the following:

NEW YORK

1786 NON VI VIRTUTE VICI

(Believed to be Head of Washington.)

	Good	Fine	V. Fine
Cent	$200	$400	$600

★Robinson

★Bolen

	Good	Fine	V. Fine
1787 Excelsior Cent, Eagle on Globe Facing Right	$125.00	$300.00	$400.00
1787 Excelsior Cent, Eagle on Globe Facing Left	100.00	225.00	300.00

1787 Cent
Large Eagle on Reverse

Arrows and Branch
Transposed (Ex. Rare) ———

1787 George Clinton Cent

	Good	Fine	V. Fine
Cent	$350	$700	$900

★Bolen

1787 Indian
N.Y. Arms

	Good	Fine	V. Fine
Cent	$350	$700	$900

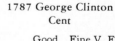

★Bolen

[25]

NEW YORK

1787 Indian Cent
Reverse Eagle
on Globe

Good.............$400.00
Fine............. 750.00
V. Fine...........1100.00

★Bolen

1787 Indian Cent
with George III
Reverse (2 known)

1787 IMMUNIS COLUMBIA
Eagle Reverse

Good...............$ 40.00
Fine................ 65.00
V. Fine............. 120.00
Ex. Fine............ 225.00

THE NOVA EBORACS

1787
NOVA EBORAC
Reverse Seated
Figure Facing Left

Good...........$15.00
Fine............ 27.50
V. Fine.......... 45.00

1787
NOVA EBORAC
Reverse Seated
Figure Facing Right

Good...........$15.00
Fine............ 27.50
V. Fine.......... 45.00

NEW YORK

1787 NOVA EBORAC
Small Head

Good.................$125.00
Fine................... 250.00
V. Fine................ 375.00

1787 NOVA EBORAC
Large Head

Good..............$ 35.00
Fine...............   90.00
V. Fine............ 150.00

CONNECTICUT

Authority for establishing a mint was granted to Samuel Bishop, Joseph Hopkins, James Hillhouse and John Goodrich in 1785.

Available records indicate that the Connecticut Cents were turned out under a sub-contract by Samuel Broome and Jeremiah Platt, former New York merchants who operated two mint houses; one at Morris Cove and the other at Westville. Abel Buel was the principal die-sinker.

1785 Cent
Bust Facing Right

Good $8.00 Fine $17.00

LIR Instead of LIB

Good $15.00 Fine $30.00

1785 Cent
African Head

Good $7.50 Fine $18.00

1785 Cent
Bust Facing Left

Good..$15.00 Fine..$45.00

CONNECTICUT

1786 Cent
ETLIB INDE

Good.............$21.00
Fine.............. 41.00

1786 Cent
Large Head Facing Right

Good.............$12.00
Fine.............. 35.00

1786 Cent
Mailed Bust Facing Left

Good.............$ 7.00
Fine.............. 12.50

1786 Cent
Mailed Bust Facing Left
Hercules Head

Good...........$ 8.50
Fine............ 24.00

1786 Cent
Draped Bust

Good...........$11.00
Fine............ 27.00

CONNECTICUT

1787 Cent
Small Head Facing Right
ETLIB INDE
Good..$12.00 Fine..$40.00

1787 Cent
Mailed Bust Facing Right
IND ET LIB
Good..$7.50 Fine..$17.50

1787 Cent
Muttonhead
Variety

Good................$ 9.00
Fine................ 31.00

	Good	Fine
1787 Cent, Mailed Bust Facing Left.....................	$ 5.00	$10.50
1787 Cent, Similar, Laughing Head Variety..............	6.00	12.50
1787 Cent, Similar, Hercules Head (see 1786)............	15.00	35.00

1787 Cent, Similar, Horned Bust Variety................	6.50	13.50
1787 Cent, Similar, CONNECT Variety..................	6.00	16.00

1787 Cent, Draped Bust Facing Left.....................	4.00	10.00
1787 Cent, Similar, AUCIORI Variety..................	6.00	12.50

CONNECTICUT

	Good	Fine
1787 Cent, Similar, **AUCTOPI** Variety	$ 7.00	$15.00
1787 Cent, Similar, **AUCTOBI** Variety	7.00	15.00
1787 Cent, Similar, **CONNFC** Variety	7.00	15.00
1787 Cent, Similar, **CONNLC** Variety	10.00	31.00
1787 Cent, Similar, **FNDE** Variety	7.00	15.00
1787 Cent, Similar, **ETLIR** Variety	7.00	15.00
1787 Cent, Similar, **ETIIB** Variety	7.00	15.00

1788 Cent, Mailed Bust Facing Right	8.00	16.00
1788 Cent, Similar, Small Head	11.00	35.00

1788 Cent, Mailed Bust Facing Left	5.50	12.50

1788 Cent, Draped Bust Facing Left	5.50	12.50
1788 Cent, Similar, **CONNLC** Variety	7.00	15.00
1788 Cent, Similar, **INDL ET LIB** Variety	7.00	15.00

MASSACHUSETTS

MASSACHUSETTS PINE TREE COPPER

Nothing is known regarding the origin of the Pine Tree pattern cent dated 1776. The obverse has a crude pine tree with an animal resembling a dog at its base; Inscription, MASSACHUSETTS STATE. The reverse has a figure probably intended to represent the Goddess of Liberty, seated on a globe and holding a liberty cap and staff. A dog sits at her feet. The legend LIBERTY AND VIRTUE surrounds the figure.

★Copley

1776 Cent (Unique).. ———

MASSACHUSETTS HALFPENNY

This pattern piece is sometimes called the "Janus Copper." There are three heads facing left, front and right on the obverse with the inscription STATE OF MASSA. ½ D. The reverse shows the Goddess of Liberty, seated resting against a globe facing right, inscribed GODDESS LIBERTY 1776.

★Copley

1776 Halfpenny, 3 Heads on Obverse (Unique).................... ———

An "Act for establishing a mint for the coinage of gold, silver and copper" was passed by the Massachusetts General Court October 17, 1786. The next year the Council directed that the design should incorporate "the figure of an Indian with a bow and arrow and a star at one side, with the word 'Commonwealth,' the reverse, a spread eagle with the words 'of Massachusetts A.D. 1787'."

A Mr. Joshua Witherle was placed in charge of the mint where he soon began coining the Massachusetts cents. There resulted many varieties, the rarest being that with arrows in the right talon. Half cents with similar devices and legends were also struck in 1787 and 1788.

Most of the dies for these coppers were made by Joseph Callender. Jacob Perkins of Newburyport probably engraved some of the dies.

The mint was abandoned early in 1789 as the venture was unprofitable to the Commonwealth.

MASSACHUSETTS

Obverse   Arrows in Eagle's Right Talon   in Left Talon

	Good	Fine	V. F.
1787 Cent, Arrows in Right Talon (Ex. Rare).....			
1787 Cent, Arrows in Left Talon.................	$6.00	$15.00	$27.50
1787 Cent, Horn (Die Break) from Eagle's Head...	7.00	17.00	30.00

1787 Half Cent

Good.................	$ 8.00
Fine.................	15.00
V. Fine...............	27.50

1788 Cent

Good.............	$ 8.00
Fine.............	15.00
V. Fine...........	27.50

★Evanson

★Evanson

	Good	Fine	V. F.
1788 Half Cent................................	$8.00	$15.00	$27.50

NEW JERSEY

Although many were dated 1786, authority for a New Jersey coinage was granted on June 1, 1787. Walter Mould, Thomas Goadsby and Albion Cox were empowered to coin coppers "of the weight of six pennyweight and six grains." They were directed to strike 10,000 pounds and deliver to the Treasurer of the state "one-tenth part of the full sum they shall strike and coin."

In an operation of this kind the contractors purchased the metal and assumed all expenses of coining. The difference between these expenses and the total face value of the coins issued represented the profit.

Later Goadsby and Cox asked authority to coin two-thirds of the total independently. Their petition was granted November 22, 1787. Mould was known to have produced his coins at Morristown, while Cox (and probably Goadsby) operated in Elizabethtown.

The series offers many varieties. The obverse shows a horse's head with plow and the legend NOVA CAESAREA (New Jersey). The reverse has a United States shield and legend E PLURIBUS UNUM (One composed of many).

1786 Cent
IMMUNIS COLUMBIA
Obverse

Good..——   Fine..——

1786 (No Date) Cent, Washington Obverse............. ——   ——
1786 Cent, Eagle Obverse............................ ——   ——
1786 Cent, Washington Obv.-Eagle Rev. (Unique)....... ——   ——

1786 Cent
Date Under Plow Handle

·Good ——   Fine ——

1786 Cent
No Coulter

Good $20.00   Fine $52.50

[33]

NEW JERSEY

	Good	Fine
1786 Cent, Narrow Shield	$ 6.00	$12.00
1786 Cent, Wide Shield	7.00	15.00
1786 Cent, Similar, Bridle Variety	8.00	16.00

Pluribs Variety
Large Planchet · Small Planchet · Outlined Shield

1787 Cent, Pronounced Outline to Shield	7.50	18.00
1787 Cent, Small Planchet, Plain Shield	5.00	12.50
1787 Cent, Large Planchet, Plain Shield	5.00	12.50
1787 Cent, Similar, PLURIBS Variety	7.50	18.00

Serpent Head · Fox Variety

1787 Cent, Serpent Head Variety	8.00	20.00
1788 Cent, Horse's Head Facing Right	5.00	12.50
1788 Cent, Similar, Running Fox before Legend	10.00	25.00

1788 Cent, Horse's Head Facing Left	12.50	32.50

TOKENS AND PATTERN COINS
THE CONTINENTAL DOLLAR

The Continental Dollars were probably a pattern issue only and never reached general circulation. It was the first silver dollar size coin ever proposed for the United States. The dies were engraved by someone whose initials were E. G. (possibly Elisha Gallaudet). Some of them have his signature "EG FECIT" on the obverse. The coins were probably struck in Philadelphia.

Varieties are caused by differences in the spelling of the word CURRENCY and the addition of EG FECIT. These coins were struck in silver, pewter and brass, those in silver probably having done service as a dollar.

"CURRENCY"   "CURENCY"

★Dickeson

Copies were struck in various metals for the 1876 Centennial Exposition in Philadelphia.

	Good	Fine	Unc.
1776 CURENCY — Brass (2 Varieties)	———	———	———
1776 CURENCY — Pewter	$90.00	$200.00	$450.00
1776 CURENCY — Silver	———	———	———
1776 CURRENCY — Pewter	105.00	225.00	500.00
1776 CURRENCY — Pewter, EG FECIT	110.00	240.00	530.00
1776 CURRENCY — Silver, EG FECIT	———	———	———
1776 CURRENCEY — Pewter	———	———	———

NOVA CONSTELLATIO PATTERNS (Silver)

These Nova Constellatio pieces undoubtedly represent the first patterns for a coinage of the United States. They were designed by Benjamin Dudley for Gouverneur Morris to carry out his ideas for a decimal coinage system. The 1000 unit designation he called a "mark," the 500 a "quint." These denominations, together with the smaller 100 unit piece, were designed to standardize the many different coin values among the several states. These pattern pieces represent the first attempt at a decimal ratio, and were the forerunners of our present system of money values. Neither the proposed denominations nor the coins advanced beyond the pattern stage. The pieces are all dated 1783 and are extremely rare. There are two types of the "quint."

NOVA CONSTELLATIO PATTERNS (Silver)

MARK

QUINT Type 1   Reverse   QUINT Type 2

★Set of
Mickley
Electrotypes

Bit 100 Units

1783 **MARK** (1000), Silver (Unique)	———	———
1783 **QUINT** (500), Silver — Type 1 (Unique)	———	———
1783 **QUINT** (500), Silver — Type 2 (Unique)	———	———
1783 Bit (100), Silver (2 known)	———	———

NOVA CONSTELLATIO COPPERS

The Nova Constellatio pieces were struck supposedly by order of Gouverneur Morris who had been Assistant Financier of the Confederation. The tokens were turned out in fairly large quantities in the years 1783 and 1785. There are a number of varieties of the 1783 and 1785 issues which are similar to the patterns heretofore described. No official records have been found stating where, or by whom the Nova Constellatio coppers were manufactured. Evidence indicates that they were struck in Birmingham from dies made there by Thomas Wyon, and imported for American circulation as a private business venture by Gouverneur Morris.

NOVA CONSTELLATIO COPPERS

1783 Cent
"CONSTELLATIO"
Pointed Rays
Small U.S.

Good	$ 7.00
Fine	17.50
Ex. Fine	40.00

1783 Cent
"CONSTELLATIO"
Pointed Rays, Large U.S.

Good	$ 8.50
Fine	25.00
Ex. Fine	45.00

1783 Cent
"CONSTELATIO"
Blunt Rays

Good	$ 7.50
Fine	19.00
Ex. Fine	50.00

1785 Cent
"CONSTELATIO"
Blunt Rays

Good	$10.00
Fine	27.50
Ex. Fine	55.00

	Good	Fine	Ex. F.
1785 Cent, CONSTELLATIO Pointed Rays	$7.50	$15.00	$40.00
1786 Cent .... (Ex. Rare)	———	———	———

[37]

IMMUNE COLUMBIA CENTS

★Edwards

These are considered experimental or pattern pieces. No laws describing them are known. There are several types with the seated figure of Justice device. These dies were possibly the work of James F. Atlee.

1785 Cent, Copper...... ———
1785 Cent, Silver........ ———

1785 Cent, Cop. Ex. Star in Border
   Copper, CONSTELLATIO
Gd.—$100 Fine—$250 V.F.—$400
Copper, CONSTELATIO,
Blunt Rays.....(2 known) ———
Gold..........(2 known) ———
A gold specimen in the National Coin Collection was acquired from Stickney in exchange for an 1804 dollar.

1785
George III Obverse
Good..$150.00   Fine..$350.00
1785
Vermon Auctori Obverse
Good..$200.00   Fine..$400.00

FRENCH COLONIES

	V. Good	Fine
1721 French Colonies, Sou, Mint Mark B for Rouen..........	$20.00	$35.00
1721 French Colonies, Sou, Mint Mark H for Rochelle........	15.00	22.00
1722 French Colonies, Sou, Mint Mark H....	10.00	17.00
1722 over 1........	12.50	22.00

1767 French Colonies, Sou
Good..................$15.00
Fine.................... 40.00
Ex. Fine.............. 75.00

FRENCH COLONIES

1767 French Colonies, Sou
Counterstamped RF for
Republic

Good................... $ 7.50
Fine.................... 20.00
Ex. Fine............... 60.00

For greater coverage of French
Colonial Coins see Charlton's
Standard Catalogue of Canadian
Coins, Tokens and Paper Money.

CONFEDERATIO CENTS

The Confederatio Cents are usually classed as experimental or pattern pieces. This will explain why the die with the CONFEDERATIO legend was combined with other designs such as bust of George Washington, Libertas et Justitia of 1785, Immunis Columbia of 1786, the "New York Excelsiors," Inimica Tyrannis Americana and others. There were in all thirteen dies struck in fourteen combinations. Some of the dies were believed to have been made by Thomas Wyon of Birmingham, England, whereas others may have been the work of James Atlee, or the New Jersey coiners.

There are two types of the Confederatio reverse. In one instance the stars are contained in a small circle; in the other larger stars are in a larger circle.

1785 Cent, Stars in Small
Circle

Fine............... ———
V. Fine............ ———

★Bolen

Typical Obverse Types

★Bolen

1785 Stars in Large Circle

Fine............ ———
V. Fine......... ———

Reverse

[39]

BRASHER'S DOUBLOONS

Perhaps the most famous piece brought out before the establishment of the mint at Philadelphia was that produced by a well-known goldsmith and jeweler, Ephraim Brasher, next door neighbor of George Washington, in New York.

Brasher produced a gold piece weighing about 408 grains, approximately equal in value to a Spanish doubloon (about $16.00).

The punch-mark EB appears in either of two positions as illustrated. This mark is found on coins of other countries as well, and probably was so used by Brasher as evidence of his approval of their value.

*Robinson

V. Fine

1787 Doubloon, Punch on Breast, Gold (Unique).................. ——

1787 Doubloon, Punch on Wing, Gold.......................... ——

1787 Half Doubloon (Unique)................................. ——

The half doubloon is struck from the usual doubloon dies, but on a smaller planchet.

AMERICAN TOKENS

Struck in America or England by Order of American Merchants
GLOUCESTER TOKENS

According to S. S. Crosby, in his book "The Early Coins of America" this piece appears to have been intended as a pattern for a shilling, a private coinage by Richard Dawson of Gloucester (county?), Virginia. The only specimens known are struck in brass, none in silver.

The denomination XII indicates that a silver coinage (one shilling) was planned but never issued. Known specimens are imperfect and a full description cannot be given.

The building may represent a warehouse or some public building, possibly a court house. The legend on the reverse may have been designed to read GLOUCESTER COURT HOUSE VIRGINIA.

1714 Shilling (2 known) Brass................................. ——

HIGLEY OR GRANBY COPPERS

John Higley owned a private copper mine near Granby, Connecticut. He worked the mine as an individual, smelting his own ore and making his own dies for the coins that he issued.

The Higley coppers were never officially authorized. All the tokens were made of pure copper. There were seven obverse and four reverse dies. The first issue, in 1737, bore the legend THE VALUE OF THREEPENCE. After a time the quantity exceeded the local demand, and a protest arose against the value of the piece. Higley, a resourceful individual, promptly created a new design, still with the Roman III, but with the inscription VALUE ME AS YOU PLEASE. On the reverse appeared the words I AM GOOD COPPER.

(Electrotypes and Casts Exist)

★Bolen

		Good	V. Good
1737 THE • VALVE • OF • THREE • PENCE. — 3 Hammers CONNECTICVT		$225.00	$425.00
1737 THE • VALVE • OF • THREE • PENCE. — 3 Hammers — I • AM • GOOD • COPPER		225.00	425.00

1737 VALUE • ME • AS • YOU • PLEASE — 3 Hammers — I • AM • GOOD • COPPER		200.00	375.00
1737 VALVE • ME • AS • YOU • PLEASE — 3 Hammers — I • AM • GOOD • COPPER		(Ex. Rare)	

(1737) VALUE • ME • AS • YOU • PLEASE — Broad Axe — J • CUT • MY • WAY • THROUGH		300.00	500.00
(1737) Similar, Wheel Design (Unique)		———	———
1739 VALUE • ME • AS • YOU • PLEASE — Broad Axe — J • CUT • MY • WAY • THROUGH		450.00	———

[41]

J. CHALMERS
Annapolis, Maryland

J. Chalmers, a goldsmith, struck a series of silver tokens at Annapolis in 1783. The shortage of change and the refusal of the people to use underweight cut Spanish coins, or "bits," prompted the issue of these pieces.

The shilling with rings on the reverse is very rare. The common type shilling has two clasped hands on the obverse. The reverse shows two doves pulling what appears to be a worm.

The sixpence has a star within a wreath on the obverse, and a cross with hands clasped on the reverse. The three pence has the clasped hands on the obverse side, and the reverse shows a branch encircled by a wreath.

	Good	Fine
1783 Shilling — Birds, Long or Short Worm	$65.00	$115.00
1783 Shilling — Rings (Ex. Rare)		

1783 Sixpence, Small Date	115.00	250.00
1783 Sixpence, Large Date	105.00	235.00
1783 Threepence	75.00	160.00

STANDISH BARRY, BALTIMORE, MARYLAND

Standish Barry, a Baltimore silversmith, circulated a silver threepence in 1790. He was a watch and clockmaker, engraver and later a silversmith. The tokens were believed to have been an advertising venture at a time when small change was scarce. The precise date, July 4, 90, on this piece may indicate that Barry intended to commemorate Independence Day, but there are no records to substantiate this belief. The head shown on the obverse is probably that of George Washington. The legend BALTIMORE TOWN JULY 4, 90 appears in the border. STANDISH BARRY THREE PENCE is on the reverse.

1790 Threepence	$110.00	$225.00

THE BAR CENT

The Bar Cent is undated and of uncertain origin.

It has thirteen parallel and disconnected bars on one side. On the other side is the large Roman USA monogram.

The significance of the design is clearly defined by its extreme simplicity. The separate thirteen states (bars) unite into a single status as symbolized by the interlocking letters (USA).

This coin is believed to have been issued at the same time as the Nova Constellatio coppers by Thomas Wyon at Birmingham, England, for America. It first circulated in New York during November, 1785. The design was supposedly copied from an old Continental button.

★Bolen (A is under S)

	Good	Fine	Unc.
Undated (about 1785) Bar Cent	$50.00	$75.00	$200.00

THE MOTT TOKEN

This was one of the first tradesman's tokens issued in America. Manufactured in England, they were issued by Messrs. Mott of New York in 1789. The firm was composed of William and John Mott, located at 240 Water Street, a fashionable section of New York at that time.

	Good	Fine	Ex. Fine
1789 Mott Token, Thick Planchet	$ 7.50	$20.00	$50.00
1789 Mott Token, Thin Planchet	10.00	27.50	70.00

TALBOT ALLUM & LEE CENTS

Talbot, Allum & Lee, engaged in the India trade and located at 241 Pearl Street, New York, placed a large quantity of English-made coppers in circulation during 1794 and 1795. ONE CENT appears on the 1794 issue, and the legend PAYABLE AT THE STORE OF—— on the edge. The denomination is not found on the 1795 reverse but the edge legend was changed to read: WE PROMISE TO PAY THE BEARER ONE CENT.

TALBOT ALLUM & LEE CENTS

1794 Cent **NEW YORK**
V. Good.............$ 6.50
V. Fine............... 25.00
Unc................... 65.00

1794 Cent without **NEW YORK**
V. Good............. 50.00
V. Fine............. 180.00
Unc................. ———

1795 Cent
V. Good............$ 6.00
V. Fine............. 12.00
Unc................ 35.00

ANGLO-AMERICAN TOKENS
Supposedly of English Origin — Speculative Ventures
CAROLINA and NEW ENGLAND ELEPHANT TOKENS

Although no law is known authorizing coinage for Carolina, two very interesting pieces known as Elephant Tokens were current with the date 1694. These copper coins were of half-penny denomination. The reverse reads GOD PRESERVE CAROLINA AND THE LORDS PROPRIETERS. 1694.

The second and more common variety has the last word spelled PROPRIETORS. The correction was made on the original die, for the E shows plainly beneath the O. The elephant's tusks nearly touch the milling on the second variety.

The Elephant Pieces were probably struck in England and perhaps intended only as tokens, or, as we might say today, as an advertising stunt to enliven interest in the Carolina Plantation.

Like the Carolina Tokens, the New England Elephant Tokens were believed to have been struck in England as a promotional piece to increase interest in the American Colonies. Some of these tokens were said to have been struck in brass.

NEW ENGLAND

★Robinson

1694 NEW ENGLAND.................................... (Ex. Rare)

CAROLINA ELEPHANT TOKENS

	Good	Fine
1694 PROPRIETERS (3 known)	———	———

★Bolen

| 1694 PROPRIETORS. . . . . | $125.00 | $250.00 |

The London Token, an early historian states, was produced during the great plague raging in London. The legend on this piece relates directly to that crisis. It has also been stated that the London Token was to have been current in Tangier, Africa, but was never used in that locality. No date appears on this coin.

(1694) Halfpenny GOD PRESERVE LONDON (Thick Planchet).	15.00	37.50
(1694) Halfpenny GOD PRESERVE LONDON (Thin Planchet).	17.50	40.00
(1694) Halfpenny GOD PRESERVE LONDON (Diagonals in center of shield).	45.00	100.00
(1694) Halfpenny, similar. Variety with sword in second quarter of shield instead of first.	———	———
(1694) Halfpenny LON DON.	55.00	115.00

VIRGINIA HALFPENNY

In 1773, George III issued this halfpenny. There are also known to have been a few specimens struck on a larger planchet with a wide milled border, known as pennies.

The Virginia piece of 1774 known as a shilling may have been a pattern piece for a halfpenny.

Halfpenny   Penny

	Good	Fine	Unc.
1773 Halfpenny, Period after GEORGIUS......	$6.00	$10.00	$ 25.00
1773 Halfpenny, No period after GEORGIUS...	7.00	12.50	45.00
1773 Penny...Proof			325.00

Virginia
Shilling
1774

1774 Shilling........................(Proof)   ———

GEORGIUS TRIUMPHO TOKEN

Although the head shown on this token bears a strong resemblance to that upon some coins of George III, many collectors consider the Georgius Triumpho (Triumphant George) a token intended to commemorate the successful termination of the Revolutionary War — a triumph justly claimed for Washington.

The reverse side shows the Goddess of Liberty behind a framework of thirteen bars and fleur de lis. She holds an olive branch in her right hand and staff of liberty in her left. VOCE POPOLI (By the Voice of the People) 1783.

	Good	Fine
1783 GEORGIUS TRIUMPHO.....................	$10.00	$22.50

AUCTORI PLEBIS TOKEN

This token is sometimes included with the coins of Connecticut as it greatly resembles issues of that state. The coin was struck in England, maker unknown, for use in America.

1787 AUCTORI PLEBIS
Good..$15.00   Fine..$35.00

KENTUCKY TOKEN

These tokens were struck in England about 1792-94. Each star in the triangle represents a state, identified by its initial letter. These pieces are usually called Kentucky Cents because the letter K (for Kentucky) happens to be at the top. Some of the edges are plain; others are engrailed with an oblique reeding, and some have the edge lettered: "PAYABLE IN LANCASTER LONDON OR BRISTOL," or "PAYABLE AT BEDWORTH NUNETON OR UNKIET."

	V. Good	V. Fine	Unc.
Cent, (1792) Plain Edge	$11.00	$21.00	$ 47.50
Cent, Engrailed Edge	20.00	50.00	150.00
Cent, Lettered Edge, PAYABLE AT BEDWORTH, Etc.	———	———	———
Cent, Lettered Edge, PAYABLE IN LANCASTER, Etc.	11.00	27.50	55.00
Cent, Lettered Edge, Thin Planchet	———	———	———

MYDDELTON TOKENS

These copper tokens were from the establishment of Boulton and Watt near Birmingham, England. They are unsurpassed in beauty and design by any piece issued for American circulation.

1796 Myddelton Token (Copper), Proof..$450.00

1796 Myddelton Token (Silver), Proof... 500.00

COPPER COMPANY OF UPPER CANADA

The reverse of this piece, according to S. S. Crosby, properly belongs upon another token and was apparently intended for Canadian circulation, or it was used to give the coin creditability.

Proof
1796 Bronze.......$125.00

NORTH WEST COMPANY TOKEN

Used among fur traders throughout western Canada, Oregon and Washington. The token was good for one beaver.

1820 North West Token,
    Brass.......V. Fine $175.00
1820 North West Token,
    Copper.............V. Rare

All but one known specimen are holed.

MISCELLANEOUS TOKENS
THE NEW YORKE TOKEN

Although only three or four specimens of this piece were known to S S. Crosby, the authority on early American coins, a number have since been discovered. From an account in the Historical Magazine for 1861, he infers that this token is of Dutch origin. The following is quoted from the magazine article mentioned.

"The style in which it is executed is more Dutch than English; and as the only existing specimen has been preserved in Holland, it is probable that the dies were originally cut there. . . . There is no date upon the token; but it evidently belongs to the period between 1664, when the name New Yorke was first adopted, and 1710, after which it was rarely spelled with an e. It should probably be referred to the latter part of this period, for the currency of the colonies was then in a very unsettled state, and the amount in circulation was not adequate to the wants of trade. . . .

"Without venturing to claim that this coin contains the earliest display of the American eagle, we think it unquestionably deserves to be considered the earliest New York token."

	Good	Fine
UNDATED Brass......	$135.00	$250.00
Pewter....	——	——

NEW ENGLAND STIVER

This token was believed to have originated in Holland and used by Dutch merchants in New Amsterdam for small change. The obverse shows two lions; the upper facing left and the lower inverted facing right.

There has been considerable conjecture concerning the significance of the letters on the obverse side. One interpretation is that they stand for "I Stiver Von Connecticut." Another suggestion has it that they were the initials of a Dutch Trader, as I. S. Van C.

There is no clue to the date of the issue. Crosby judges the time as "that of the seventeenth century."

UNDATED (1650) (Unique)................................... ———

FLORIDA TOKEN

★19th Century
   Restrikes
   Exist

	Good	Fine	Unc.
(1688) Florida, James II Plantation Token, 1/24 part real — Pewter	$15.00	$ 27.50	$ 60.00
(1688) Florida, James II Plantation Token, 1/24 part real — Pewter. Sidewise 4 in 24	50.00	100.00	250.00

NORTH AMERICAN TOKEN

This piece was struck in Dublin, Ireland. The obverse shows the seated figure of Hibernia facing left. The date of issue is believed to have been much later than that shown on the coins.

Like many Irish tokens, this issue found its way to America in large quantities and was readily accepted owing to a scarcity of small change.

	Good	Fine
1781	$7.50	$12.50

FRANKLIN PRESS CENT

This piece is an English token but has often been associated with Benjamin Franklin, and has accordingly been placed in American collections.

1794 Franklin Press Cent

Good	Fine	Unc.
$11.00	$25.00	$55.00

HIBERNIA-VOCE POPULI

These coins, struck in the year 1760, were prepared by one Roche, of King Street Dublin, who was at that period engaged in the manufacture of buttons for the army, for which he held a contract with home government. Like other Irish tokens, many of these pieces found their way to Colonial America. The piece dated 1700 is probably a die-cutter's error. It no doubt circulated in Colonies with numerous other counterfeit halfpence and "Bungtown Tokens."

Halfpenny 1700   Halfpenny 1760

VOOE POPULI   1760 Farthing

	Good	Fin
1700 Halfpenny	———	—
1760 Halfpenny	$ 7.50	$15.
1760 Halfpenny VOOE POPULI	16.00	35.
1760 Farthing Lg. Letters..	35.00	70.0
1760 Farthing Sm. Letters.	———	—

PITT TOKENS

William Pitt, who endeared himself to America, is the subject of these pieces, probably intended as commemorative medalets. The halfpenny served as currency during a shortage of regular coinage. Mr. Smithers of Philadelphia struck the coins which were designed by Colonel Revere of Boston. The reverse legend refers to Pitt's efforts to have the stamp act repealed. The Pitt farthing-size token, found in brass or copper, is rare.

	Good	Fine	Unc.
1766 Halfpenny	$16.00	$37.50	$75.00
1766 Farthing	———	———	———

RHODE ISLAND SHIP TOKEN

Although this medal has a Dutch inscription, the spelling and design indicate an English or Anglo-American origin. Specimens are known in brass, copper, tin and pewter.

1778-1779 Rhode Island
      Ship Token

Wreath below ship......
V.F. $50.00   E.F. $90.00

No Wreath below ship...
V.F. $45.00   E.F. $85.00

VLUGTENDE below
ship. V.F. ——— E.F. ———

★Grant

THE CASTORLAND MEDAL

This piece is dated 1796 and relates to a settlement of Frenchmen known as Castorland in Carthage, New York, at the time of the French Revolution.

    The dies are still available and have been used for restriking throughout the years.

            Matte
            Proof

	Matte Proof
1796 Silver Original (Reeded edge)	———
1796 Copper Original	———
1796 Copper Restrike (thin)	$10.00

WASHINGTON PIECES

An interesting series of coins and tokens was struck during the period from 1783 to 1795, bearing the portrait of George Washington. The likenesses in most instances were faithfully reproduced and were designed to please Washington. Some of these pieces were of English origin.

    The legends generally signify a strong unity among the states and a marked display of patriotism which pervaded the new nation during that period. We find among these tokens an employment of what were soon to become our official coin devices, namely, the American eagle, the United States shield and stars. The one cent value is used in several instances, while on some of the English pieces the halfpenny value will be found. Several pieces were intended to be patterns for half dollars.

Small Military Bust

	Good	Fine	V.Fine
Plain edge...$	9.00	$16.00	$37.50
Engrailed edge...	11.00	20.00	55.00
Large Military Bust →			
	8.00	15.00	25.00

WASHINGTON PIECES

1783 Draped Bust No Button
Plain Edge

Good...................$ 8.00
Fine................... 13.50
V. Fine............... 22.50

1783 Draped Bust with Button
Plain Edge

Good................... 15.00
Fine................... 30.00
V. Fine............... 55.00

1783 Draped Bust, Copper Restrike, plain edge...............Proof 90.00
1783 Draped Bust, Copper Restrike, engrailed edge...........Proof 37.50
1783 Draped Bust, Silver Restrike, engrailed edge............Proof 90.00

UNITY STATES

Good..............$ 7.00
Fine.............. 14.00
V. Fine........... 27.50

Undated (1783)
Double Head
Cent

Good...............$10.00
Fine............... 25.00
V. Fine............ 37.50

Ugly Head

1784 Ugly Head.....(Ex. Rare)

Presumably of American origin.

1791 Cent
Small Eagle

Lettered edge—United
States of America

Good.........$12.50
Fine.......... 27.50
Unc........... 75.00

WASHINGTON PIECES

1791 Cent
Large Eagle

Lettered edge —
UNITED STATES
OF AMERICA

Good.........$12.50
Fine......... 27.50
Unc.......... 65.00

1791 Liverpool
Halfpenny

Lettered edge

Good........... $ 50.00
Fine............ 110.00
Unc............ 225.00

1792 Eagle Half Dollar
Copper........ ———

1792 Eagle Half Dollar
Silver........... ———

1792 Eagle Half Dollar
Gold.......... ———

1792 Cent
"WASHINGTON —
PRESIDENT"

Fine
Plain edge....... $225.00
Lettered edge.... ———

Undated
(1792) Cent
"WASHINGTON
BORN VIRGINIA"

Fine
Copper....... $200.00
Silver....... ———
(Restrike of obverse by
Albert Collis, 1960.)

WASHINGTON PIECES

1792 Half Dollar, Silver
Good...........——
Fine...........——
1792 Half Dollar, Copper
Good.........$175.00
Fine........... 350.00
1792 Half Dollar, Copper
Ornamented edge —
(Circles and Squares)
Good $400   Fine $750
1792 same Silver——

★ Idler

1792 Half Dollar, Large
Eagle (Unique).. ——

1792 Cent
Roman Head

Lettered edge—
UNITED STATES
OF AMERICA

Proof.......$500.00

1793 Ship
Halfpenny

Lettered Edge

Good............$10.00
Fine............. 20.00
V. Fine........... 40.00

1795 Grate Cent
Oblique Reeding
Good...............$10.00
Fine............... 20.00
Unc................. 50.00
Lettered Edge
Good...............$30.00
Fine............... 70.00
Unc............... 100.00

[54]

WASHINGTON PIECES

	Good	Fine	Ex. Fine
1795 Halfpenny, Plain edge...................	$15.00	$35.00	$ 75.00
1795 Halfpenny, Lettered edge................	9.00	17.50	35.00
1795 Halfpenny, Edge: AN ASYLUM FOR THE OPPRESSED OF ALL NATIONS.......	20.00	80.00	120.00
1795 Penny, Similar to Halfpenny (Ex. Rare)...	———	———	———

Undated (1795) Penny
Lettered Edge

Good............$12.50
Fine............. 25.00
Unc.............. 75.00

SUCCESS TOKENS

Good Fine

SUCCESS Token, Large
Plain, or Reeded Edge.$12.50 $30.00

Good Fine

SUCCESS Token, Small
Plain, or Reeded Edge.$12.50 $30.00

NORTH WALES HALFPENNY

	Good	Fine
1795 NORTH WALES Halfpenny, brass.	$10.00	$25.00
Copper, lettered edge...	——	——
Copper, two stars either side of harp......	——	——

THE FUGIO CENTS

The first coins issued by authority of the United States were the "Fugio" cents. Entries in the Journal of Congress supply interesting information about proceedings relating to this coinage.

"Saturday, April 21, 1787. . . .

"That the board of treasury be authorized to contract for three hundred tons of copper coin of the federal standard, agreeable to the proposition of Mr. James Jarvis, ... That it be coined at the expense of the contractor, etc."

On Friday, July 6, 1786, there was "Resolved, that the board of treasury direct the contractor for the copper coinage to stamp on one side of each piece the following device, viz: thirteen circles linked together, a small circle in the middle, with the words 'United States,' round it; and in the centre, the words 'We are one'; on the other side of the same piece the following device, viz: a dial with the hours expressed on the face of it; a meridian sun above on one side of which is the word 'Fugio,' (The meaning is, 'time flies' and on the other the year in figures '1787' below the dial, the words 'Mind Your Business.' "

The legends have been credited to Benjamin Franklin by many, and the coin, as a consequence, has been referred to as the Franklin Cent.

These cents were coined in New Haven, Conn., and it has been suggested, also in New York City, Rupert, Vt. and elsewhere. Most of the copper used in this coinage came from military stores. It is believed to have been the copper bands which held together the powder kegs sent to us by the French. The dies were made by Abel Buel of New Haven.

We list below major varieties, some of considerable rarity:

WITH CLUB RAYS
1787

	Good	Fine	Unc.
Club Rays, concave ends to rays: FUCIO (C instead of G)	—	—	—
Club Rays, concave ends, FUGIO (Ex. Rare)	—	—	—
Club Rays, rounded ends	$17.50	$35.00	—

WITH POINTED RAYS
1787

	Good	Fine	Unc.
UNITED above, STATES below (Rare)	—	—	$200.00
UNITED STATES at sides of circle	$15.00	$27.50	80.00

THE FUGIO CENTS

	Good	Fine	Unc.
STATES UNITED at sides of circle. Cinquefoils (small, five bladed clover design) on label.....	$12.00	$22.50	$70.00
STATES UNITED. Eight-pointed stars on label	18.50	45.00	———
STATES UNITED. Label with raised rims (simply two concentric circles). Large letters in WE ARE ONE............................	30.00	65.00	———

Note: The preceding types with pointed rays have regular obverses punctuated with four cinquefoils.

Obv. no cinquefoils. Cross after date.

Rev. UNITED STATES. (Very Rare)........	———	———	———
Same Obv., Rev. STATES UNITED. (Very Rare)	———	———	———
Same Obv., Rev. label with raised rims. (Ex. Rare)	———	———	———

American Congress   New Haven Restrike

Copper Pattern. Same obv.; reverse with rays and AMERICAN CONGRESS. (Ex. Rare).......	———	———	———
New Haven Restrikes. Narrow rings on reverse.			
Gold (2 known)............................	———	———	———
Silver....................................	———	———	190.00
Copper...................................	———	———	50.00
Brass....................................	———	———	55.00

New Haven Restrikes were struck from dies discovered by the fourteen-year-old C. Wyllys Betts in 1858 on the site of the Broom & Platt Store in New Haven, Conn., where the originals were made. Three pairs of dies were found and are still extant.

BIBLIOGRAPHY — Early American Coins

Crosby, S. S., Early Coins of America................1875 (Reprint 1945)
Dickeson, Dr. M. W., American Numismatic Manual................1859
Maris, Dr. Edward, New Jersey Cents....................(Reprint 1925)
Miller-Ryder, The State Coinage of New England....................1920
Nelson, Philip, The Coinage of William Wood (1722-1733)............1903
Newman, Eric, Secret of Good Samaritan Shilling....................1959
Noe, Sydney P., The New England and Willow Tree Coinages
     of Massachusetts.... 1943
Wurtzbach, Carl, Massachusetts Colonial Silver Money...............1937

FIRST UNITED STATES MINT ISSUES

Many members of the House favored a representation of the president's head on the obverse of each coin. Others considered the idea a monarchial practice. Washington is believed to have expressed disapproval of the use of his portrait on our coins.

The majority considered a figure emblematic of Liberty more appropriate and the Senate finally concurred in this opinion. Robert Birch was an engraver employed at designing proposed devices for our coins. He engraved the dies for the disme and half-disme. He has also been associated with a large copper cent of unusual design, which is known as the Birch Cent.

DISME

	Good	Fine	Unc.
1792 Silver (3 Known)....	——	——	——
1792 Copper.....	——	——	——

HALF DISME

	Good	Fine	V. Fine
1792 Silver.....	$350	$600	$1000
1792 Copper (Unique)			

1792 SILVER CENTER CENT

	Fine	Ex. Fine
1792 Silver Center Cent.	——	——
1792 Cent, No Silver Center.....	——	——

1792 BIRCH CENT (Very Rare)

Copper...................... ——

G.W. Pt. Below Wreath
White Metal (Unique)

1792 PATTERN HALF EAGLE

Copper....... (2 Known)
White Metal... (Unique)

MINTS AND MINT MARKS

Coins struck at Philadelphia (excepting 1942 and later silver five-cent pieces) do not carry a mint mark. The mint mark is found only on coins struck at the branch mints. It is a small letter, usually found on the reverse side (the Lincoln cent is one exception to the rule; there are other exceptions, too). The letters to signify the various mints are as follows:

"C" for Charlotte, North Carolina (on gold coins only).
"CC" for Carson City, Nevada.
"D" for Dahlonega, Georgia (gold coins only, 1838 to 1861).
"D" for Denver, Colorado (from 1906 to date).
"O" for New Orleans, Louisiana.
"P" for Philadelphia, Pennsylvania.
"S" for San Francisco, California.

Location of Mint Marks

The mint mark is of utmost importance to collectors because of the fact that the coinage at the branch mints has usually been much smaller than at Philadelphia and many of the branch mint pieces are very scarce.

Half Cents — All coined at Philadelphia, no mint mark.
Large Cents — All coined at Philadelphia, no mint mark.
Flying Eagle Cents — All coined at Philadelphia, no mint mark.
Indian Cents — 1908 and 1909, under the wreath on reverse side.
Lincoln Cents — Under the date.
Two Cents, Three Cents Nickel — All coined at Philadelphia, no mint mark.
Three Cents Silver — All coined at Philadelphia, except 1851 New Orleans mint — reverse side.
Shield Nickels — All coined at Philadelphia, no mint mark.
Liberty Nickels — All coined at Philadelphia except 1912 S and D — reverse side to left of word CENTS.
Buffalo Nickels — Reverse side under words FIVE CENTS.
Jefferson Nickels — Reverse side at right of the building.
Jefferson Five-Cent Pieces (1942 to 1945 silver) — above dome on reverse.
Half Dimes — Reverse side either within or below the wreath.
Dimes — Old types on reverse side below or within wreath; Mercury type (1916 to 1945) on the reverse to left of fasces. Roosevelt type, left of bottom of torch on reverse.
Twenty Cents — Reverse, under the eagle.
Quarter Dollars — Old types on reverse under eagle; Standing Liberty type obverse to left of date; Washington type on reverse under eagle.
Half Dollars — 1838 and 1839 O mint mark above date; other dates to 1915 on reverse under eagle. 1916 on obverse, 1917 on obverse and reverse. After 1917 on lower left reverse. Franklin type, above bell beam.
Dollars — Old types, on reverse under eagle; Peace type (1921 and after) on reverse above eagle's tail feathers.
Trade Dollars — On reverse under eagle.
Gold Dollars — Reverse under wreath.
Quarter Eagles ($2.50) — 1838 and 1839 over the date; other dates previous to 1907 on reverse under the eagle; Indian type (1908-29) on reverse lower left.
Three Dollar Pieces — Reverse under the wreath.
Half Eagles ($5.00) — Same as quarter eagles.
Eagles ($10.00) — Reverse under eagle; after 1907 at left of value.
Double Eagles ($20.00) — Old types on reverse under eagle; St. Gaudens (after 1907) above the date.

PROOF COINS

A "proof" is a specimen striking of coinage for presentation, souvenir, exhibition and/or numismatic purposes. Proofs come only from the Philadelphia Mint.

A proof coin has a glittering, mirror-like, perfect appearance. Regular production coins in mint state have a coruscating, frosty lustre with small detail and lettering larger-spread and not always in full relief.

Matte proofs have a sandblast surface instead of the mirror one. Matte cent, nickel and gold proofs were issued from 1908 to 1916; a few 1921 and 1922 matte silver dollars are known.

"New-die-proofs" are the first impressions off regular production dies. They are the best examples from long periods of mintage when there were no specimen proof strikings and of issues from branch mints which never coin regular proofs.

How A Proof Coin Is Made . . .

Carefully selected metal blanks free of imperfections are washed with a solution of Cream of Tartar, rinsed in water and dipped in alcohol.

The dies for proofs receive a special polish resulting in a mirror-like surface not unlike the finished brilliant proof coin and are occasionally wiped with an oily cloth to retain a clean, polished surface. Unlike ordinary coinage produced by mechanical pressure at the rate of 90 to 130 coins per minute, proofs are struck by hydraulic pressure at a slower rate. The coins are carefully handled and never allowed to come in contact with other coins.

Proof coins struck prior to 1855 are very rare. Because they are offered infrequently, they are not listed in this catalog.

Collectors should beware of coins which have been buffed to look like proofs and should use a magnifying glass. Buffed coins have myriad hair lines and lack perfect detail.

MODERN PROOF COINS

After a lapse of twenty years proof coins were struck at the Philadelphia Mint from 1936 to 1942 inclusive. In 1942 when the content of the five-cent piece was changed, there were two types of this denomination available to collectors. The striking of proof coins was temporarily suspended from 1942 to 1950. The present cost of proof sets directly from the Mint in Philadelphia is $2.10 postpaid.

RECENT PROOF SETS

Cent—Nickel—Dime—Quarter—Half

1936 (3,837)............\$425.00		1955 (378,200).............\$ 11.50
1937 (5,542)............ 210.00		1956 (669,384)............. 6.50
1938 (8,045)............ 105.00		1957 (1,247,952)........... 4.00
1939 (8,795)............ 90.00		1958 (875,652)............. 9.00
1940 (11,246)............ 65.00		1959 (1,149,291)........... 4.00
1941 (15,287)............ 60.00		1960 Large Date Cent...... 3.75
1942 with both nickels (21,120) 55.00		1960 Small Date Cent
1950 (51,386)............ 70.00		(1,691,602 both kinds).. 20.00
1951 (57,500)............ 37.50		1961 (3,028,244)........... 3.00
1952 (81,980)............ 30.00		1962 (3,218,019)............ 3.00
1953 (128,800)............ 17.50		1963..................... 3.00
1954 (233,300)............ 13.50		

Figures in parentheses represent the total number of full sets minted.

UNITED STATES REGULAR ISSUES

HALF CENTS — 1793-1857

From the standpoint of face value the half cent is the smallest coin struck by the United States. All half cents are scarce, but the series has never enjoyed the popularity of some of the other series, hence the more common dates are reasonably priced.

There were various intermissions in coinage, and during the period 1831 to 1849 the coinage was very small causing a very noticeable lapse in the series for the average collector.

While 1796 is the rarest date the originals and restrikes of 1831, 1836, 1840, 1841, 1842, 1843, 1844, 1845, 1846, 1847, 1848, and 1849 are difficult to obtain.

The half cent was authorized to be coined April 2, 1792. Originally the weight was to have been 132 grains, but this was changed to 104 grains by the Act of January 14, 1793, before coinage commenced. The weight was again changed January 26, 1796 by presidential proclamation in conformity with the Act of March 3, 1795 to 84 grains. Coinage was discontinued by the Act of February 21, 1857.

Fair — Clear enough to identify.

Good — Outline of bust clear, no details. Date readable.
*   Reverse lettering incomplete.*

Very Good — Some hair details. Reverse lettering complete.

Fine — Most of hair detail shows.

Very Fine — Hair near ear and forehead worn, other areas distinct.

LIBERTY CAP TYPE

1793   1794

	Quan. Minted	Fair	Good	V. Good	Fine	V. Fine
1793	31,934	$60.00	$120.00	$150.00	$275.00	$475.00
1794	81,600	20.00	47.50	60.00	77.50	125.00

1795 Lettered Edge, Pole   No Pole to Cap   Pole to Cap

1795 Let. Edge Pole					
All Kinds 25,600	20.00	42.50	52.50	75.00	110.00
1795 Plain Edge, No Pole	20.00	37.50	50.00	67.50	110.00

HALF CENTS

1795 Lettered Edge, Punctuated Date   1796 Plain Edge, No Pole

	Quan. Minted	Fair	Good	V. Good	Fine	V. Fine
1795 Let. Edge, Punct. Date ...		$ 20.00	$ 32.50	$ 52.50	$ 75.00	$115.00
1795 Plain Edge, Punct. Date ..		20.00	32.50	52.50	75.00	115.00
*1796 Plain Edge, Pole						
All Kinds	115,480	200.00	400.00	600.00	950.00	1350.00
1796 Plain Edge, No Pole		300.00	575.00	750.00	1100.00	1750.00

1797 Plain Edge   1797 1 Above 1, Plain Edge

1797 Plain Edge						
All Kinds	107,048	15.00	35.00	45.00	75.00	110.00
1797 Let. Edge		70.00	125.00	175.00	275.00	450.00
1797 1 above 1, Plain Edge....		12.50	32.00	42.50	65.00	110.00

DRAPED BUST TYPE

Fair — Clear enough to identify.

Good — Bust outline clear, no details, date readable.
Reverse lettering worn and incomplete.

Very Good — Some drapery shows. Date and legends complete.

Fine — Shoulder drapery and hair over brow worn smooth.

Very Fine — Only slight wear in above areas. Slight wear on reverse.

1800	211,530	4.00	7.00	12.00	17.50	25.00
1802 over 1800 (As all are)						
All Kinds	14,366	30.00	57.50	82.50	120.00	175.00
1802 Rev. of 1800		50.00	120.00	210.00	275.00	400.00
1803	97,900	4.00	7.00	10.00	15.00	20.00

*A deceptive copy of this coin was made by Edwards.

HALF CENTS

Plain 4	Crosslet 4	Stemless Wreath	Stems to Wreath

	Quan. Minted	Fair	Good	V. Good	Fine	V. Fine
1804 Plain 4, Stemless						
All Kinds......1,055,312		$ 4.00	$ 5.00	$ 6.00	$ 9.50	$17.50
1804 Plain 4, Stems..........		10.00	15.50	23.00	35.00	50.00
1804 Crosslet 4, Stemless......		4.00	7.50	9.50	15.00	23.00
1804 Crosslet 4, Stems........		3.50	6.00	7.50	10.50	18.00

1804 Spiked Chin Variety		Small 5	Large 5		

1804 Spiked Chin Var........	4.00	6.50	8.50	12.00	24.00
1805 Small 5, Stemless					
All Kinds........814,464	4.00	7.25	10.00	14.00	21.00
1805 Small 5, Stems..........	20.00	35.00	60.00	105.00	150.00
1805 Large 5, Stems..........	4.00	6.50	9.75	13.50	19.00

Small 6	Large 6	1808 over 7	Normal Date		

1806 Small 6, Stems					
All Kinds........356,000	11.00	23.00	36.00	56.50	81.50
1806 Small 6, Stemless........	4.00	6.00	9.00	13.00	18.00
1806 Large 6, Stems..........	4.00	6.00	8.50	12.00	16.50
1807................476,000	4.25	6.50	9.00	13.00	20.00
1808 over 7, All Kinds..400,000	15.50	24.50	38.50	62.50	115.00
1808 Normal Date...........	4.00	6.50	10.00	13.50	20.00

TURBAN HEAD TYPE

Fair — Worn, but clear enough to identify.
Good — LIBERTY only partly visible on hair band. Lettering, date, stars, worn but visible.
Very Good — LIBERTY entirely visible on hair band. Lower curls worn.
Fine — Only part wear on LIBERTY and hair at top worn in spots.
Very Fine — Lettering clear-cut. Hair only slightly worn.

HALF CENTS

| 1809 Circle Inside O | | | | 1809 Normal Date | |

	Quan. Minted	Good	V. Good	Fine	V. Fine	Unc.
1809 Circle Inside 0						
All Kinds	1,154,572	$ 6.50	$ 9.00	$14.00	$21.00	$47.50
1809 over 6		6.50	9.00	14.00	21.00	55.00
1809 Normal Date		5.50	7.50	10.00	14.00	38.50
1810	215,000	8.50	12.50	20.00	28.50	125.00
1811	63,140	29.00	38.50	55.00	90.00	350.00
1811 Restrike Rev. of 1802				Very Rare		
1825	63,000	5.00	6.50	9.00	12.00	35.00
1826	234,000	5.00	6.50	9.00	12.00	30.00

13 Stars   12 Stars

	Quan. Minted	Good	V. Good	Fine	V. Fine	Unc.
1828 13 Stars						
All Kinds	606,000	4.50	6.00	7.50	13.00	28.50
1828 12 Stars		7.50	9.50	13.50	25.00	65.00
1829	487,000	5.00	6.00	8.50	14.50	30.00

 Original Large Berries Restrike Small Berries

	Quan. Minted	V. Good	Fine	V. Fine	Unc.	Proof
1831 Original (Beware of altered date)						
All Kinds	2,200					445.00
1831 Restrike Large Berries (Rev. of 1836)						365.00
1831 Restrike Small Berries (Rev. of 1852)						370.00
1832	154,000*	5.00	7.50	13.50	31.00	
1833	120,000*	4.50	7.00	12.00	35.00	135.00
1834	141,000*	4.75	7.00	12.00	35.00	135.00
1835	398,000*	4.50	7.00	12.00	35.00	135.00
1836 Original						400.00
1836 Restrike (Rev. of 1852)						360.00
1837 Token (not a coin)		14.00	27.50	42.50	63.50	

*Considered to be correct.

HALF CENTS

BRAIDED HAIR TYPE

Proofs only 1840 to 1849 and 1852. No Mint totals available.

	Proof		Proof
1840 Original	$450.00	1845 Original	$450.00
1840 Restrike	450.00	1845 Restrike	450.00
1841 Original	450.00	1846 Original	450.00
1841 Restrike	450.00	1846 Restrike	450.00
1842 Original	450.00	1847 Original	450.00
1842 Restrike	450.00	1847 Restrike	450.00
1843 Original	450.00	1848 Original	450.00
1843 Restrike	450.00	1848 Restrike	450.00
1844 Original	450.00	1849 Original - Small Date	450.00
1844 Restrike	450.00	1849 Restrike - Small Date	450.00

Good — Some of LIBERTY shows and beads partly distinct.
Very Good — Beads uniformly distinct. Hairlines show in spots.
Fine — Hairlines above ear worn. Beads sharp.
Very Fine — Lowest curl shows wear, hair otherwise distinct.

Brilliant or Red Uncirculated Half Cents Are Worth More Than Prices Shown.

		Small Date			Large Date	
	Quan. Minted	V. Good	Fine	V. Fine	Unc.	Proof
1849 Large Date	39,864	$ 7.50	$17.50	$30.00	$57.50	
1850	39,812	6.00	12.50	21.00	33.00	
1851	147,672	5.00	7.50	15.00	26.50	
1852 Original						
1852 Restrike						450.00
1853	129,694	5.00	7.50	15.00	26.50	
1854	55,358	5.50	9.25	17.00	29.00	160.00
1855	56,500	5.50	9.25	17.00	29.00	160.00
1856	40,430	6.00	10.25	18.00	31.00	160.00
1857	35,180	10.00	18.00	27.00	52.50	200.00

BIBLIOGRAPHY

Crosby, S. S., United States Coinage of 1793 (Cents and Half Cents). 1897. Reprint 1933.

Frossard, Ed., U. S. Cents and Half Cents 1793-1857. 1879.

Gilbert, Ebenezer, The United States Half Cents. 1916.

LARGE CENTS — 1793-1857

Laws affecting large cents were the same as half cents. The weights of cents are twice those of the half cents. Proofs are known to exist of some dates; all are rare.

THE 1793 CHAIN OR LINK CENT

Dies for first type cent were believed to been cut by Jean Pierre Droz, a Swiss.

THE WREATH CENTS OF 1793

These cents might be more easily identified if they were called single-bow Wreath Cents. The Liberty Cap Cents also have wreaths but the stems are tied with a double bow knot. There are other differences to be seen on the Wreath type cents such as a bolder relief to the head of Liberty, more loosely flowing hair and a three-leaf sprig above the date. Some types have the vine and bars, and one variety has ONE HUNDRED FOR A DOLLAR on the edge.

LARGE CENTS

Fair — Date and devices clear enough to identify.
Good — Lettering worn but readable. Bust has no detail.
Very Good — Date and lettering distinct, some details of head visible.
Fine — About half of hair, etc. details show.
Very Fine — Ear visible. Most of details can be seen.

	Quan. Minted	Fair	Good	V. Good	Fine	V. Fine
1793 Chain type, AMERI.						
All Kinds........	112,212	$110.00	$190.00	$310.00	$520.00	$825.00
1793 Chain type, AMERICA..		95.00	155.00	262.50	420.00	650.00

Wreath Type

1793 Chain type, Period after					
date and Liberty........	95.00	155.00	262.50	400.00	615.00
1793 Wreath type, Edge					
has Vine and Bars.......	65.00	112.50	170.00	262.50	420.00
1793 Wreath type, Lettered					
edge one Leaf on Edge...	65.00	115.00	180.00	290.00	500.00
1793 Wreath type, Lettered					
edge, Double Leaf Edge..	70.00	117.50	185.00	295.00	520.00

1793 Strawberry Leaf Var.   1793 Liberty Cap Type

1793 Wreath type, strawberry						
leaf variety.......101,156			(Ex. Rare)			
1793 Liberty Cap type						
All Kinds.........11,056	180.00	295.00	480.00	750.00	1045.00	

[66]

LARGE CENTS

Jefferson
Head

	Quan. Minted	Fair	Good	V. Good	Fine	V. Fine
1794 (Many Varieties)						
All Kinds	918,521	$11.00	$ 21.00	$ 30.00	$ 50.00	$ 75.00
1794 Head of 1793		18.50	33.00	50.00	80.00	125.00
1794 Head of 1795		12.50	24.00	30.00	50.00	80.00
1794 No fraction Bar		17.50	30.00	42.50	65.00	90.00
1795 Jeff. Hd. (Not Regular Issue)		75.00	125.00	175.00	275.00	475.00

One Cent in Center of Wreath   High in Wreath

1795 Lettered Edge ONE CENT in Center of Wreath					
All Kinds	82,000	17.00	30.00	45.00	70.00	100.00
1795 Lettered Edge ONE CENT High in Wreath		26.00	55.00	77.00	117.00	185.00
1795 Plain Edge, ONE CENT, Center of Wreath		9.00	20.00	26.50	40.00	50.00
1795 Plain Edge, ONE CENT High in Wreath		8.25	20.00	26.50	40.00	50.00
1795 Reeded Edge				(Very Rare)		

1796 Lib. Cap All Kinds 974,700	16.00	28.50	45.00	67.50	95.00

DRAPED BUST TYPE

Fair — Clear enough to identify.
Good — Lettering worn, but clear; date clear. Bust lacks details.
Very Good — Drapery partly visible. Less wear in date and lettering.
Fine — Hair over brow is smooth, some detail showing elsewhere.
Very Fine — Hairlines slightly worn. Hair over brow better defined.

LARGE CENTS

Draped Bust Type

LIHERTY Variety

	Quan. Minted	Fair	Good	V. Good	Fine	V. Fine
1796 Draped Bust............		$16.00	$25.00	$35.00	$ 60.00	$ 90.00
1796 LIHERTY Var. (error)..		20.00	35.00	60.00	100.00	140.00

Gripped or Milled Edge

		Stems		Stemless		
1797 Stems on Wreath All Kinds........897,510		6.50	10.00	15.00	25.00	40.00
1797 Stemless Wreath........		20.00	37.50	62.50	105.00	150.00
1797 Crudely Gripped or Milled Edge. Rev. of 1796		10.00	17.50	32.50	55.00	75.00
1797 Plain Edge. Rev. of 1796.		11.00	19.00	32.50	55.00	80.00

1798 Over 97   Small Date   Large Date

1798 over 97-All Kinds.979,700		11.00	17.50	35.00	60.00	80.00
1798 Small Date............		4.50	8.00	12.00	18.50	25.00
1798 Large Date............		5.50	9.00	13.00	20.00	28.50

Reverse of 1796

1798 Rev. of 1796, Wide date..

Fair	Good	V.G'd	Fine	V. Fine
11.00	22.00	35.00	57.50	90.00

1798 Rev. of 1796, Close date (Very Rare)

Wide Date——>

[68]

LARGE CENTS

1799 Over 98

$\leftarrow$

$\rightarrow$

(Normal Date)   Chip Reverse

$\rightarrow$

	Quan. Minted	Fair	Good	V. Good	Fine	V. Fine
1799 over 98-All Kinds	904,585	$135.00	$225.00	$350.00	$600.00	$900.00
1799 Normal Date	125.00	200.00	350.00	550.00	900.00

Genuine coins identified by the chip in the reverse die, (see arrow).

$\leftarrow$ 1800 Over 1798 $\rightarrow$ Normal Date

1800 over 1798 All Kinds	2,822,175	5.50	9.00	15.00	25.00	37.50
1800 over 179		5.50	8.00	12.00	19.50	28.50
1800 Normal Date		4.50	7.00	11.00	19.00	27.50

Normal Dies   1801 Reverse 3 Errors

$\rightarrow$

1801 Normal Dies — Blunt 1's All Kinds	1,362,837	4.00	8.00	12.00	20.00	26.00
1801 First 1 Perfect		5.00	9.50	16.00	27.00	38.00
1801 3 errors — 1/000, one stem and IINITED		15.00	25.00	45.00	75.00	100.00

1801 Error $\frac{1}{000}$

$\frac{1}{100}$ Over $\frac{1}{000}$

1801 Fraction 1/000		6.00	13.00	20.00	29.00	40.00
1801 Fraction 1/100 over 1/000		7.50	16.00	25.00	42.50	55.00

LARGE CENTS

	Quan. Minted	Fair	Good	V. Good	Fine	V. Fine
	Normal Dies			Stemless Wreath Double Fraction Bar		
1802 Normal Dies						
All Kinds.......3,435,100		$3.00	$6.50	$ 9.00	$13.50	$22.50
1802 Stemless Wreath —						
Single Fraction Bar......		3.50	7.50	12.00	20.00	27.50
1802 Stemless Wreath —						
Double Fraction Bar.....		4.00	8.50	14.00	25.00	32.50
1802 Fraction 1/000.........		4.75	9.50	16.00	27.00	40.00

1803 Small Date   Small Fraction   Large Fraction

	Fair	Good	V. Good	Fine	V. Fine
1803 Sm. Date — Sm. Fraction					
(Blunt 1) All Kinds. 2,471,353	3.50	6.00	9.50	15.00	35.00
1803 Sm. Date — Lg. Fraction					
(Blunt 1 in date)........	3.50	6.00	9.50	15.00	35.00
1803 Lg. Date — Sm. Fraction					
(Pointed 1 in date)......	40.00	80.00	130.00	225.00	300.00
1803 Lg. Date — Lg. Fraction					
(Pointed 1 in date)......	25.00	45.00	75.00	140.00	200.00
1803 Stemless Wreath........	7.00	12.00	20.00	30.00	42.50
1803 1/100 over 1/000........	7.50	13.50	23.00	38.00	48.00

On all genuine 1804 Cents
the O of the date is in line
with the O in OF on the
reverse of the coin.

		Fair	Good	V. Good	Fine	V. Fine
1804 Normal Dies						
All Kinds........756,838		85.00	130.00	190.00	300.00	420.00

LARGE CENTS

	Quan. Minted	Fair	Good	V. Good	Fine	V. Fine
1804 Broken Obv. Die		$70.00	$115.00	$170.00	$270.00	$365.00
1804 Broken Obv. & Rev. Dies.		70.00	115.00	170.00	270.00	365.00

RESTRIKE OF 1804 CENT

A fake 1804 was manufactured in the U. S. Mint by some employees of that institution about the year 1860 to satisfy the demand for this rare date. Known as the "restrike" it was a patchwork job and easily distinguished from a genuine 1804 cent.

1804 Restrike of 1860 . . . . Unc. $75.00

Blunt 1 in Date   Pointed 1

	Fair	Good	V. Good	Fine	V. Fine
1805 Blunt 1 in date					
All Kinds 941,116	4.00	7.50	12.00	18.00	26.00
1805 Pointed 1 in date	4.50	8.50	14.00	24.00	35.00

1807
Over 6

	Fair	Good	V. Good	Fine	V. Fine
1806 All Kinds 348,000	8.00	16.00	30.00	50.00	75.00
1807 over 6, Large 7					
All Kinds 727,221	4.00	7.50	12.50	21.00	27.50
1807 over 6, Small 7	28.00	45.00	62.50	115.00	175.00

LARGE CENTS

Small Fraction

Large Fraction

1807 Comet Variety

	Quan. Minted	Fair	Good	V. Good	Fine	V. Fine
1807 Small Fraction		$3.25	$ 7.25	$12.00	$18.50	$25.00
1807 Large Fraction		3.25	7.25	12.00	18.50	25.00
1807 Comet Variety						
Die Break Behind Head		6.00	11.00	20.00	35.00	50.00

TURBAN HEAD TYPE

1808 to 1814 — This group does not compare in sharpness and quality to those struck before, (1793-1807), nor to those struck after (1816 on). The copper used was "softer," having less alloy. This impaired the wearing quality of the series. For this reason collectors find greater difficulty in obtaining these dates in choice condition.

Fair — Details clear enough to identify.
Good — Legends, stars, date worn, but plain.
V. Good — LIBERTY all readable. Ear shows. Details worn but plain.
Fine — Hair on forehead and before ear nearly smooth. Ear and hair under ear sharp.
V. Fine — All hairlines show some detail. Leaves on rev. show wear.

13 Stars   12 Stars Caused by Die Break

		Fair	Good	V. Good	Fine	V. Fine
1808 13 Stars						
All Kinds	1,109,000	5.00	10.00	17.50	30.00	60.00
1808 12 Stars		5.50	12.00	22.00	37.50	65.00

		Fair	Good	V. Good	Fine	V. Fine
1809	222,867	25.00	50.00	80.00	125.00	250.00

LARGE CENTS

	Quan. Minted	Fair	Good	V. Good	Fine	V. Fine
1810 Over 9					Normal Date	
1810 over 9 All Kinds	1,458,500	$ 4.25	$ 9.50	$14.50	$20.00	$40.00
1810 Normal Date		3.50	8.50	12.75	18.50	35.00

1811 Over 10					Normal Date	
1811 over 10 All Kinds	218,025	17.00	21.00	32.00	62.50	97.50
1811 Normal Date		15.00	20.00	31.00	60.00	87.50

1812 Large Date				1813		
1812 Sm. Date All Kds.	1,075,500	3.50	7.50	12.00	17.50	33.50
1812 Large Date		4.00	8.00	14.00	19.00	35.00
1813	418,000	7.50	16.00	25.00	45.00	65.00

1814 Plain 4				1814 Crosslet 4	
1814 Plain 4 All Kinds	357,830	3.50	6.00	10.00	17.50	27.50
1814 Crosslet 4		3.50	6.00	10.00	17.50	27.50

LARGE CENTS

CORONET TYPE

Red to bright red uncirculated large cents (not cleaned) command higher prices

Good — Head details partly visible. Even wear in date and legends.
V. Good—LIBERTY, date, stars, legends clear. Part of hair cord visible
Fine — All hairlines show. Hair cords show uniformly.
V. Fine — Hair cords only slightly worn. Hairlines only partly worn
all well defined.

	Quan. Minted	Good	V. Good	Fine	V. Fine	Unc.
1816	2,820,982	$3.50	$5.00	$ 8.00	$12.50	$45.0

1817 Wide Date   **1817 Close Date**   **1817 15 Stars**

1817 Wide Date						
All Kinds	3,948,400	3.00	5.00	8.00	12.00	45.0
1817 Close Date		3.00	4.50	7.00	10.00	40.0
1817 15 Stars		5.00	9.00	15.00	22.50	75.0
1818	3,167,000	3.00	4.00	6.00	9.00	30.0

1819 Over 18   **1819 Small Date**   **1819 Large Date**

1819 over 18 All Kinds	2,671,000	4.00	5.50	8.50	14.00	60.0
1819 Small Date		3.00	4.00	6.00	9.00	33.0
1819 Large Date		3.25	4.75	7.00	11.50	37.5

1820 Over 19   **1820 Small Date**   **1820 Large Date**

1820 over 19 All Kinds	4,407,550	3.00	4.50	7.00	12.00	45.

LARGE CENTS

	Quan. Minted	Good	V. Good	Fine	V. Fine	Unc.
1820 Small Date............		$ 2.50	$ 4.25	$ 7.00	$10.00	$38.00
1820 Large Date............		2.50	3.50	6.00	9.00	28.00

1821 Wide Date   1821 Close Date

1821 Wide Date					
All Kinds........389,000	9.50	15.00	26.00	42.00	150.00
1821 Close Date............	11.50	21.00	34.00	47.50	175.00

1822 Wide Date   1822 Close Date

1822 Wide Date					
All Kinds.......2,072,339	3.50	5.25	8.00	15.00	75.00
1822 Close Date............	3.50	5.25	8.00	15.00	75.00

1823 Over 22   1823 Normal Date

1823 over 22 All Kinds.855,730	17.00	25.00	38.00	63.00	700.00
1823 Normal Date...........	20.00	30.00	47.00	80.00	1250.00
1823 Restrike, from broken obverse die.					60.00

LARGE CENTS

1824 Over 22   1824 Wide Date   1824 Close Date

	Quan. Minted	Good	V. Good	Fine	V. Fine	Unc.
1824 over 22						
All Kinds	1,262,000	$10.00	$15.00	$23.00	$38.00	$200.00
1824 Wide Date		4.25	6.00	10.00	20.00	125.00
1824 Close Date		4.25	6.00	10.00	20.00	125.00

1825 Small A's   1825 Large A's

1825 Small A's in Legend					
All Kinds	1,461,100	4.00	5.50	9.50	15.00	80.00
1825 Large A's in Legend		4.00	5.50	9.50	15.00	80.00

1826 Over 25   1826 Wide Date   1826 Close Date

1826 over 25 (Trace of 5 inside					
of 6) All Kinds	1,517,425	9.50	15.00	23.50	35.00	110.00
1826 Wide Date		3.75	5.50	9.00	15.00	77.50
1826 Close Date		3.50	5.00	8.00	13.00	72.50

LARGE CENTS

	Quan. Minted	Good	V. Good	Fine	V. Fine	Unc.
1827	2,357,732	$2.75	$ 4.00	$ 6.00	$11.00	$60.00

1828 Small Date   **1828 Large Date**

1828 Small Date						
All Kinds	2,260,624	6.25	9.50	15.00	22.00	105.00
1828 Large Date		3.25	5.00	7.00	13.00	57.50

1829 Small Letters   **1829 Large Letters**

1829 Small Letters						
All Kinds	1,414,500	5.00	7.50	11.50	19.00	82.50
1829 Large Letters		3.00	4.50	6.50	11.50	47.50
1830 Small Letters						
All Kinds	1,711,500	9.50	16.00	25.00	45.00	165.00
1830 Large Letters		3.25	4.50	6.50	11.50	55.00
1831 Small Letters						
All Kinds	3,359,260	2.75	3.50	5.50	9.00	42.50
1831 Large Letters		2.75	3.50	5.50	9.00	42.50
1832 Small Letters						
All Kinds	2,362,000	3.00	4.00	6.50	11.50	52.50
1832 Large Letters		3.00	4.00	6.50	11.50	52.50
1833 Small Letters						
All Kinds	2,739,000	2.75	3.75	6.00	9.00	40.00
1833 Large Letters		2.75	3.75	6.00	9.00	40.00

LARGE CENTS

Large Date, Large Stars Small Date, Large Stars Large Date, Small Stars

	Quan. Minted	Good	V. Good	Fine	V. Fine	Unc.
1834 Lg. Date, Lg. Stars, Lg. Let. on Rev. All Kinds	1,855,100	$4.75	$8.00	$12.50	$20.00	$65.00
1834 Sm. Date, Lg. Stars, Sm. Let. on Rev		3.75	5.50	9.00	13.00	45.00
1834 Lg. Date, Sm. Stars, Sm. Let. on Rev		4.50	7.00	11.50	17.00	57.00

Good — Considerably worn. LIBERTY readable.
V. Good — Hairlines smooth but visible, outline of ear clearly defined.
Fine — Hairlines at top of head and behind ear worn but visible.
Braid over brow plain, ear clear.
V. Fine—All details more sharp. Hair over brow shows only slight wear.

Large Date, Large Stars Small Date, Small Stars Type of 1836

1835 Lg. Date, Lg. Stars All Kinds	3,878,400	4.00	6.00	9.00	14.00	45.00
1835 Sm. Date, Sm. Stars		4.50	7.00	9.50	16.00	50.00
1835 Type of 1836		3.25	4.50	7.00	10.00	37.50

1836	2,111,000	3.00	4.50	7.50	11.50	47.50

LARGE CENTS

1837
Plain Hair
Cord

1837
Beaded
Hair
Cord

	Quan. Minted	Good	V. Good	Fine	V. Fine	Unc.
1837 Plain Hair Cord, Sm. Let. All Kinds	5,558,300	$ 4.50	$ 6.50	$ 9.50	$15.00	$55.00
1837 Plain Hair Cord, Lg. Let.		2.75	4.00	6.00	9.00	32.50
1837 Beaded Hair Cd., Sm. Let.		2.50	4.25	7.00	10.00	35.00
1838	6,370,200	2.50	3.75	5.00	9.00	25.00

1839 over 36

Line Under
CENT
No Center
Dot

	Good	V. Good	Fine	V. Fine	Unc.
1839 over 36 Line under CENT; No ctr. dot. All kinds . 3,128,661	75.00	110.00	160.00	235.00	———

Type of
1838

Silly Head
Variety

	Good	V. Good	Fine	V. Fine	Unc.
1839 Type 1838, Line under CENT	5.50	8.00	12.50	18.00	70.00
1839 Silly Head, Line under CENT; No center dot	6.50	9.00	15.00	20.00	85.00

Booby Head Variety, No Line Under CENT				1839 Type of 1840	
1839 Booby Head, no line und. CENT	4.50	7.00	10.00	14.00	65.00
1839 Type of 1840, no line und. CENT	5.50	8.00	12.50	17.50	72.50

LARGE CENTS
BRAIDED HAIR TYPE

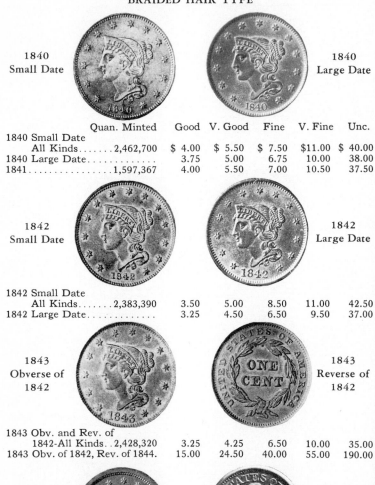

1840
Small Date

1840
Large Date

1842
Small Date

1842
Large Date

1843
Obverse of
1842

1843
Reverse of
1842

1843
Obverse of
1844

1843
Reverse of
1844

	Quan. Minted	Good	V. Good	Fine	V. Fine	Unc.
1840 Small Date						
All Kinds......	2,462,700	$ 4.00	$ 5.50	$ 7.50	$11.00	$ 40.00
1840 Large Date............		3.75	5.00	6.75	10.00	38.00
1841..............	1,597,367	4.00	5.50	7.00	10.50	37.50
1842 Small Date						
All Kinds......	2,383,390	3.50	5.00	8.50	11.00	42.50
1842 Large Date............		3.25	4.50	6.50	9.50	37.00
1843 Obv. and Rev. of						
1842-All Kinds..	2,428,320	3.25	4.25	6.50	10.00	35.00
1843 Obv. of 1842, Rev. of 1844.		15.00	24.50	40.00	55.00	190.00
1843 Obv. and Rev. of 1844 ...		4.50	7.00	10.00	15.00	65.00

LARGE CENTS

1844

1844
Over
81

	Quan. Minted	Good	V. Good	Fine	V. Fine	Unc.
1844 All Kinds.......	2,398,752	$3.00	$4.00	$ 5.00	$ 7.50	$30.00
1844 over 81 (die error).......		5.00	7.00	9.50	15.00	50.00
1845...............	3,894,804	2.50	3.50	5.00	6.50	21.00

1846
Small
Date

1846
Tall
Date

1846 Small Date						
All Kinds.......	4,120,800	2.00	2.50	3.50	6.00	21.00
1846 Medium Date...........		2.25	3.00	4.00	6.25	23.50
1846 Tall Date..............		2.75	3.50	5.50	9.50	30.00
1847...............	6,183,669	2.00	2.75	4.00	6.00	20.00

1848...............	6,415,799	2.00	2.75	4.00	6.00	20.00
1849...............	4,178,500	2.00	2.75	4.00	6.00	21.00
1850...............	4,426,844	2.00	2.75	4.00	6.00	20.00
1851 All Kinds.......	9,889,707	2.00	2.75	3.50	5.50	19.00
1851 over 81 (die error).......		4.75	5.50	10.00	15.00	60.00
1852...............	5,063,094	2.00	2.75	4.00	5.75	19.00
1853...............	6,641,131	2.00	2.75	4.00	5.75	19.00
1854...............	4,236,156	2.00	2.75	4.00	5.75	20.00

LARGE CENTS

1855
Upright 5's

1855
Slanting 5's

Original sketches of Engraver James B. Longacre's work reveal that slanting 5's were a peculiarity of his work. The upright 5's were probably the work of an apprentice.

	Quan. Minted	Good	V. Good	Fine	V. Fine	Unc.
1855 Upright 5's						
All Kinds	1,574,829	$ 2.50	$ 3.25	$ 4.50	$ 6.50	$20.00
1855 Slanting 5's		2.50	3.50	5.25	8.00	26.00
1855 Slanting 5's Knob on Ear		3.00	4.25	5.75	9.00	30.00

1856
Upright 5

1856
Slanting 5

1856 Upright 5						
All Kinds	2,690,463	2.50	3.50	4.50	6.50	20.00
1856 Slanting 5		2.50	3.50	4.50	6.50	20.00

1857
Small Date

1857
Large Date

1857 Small Date						
All Kinds	333,456	15.00	19.00	24.00	33.00	65.00
1857 Large Date		15.00	17.50	22.50	30.00	65.00

BIBLIOGRAPHY

Crosby, S. S., The Cents and Half Cents of 1793.
Hays, W. W., The Cents of 1794.
Gilbert-Elder, The Cents of 1796.
Doughty, Francis W., United States Cents.
Clapp, Geo. H., Cents of 1798 and 1799.
Newcomb, H. R., United States Copper Cents 1816-1857.
Sheldon, Wm. H., Penny Whimsy (1793-1814).

FLYING EAGLE CENTS — 1856-1858
Copper-Nickel or "White" Cents

The Act of February 21, 1857 provided for the coinage of the small cent, and made uncurrent the coins of other countries, particularly the Spanish and Mexican dollars. The new cents weighed 72 grains.

The 1858 cent is found in two major varieties. The A and M in the word AMERICA are joined in the large letter variety, and separated in the small letter variety. The reverse design of the eagle cents is dominated by a wreath of corn, wheat, cotton and tobacco.

Good — All details worn, but readable.
V. Good — Feather details and eye of Eagle are evident, but worn.
Fine — Eagle head details and feather tips sharp.
Ex. Fine — Slight wear, all details sharp.

THE 1856 FLYING EAGLE CENT

The 1856 Eagle Cent was not an authorized mint issue, as the law governing the new size coin was enacted after the date of issue. It is believed that about 1000 of these pieces were struck. They are usually referred to as patterns.

1858 Large Letters

1858 Small Letters

1858 Cent

	Quan. Minted	Good	V.G.	Fine	V.F.	E.F.	Unc.	Proof
1856	....	500.00	575.00	700.00	900.00	1300.00	2100.00	2300.00
1857	17,450,000	4.00	5.25	8.75	13.00	20.00	57.50	400.00
1858 All Kinds - 24,600,000 (Proofs, L.L. 80; S.L. 200)								
Large Letters..		5.00	7.25	11.50	20.00	31.00	95.00	500.00
1858 Small Letters..		5.00	7.25	11.50	20.00	31.00	105.00	525.00

INDIAN HEAD CENTS
1859-1864
Copper-Nickel

The small cent was redesigned in 1859, and a representation of an Indian girl was adopted as the obverse device. The 1859 reverse was also changed to represent a laurel wreath. In 1860 the reverse only was modified to display an oak wreath with a small shield at the top. The weight and composition of the coin was not changed.

Good — No LIBERTY visible.

V. Good — At least half of LIBERTY readable.

Fine — LIBERTY completely visible.

V. Fine — Slight but even wear on LIBERTY.

Ex. Fine — LIBERTY sharp. All other details sharp. Only slight wear on ribbon end.

1859 Only
Without shield
at top of wreath
on reverse

1860 to 1909
With shield
on reverse

	Quan. Minted	Good	V.G.	Fine	V.F.	E.F.	Unc.	Proof
1859	36,400,000	$3.50	$4.25	$ 8.50	$13.00	$19.50	$65.00	$ 275.00
1860..(400)	20,566,000	2.75	4.50	7.00	11.00	16.00	45.00	200.00
1861..(375)	10,100,000	7.50	9.50	15.00	18.50	26.00	70.00	250.00
1862..(450)	28,075,000	1.75	3.00	5.00	7.00	9.00	18.00	150.00
1863..(460)	49,840,000	1.75	2.75	4.00	5.50	7.00	20.00	150.00
1864..(300)	13,740,000	4.75	6.75	10.50	14.50	20.00	40.00	250.00

1864-1909 Bronze

During the year 1864 the alloy of the cent was changed to 95 per cent copper and five per cent tin and zinc. The weight was reduced to 48 grains, resulting in a thinner coin than the "White" Cents. The design remained unchanged. The first 1864 bronze cents did not have the designer's initial L on the bonnet ribbon. Later in the year the letter appeared on only a small quantity. The initial appeared on all dates of Indian Cents thereafter. Consult the illustration details.

1864 (No L on ribbon)

....(150)	39,233,714	2.25	4.50	8.50	12.00	15.50	40.00	400.00

1864 Bronze
Indian Head Cent With "L"

If the coin is turned slightly (so Indian faces observer) the highlighted details of the "L" will appear to better advantage. The point of the bust is pointed on the variety with "L"; rounded without "L." The "L" is the initial of the engraver, Longacre.

SMALL CENTS

Closed 3   Open 3

Select brilliant Unc. and Proof small cents command higher prices.

	Quan. Minted	Good	V.G.	Fine	V.F.	E.F.	Unc.	Proof
1864 (L on ribbon must show)								
....(20)	Unknown	$16.00	$30.00	$60.00	$77.50	$95.00	$225.00	$——
1865..(500)	35,429,286	2.25	3.25	5.75	8.25	13.75	31.50	150.00
1866..(725)	9,826,500	10.00	15.00	25.00	40.00	52.50	95.00	190.00
1867..(625)	9,821,000	9.00	14.00	23.00	37.00	50.00	100.00	200.00
1868..(600)	10,266,500	9.00	14.00	23.00	37.00	50.00	100.00	200.00
‡1869 over 8 All Kinds								
....(600)	6,420,000	45.00	55.00	75.00	95.00	125.00	270.00	
1869..............		14.00	23.50	45.00	62.50	82.50	170.00	300.00
1870 (1,000)	5,275,000	13.00	20.00	35.00	45.00	65.00	125.00	250.00
1871..(960)	3,929,500	19.00	28.50	47.50	65.00	80.00	155.00	300.00
1872..(950)	4,042,000	22.50	35.00	55.00	75.00	95.00	205.00	350.00
1873 Closed 3 All Kinds								
....(600)	11,676,500	5.50	8.25	14.25	21.25	31.00	70.00	125.00
1873 Open 3.........		5.00	8.00	14.00	20.50	30.00	65.00	
1874..(700)	14,187,500	4.50	7.75	14.00	20.00	29.00	65.00	120.00
1875..(700)	13,528,000	5.00	8.00	14.50	21.00	30.00	70.00	120.00
1876 (1,150)	7,944,000	7.00	11.50	19.00	27.00	35.00	75.00	115.00
1877..(510)	852,500	80.00	105.00	170.00	230.00	350.00	680.00	1100.00
1878 (2,350)	5,799,850	8.25	12.50	19.00	27.50	35.00	65.00	110.00
1879 (3,200)	16,231,200	2.00	3.50	5.50	8.00	9.25	28.00	50.00
1880 (3,955)	38,964,955	1.50	2.50	4.50	6.25	9.00	26.00	42.50
1881 (3,575)	39,211,575	1.50	2.50	4.50	6.25	9.00	26.00	42.50
1882 (3,100)	38,581,100	1.50	2.50	4.50	6.25	9.00	26.00	55.00
1883 (6,609)	45,598,109	1.25	2.25	3.50	5.25	8.00	22.00	45.00
1884 (3,942)	23,261,742	2.25	3.50	6.00	9.50	13.50	31.00	55.00
1885 (3,790)	11,765,384	4.00	7.00	12.75	17.25	22.00	41.50	62.50
1886 (*Var. 1) All Kinds								
(4,290)	17,654,290	2.50	3.50	7.00	11.50	15.50	32.50	60.00
1886 (*Var. 2).......		2.50	3.50	7.00	11.50	15.50	32.50	60.00
1887 (2,960)	45,226,483	.65	1.30	2.75	4.65	8.00	18.50	45.00
1888 (4,582)	37,494,414	.70	1.50	2.75	4.65	8.00	21.00	42.50
1889 (3,336)	48,869,361	.65	1.30	2.40	4.25	6.75	17.00	42.50
1890 (2,740)	57,182,854	.65	1.30	2.40	4.25	6.75	17.00	42.50
1891 (2,350)	47,072,350	.65	1.30	2.40	4.25	6.75	17.00	42.50
1892 (2,745)	37,649,832	.70	1.45	2.70	5.25	8.50	18.50	42.50
1893 (2,195)	46,642,195	.60	1.30	2.50	4.25	6.25	15.00	42.50
1894 (2,632)	16,752,132	1.50	4.00	7.00	9.50	12.50	32.50	50.00
1895 (2,062)	38,343,636	.60	1.20	2.50	4.50	7.25	16.50	47.50
1896 (1,862)	39,057,293	.60	1.20	2.50	4.50	7.25	20.00	55.00
1897 (1,938)	50,466,330	.55	1.20	2.25	4.00	6.75	17.50	47.50
1898 (1,795)	49,823,079	.55	1.10	2.15	4.00	6.00	16.75	47.50

‡Do not confuse with recut variety.
*1886 VAR. 1 Last feather points between I and C.
*1886 VAR. 2 Last feather points between C and A.

SMALL CENTS

	Quan. Minted	Good	V.G.	Fine	V.F.	E.F.	Unc.	Proof
1899..(2,031)	53,600,031	$ .50	$ 1.10	$ 2.00	$ 3.50	$ 4.50	$16.00	$45.00
1900..(2,262)	66,833,764	.45	.80	1.50	2.50	3.50	12.00	42.50
1901..(1,985)	79,611,143	.40	.75	1.15	2.25	3.50	8.00	38.00
1902..(2,018)	87,376,722	.40	.75	1.15	2.25	3.50	8.00	38.00
1903..(1,790)	85,094,493	.40	.75	1.15	2.25	3.50	8.00	38.00
1904..(1,817)	61,328,015	.40	.75	1.15	2.25	3.50	8.00	38.00
1905..(2,152)	80,719,163	.40	.75	1.15	2.25	3.50	8.00	38.00
1906..(1,725)	96,022,255	.40	.75	1.15	2.25	3.50	8.00	38.00
1907..(1,475)	108,138,618	.40	.75	1.15	2.25	3.50	8.00	42.50
1908..(1,620)	32,327,987	.50	.90	1.30	2.40	3.80	11.00	45.00
1908S	1,115,000	16.25	20.00	25.00	35.00	45.00	92.50	
1909..(2,175)	14,370,645	.85	1.25	2.00	3.00	5.00	12.00	50.00
1909S	309,000	66.50	75.00	87.50	97.50	155.00	280.00	

Lincoln Head Type — 1909 to Date

Victor D. Brenner designed this cent which was issued to commemorate the hundredth anniversary of Lincoln's birth. The designer's initials VDB appear on a limited quantity of cents of 1909. The San Francisco mint produced the smallest issue before the initials were removed, creating the scarcest though not the highest priced Lincoln Head Cent. The initials were restored, in 1918, to the obverse side as illustrated below. This type cent was the first to have the motto "In God We Trust."

Select brilliant uncirculated cents command higher prices.

Cents with well-struck mint marks are also worth more.

Matte Proof

		Good	V.G.	Fine	V.F.	E.F.	Unc.	Proof
1909 V. D. B. ....(420)	27,995,000	.50	.65	.85	1.10	1.40	4.25	185.00
1909S, V. D. B..	484,000	115.00	130.00	147.50	170.00	200.00	310.00	

Good — *Date worn but apparent. Lines in wheat ears missing.*

V. Good — *Lines show in upper wheat ears.*

Fine — *Wheat lines worn but visible.*

V. Fine—*Cheek, and jaw bones worn but separated. No worn spots on wheat ears.*

Ex. Fine — *Slight wear. All details sharp.*

No
V. D. B.
on
Reverse

1909..(2,198)	72,702,618	.35	.45	.65	.90	1.35	6.00	47.50
1909S	1,825,000	25.00	28.50	33.50	37.50	55.00	87.50	
1910..(2,405)	146,801,218	.15	.25	.45	.85	1.50	7.00	48.50
1910S	6,045,000	3.00	4.25	5.50	8.00	10.50	40.00	
1911..(1,733)	101,177,787	.20	.30	.50	1.00	1.75	8.25	42.50
1911D	12,672,000	1.30	2.00	3.25	6.25	10.00	30.00	
1911S	4,026,000	8.50	10.50	13.50	17.50	22.50	50.00	
1912..(2,145)	68,153,060	.15	.30	.50	1.25	1.75	10.00	42.50
1912D	10,411,000	1.50	2.25	4.25	9.00	14.50	42.50	
1912S	4,431,000	4.50	5.50	7.00	11.00	17.50	40.00	
1913..(2,848)	76,532,352	.15	.30	.50	.95	1.50	8.50	40.00
1913D	15,804,000	.65	1.50	3.50	6.50	10.00	42.50	
1913S	6,101,000	3.50	4.50	6.00	8.50	12.50	42.50	

[86]

SMALL CENTS

	Quan. Minted	Good	V.G.	Fine	V.F.	E.F.	Unc.	Matte Proof
1914..(1,365)	75,238,432	$ .40	$ 1.10	$ 2.30	$ 3.60	$ 5.00	$25.00	$75.00
*1914D	1,193,000	38.00	47.50	68.50	110.00	175.00	500.00	
1914S	4,137,000	4.50	5.50	6.75	13.50	20.00	85.00	
1915..(1,150)	29,092,120	.50	1.75	4.00	6.00	12.50	80.00	120.00
1915D	22,050,000	.50	1.25	2.35	3.75	7.00	23.50	
1915S	4,833,000	3.50	5.00	6.25	8.00	12.50	42.50	
1916..(1,050)	131,833,677	.15	.30	.50	.90	1.50	8.00	120.00
1916D	35,956,000	.35	.60	2.00	3.25	5.50	17.50	
1916S	22,510,000	.60	1.25	2.50	4.40	7.50	30.00	
1917	196,429,785	.15	.30	.50	.75	1.50	7.00	
1917D	55,120,000	.35	.75	1.40	4.25	7.25	24.00	
1917S	32,620,000	35	.75	1.40	4.25	7.25	24.00	

Designer's
Initials
Restored

1918	288,104,634	.20	.35	.50	1.00	1.50	8.00	
1918D	47,830,000	.30	.80	1.75	4.00	7.00	30.00	
1918S	34,680,000	.30	.80	1.75	4.00	7.00	32.50	
1919	392,021,000	.15	.24	.40	.85	1.50	7.50	
1919D	57,154,000	.30	.65	1.25	3.00	5.00	21.00	
1919S	139,760,000	.30	.65	1.25	3.00	5.00	21.00	
1920	310,165,000	.15	.30	.50	1.00	1.35	7.00	
1920D	49,280,000	.30	.75	1.50	4.00	6.50	35.00	
1920S	46,220,000	.30	.75	1.50	4.00	6.50	35.00	
1921	39,157,000	.30	.75	1.50	3.25	5.00	17.50	
1921S	15,274,000	.75	1.65	3.50	13.00	22.50	140.00	
1922D All K.	7,160,000	2.70	4.00	5.75	8.50	12.50	35.00	
1922 Plain (Filled die, D missing)								
		18.50	25.00	37.50	57.50	90.00	325.00	
1923	74,723,000	.15	.25	.40	.85	1.50	8.00	
1923S	8,700,000	1.00	2.50	4.50	13.50	25.00	200.00	
1924	75,178,000	.20	.25	.30	1.00	2.00	15.00	
1924D	2,520,000	10.00	14.50	17.50	24.50	32.50	110.00	
1924S	11,696,000	1.20	1.75	3.00	9.00	16.00	70.00	
1925	139,949,000	.20	.25	.35	.65	1.25	6.25	
1925D	22,580,000	.30	.60	1.25	2.25	4.00	20.00	
1925S	26,380,000	.50	1.00	2.50	3.50	6.00	32.50	
1926	157,088,000	.20	.25	.35	.90	1.50	4.00	
1926D	28,020,000	.25	.55	1.10	2.00	3.50	20.00	
1926S	4,550,000	2.25	4.00	5.50	12.00	20.00	80.00	
1927	144,440,000	.20	.25	.45	.90	1.35	4.25	
1927D	27,170,000	.30	.60	1.10	2.60	4.00	15.50	
1927S	14,276,000	.40	1.00	2.25	4.50	7.00	35.00	
1928	134,116,000	.15	.25	.40	.65	1.00	3.75	
1928D	31,170,000	.30	.50	.85	2.25	3.50	13.50	
1928S	17,266,000	.30	.55	1.10	2.50	4.50	22.50	

*Beware of Altered Date. No VDB on Lincoln's Shoulder on Genuine 1914D Coin.

SMALL CENTS

	Quan. Minted	Good	V.G.	Fine	V.F.	E.F.	Unc.	Proof
1929	185,262,000	$ .10	$ .15	$ .20	$ .30	$ .65	$ 3.50	
1929D	41,730,000	.15	.20	.30	.60	.85	7.50	
1929S	50,148,000	.15	.20	.30	.60	.90	4.00	
1930	157,415,000	.15	.20	.30	.40	.50	2.00	
1930D	40,100,000	.25	.30	.40	.75	1.10	6.75	
1930S	24,286,000	.25	.30	.40	.65	.85	4.25	
1931	19,396,000	.25	.45	.75	1.25	1.75	11.50	
1931D	4,480,000	2.50	3.75	6.00	8.00	12.50	60.00	
1931S	866,000	22.50	25.00	30.00	35.00	45.00	72.50	
1932	9,062,000	.40	.55	1.25	1.75	2.25	11.50	
1932D	10,500,000	.40	.55	1.25	1.75	2.25	11.50	
1933	14,360,000	.60	.85	2.00	3.00	4.00	17.50	
1933D	6,200,000	1.25	1.50	2.50	3.50	4.50	22.50	
1934	219,080,000						3.25	
1934D	28,446,000						8.00	
1935	245,388,000						1.35	
1935D	47,000,000						2.60	
1935S	38,702,000						3.50	
1936..(5,569)	309,637,569						1.25	$55.00
1936D	40,620,000						1.50	
1936S	29,130,000						2.00	
1937..(9,320)	309,179,320						1.00	25.00
1937D	50,430,000						1.40	
1937S	34,500,000						1.75	
1938 (14,734)	156,696,734						1.75	7.00
1938D	20,010,000						2.00	
1938S	15,180,000						3.50	
1939 (13,520)	316,479,520						1.00	5.50
1939D	15,160,000	.50	.65	.75	1.10	1.50	4.75	
1939S	52,070,000						1.95	
1940 (15,872)	586,825,872						.85	4.25
1940D	81,390,000						1.00	
1940S	112,940,000						1.10	
1941 (21,100)	887,039,100						.70	4.00
1941D	128,700,000						.95	
1941S	92,360,000						1.00	
1942 (32,600)	657,828,600						.55	3.00
1942D	206,698,000						.60	
1942S	85,590,000						3.00	

WARTIME STEEL CENTS

Owing to a shortage of copper during the critical war year 1943 the Treasury Department resorted to the use of zinc coated steel for our cents. No bronze cents were officially issued in 1943. A few specimens struck on bronze planchets by error are known to exist. Through a similar error, a few of the 1944 cents were struck on steel planchets.

1943	684,628,670	.75
1943D	217,660,000	.85
1943S	191,550,000	2.00

"SHELL CASE" COPPER

Shell cases were salvaged for coinage in 1944. Although the color is a little different, the coin has proved satisfactory in every respect.

1944	1,435,400,000	.50

SMALL CENTS

	Quan. Minted	Unc.	Proof
1944D	430,578,000	$ .50	
1944S	282,760,000	.65	
1945	1,040,515,000	.60	
1945D	226,268,000	.55	
1945S	181,770,000	.60	

BRONZE PRE-WAR COMPOSITION RESUMED

	Quan. Minted	Unc.	Proof
1946	991,655,000	.50	
1946D	315,690,000	.50	
1946S	198,100,000	.60	
1947	190,555,000	1.00	
1947D	194,750,000	.55	
1947S	99,000,000	.80	
1948	317,570,000	.70	
1948D	172,637,500	.75	
1948S	81,735,000	.90	
1949	217,490,000	1.00	
1949D	154,370,500	1.00	
1949S	64,290,000	1.75	
1950	(51,386) 272,686,386	.70	$21.00
1950D	334,950,000	.50	
1950S	118,505,000	1.00	
1951	(57,500) 294,633,500	.60	10.00
1951D	625,355,000	.50	
1951S	100,890,000	1.35	
1952	(81,980) 186,856,980	.60	8.00
1952D	746,130,000	.45	
1952S	137,800,004	1.00	
1953	(128,800) 256,883,800	.40	5.50
1953D	700,515,000	.40	
1953S	181,835,000	.75	
1954	(233,300) 71,873,350	.80	3.50
1954D	251,552,500	.35	
1954S	96,190,000	.60	
1955 All Kinds	(378,200) 330,958,200	.30	2.75

	Quan. Minted	Unc.	Proof
1955 Doubled Die Obv		———	
1955D	563,257,500	.30	
1955S	44,610,000	.90	
1956	(669,384) 421,414,384	.20	2.00
1956D	1,098,201,100	.15	

SMALL CENTS

	Quan. Minted		Unc.	Proof
1957	(1,247,952)	283,787,952	$ .15	$1.25
1957D		1,051,342,000	.15	
1958	(875,652)	253,400,652	.20	2.75
1958D		800,953,000	.15	

Frank Gasparro designed the Lincoln Memorial reverse which was introduced on the 150th anniversary of Lincoln's birth in 1959.

1959	(1,149,291)	610,864,291	.15	1.25
1959D		1,279,760,000	.10	

Small Date	**Large Date**

1960 Large date - All Kinds	(1,691,602)	588,096,602	.10	1.25
1960 Small date			4.00	17.00
1960D Large date - All Kinds		1,580,884,000	.10	
1960D Small date			.40	
1961	(3,028,244)	756,373,244	.05	.75
1961D		1,753,266,700	.05	

COMPOSITION CHANGED TO 95% COPPER, 5% ZINC

1962	(3,218,019)	609,263,019	.05	.75
1962D		1,793,148,400	.05	
1963			.05	.75
1963D			.05	

TWO-CENT PIECES — 1864-1873 Bronze

The Act of April 22, 1864 which changed the weight and composition of the cent included a provision for the bronze two-cent piece. The weight was specified as 96 grains, the alloy being the same as for the cent.

The two-cent piece is one of the short-lived issues of United States coinage. The motto "In God We Trust" appeared for the first time. Its presence on the new coin was due largely to the increased religious sentiment during the Civil War crisis.

There are two varieties for the first year of issue, 1864: the small motto and the large motto. The differences are explained in the illustrations below. The small motto variety of 1864 is scarce.

It will be noted that the shield device is very similar to the nickel five-cent piece introduced in 1866.

Select uncirculated and proof coins command higher prices.

Good — At least IN GOD visible.

V. Good — WE weakly visible.

Fine — Complete Motto visible. WE weak.

Ex. Fine — WE is bold.

TWO-CENT PIECES

Small Motto   TWO CENTS OF 1864   Large Motto

Details explain the differences in these two well-known varieties. On the obverse the D in God is narrow on the large motto. The stem to the leaf shows plainly on the small motto variety. There is no stem on the large motto coin.

Letter T in TRUST touches ribbon crease at left on small motto variety; there is a 1/32″ gap on the large motto variety.

	Quan. Minted	Good	V.G.	Fine	E.F.	Unc.	Proof
1864 Small Motto							
All Kinds	19,847,500	$35.00	$42.50	$55.00	$90.00	$210.00	$———
1864 Large Motto		1.50	2.25	3.25	7.00	11.50	125.00
1865	13,640,000	1.75	2.50	3.50	7.25	12.00	70.00
1866	3,177,000	1.75	3.00	5.00	8.50	22.50	57.50
1867	2,938,750	1.75	3.00	5.00	8.50	20.00	57.50
1868	2,803,750	1.75	3.00	5.00	8.50	20.00	57.50
1869	1,546,500	2.00	3.50	6.00	10.00	22.00	60.00
1870	861,250	3.00	5.00	8.00	13.00	30.00	65.00
1871	721,250	4.00	5.75	9.00	17.50	40.00	72.50
1872	65,000	25.00	28.50	35.00	47.50	77.50	120.00
1873 Proofs only (Closed 3)							340.00
1873 Proofs only (Open 3)							340.00
(See page 85.)							

THREE-CENT PIECES (NICKEL) 1865-1889

Dr. Lewis Feuchtwanger produced a metal which was really a variety of German silver consisting of nickel, copper and some zinc. He suggested as early as 1837 to Congress that his metal be substituted for copper. He made some one-cent and three-cent trial pieces in this metal at that time.

The regular series which was issued uninterruptedly from 1865 until 1889 offers no type variations. The edge is plain.

Good — Date and legends complete though worn. III smooth.

V. Good — III is half worn. Rims complete.

Fine — Hair curls well defined.

Ex. Fine — Slight, even wear.

1865	11,382,000	1.10	1.40	1.75	3.75	8.50	300.00
1866	4,801,000	1.30	1.60	2.25	4.00	9.00	65.00
1867	3,915,000	1.25	1.60	2.25	4.00	9.00	40.00
1868	3,252,000	1.30	1.65	2.25	4.00	9.00	40.00
1869	1,604,000	1.50	2.00	2.75	4.50	9.00	40.00
1870	1,335,000	1.65	2.10	3.00	5.00	10.00	40.00
1871	604,000	2.60	3.50	5.00	7.25	16.00	42.50
1872	862,000	2.30	3.25	4.60	7.00	15.00	40.00

THREE-CENT PIECES (NICKEL)

	Quan. Minted	Good	V.G.	Fine	E.F.	Unc.	Proof
1873 (Closed 3)							
All Kinds.....	1,173,000	$2.25	$3.00	$4.00	$7.00	$12.00	$25.00
1873 (Open 3).............		1.00	1.40	2.00	4.00	10.00	
1874...............	790,000	2.50	3.50	4.75	10.00	17.00	42.50
1875...............	228,000	4.25	5.75	8.25	13.50	25.00	45.00
1876...............	162,000	4.00	5.25	7.50	12.50	24.00	37.50
1877 (Proofs Only).........							295.00
1878........(2,350)	2,350						100.00
1879........(3,200)	41,200	3.00	4.00	5.50	8.75	14.00	30.00
1880........(3,955)	24,955	3.00	4.00	5.50	8.75	14.00	23.00
1881........(3,575)	1,080,575	1.25	1.45	1.75	4.00	7.50	22.00
1882........(3,100)	25,300	2.75	3.50	4.50	8.00	14.00	22.00
1883........(6,609)	10,609	2.75	3.50	4.50	8.00	14.00	22.00
1884........(3,942)	5,642	3.25	4.25	5.50	8.00	14.00	26.00
1885........(3,790)	4,790	3.25	4.25	5.50	8.00	14.00	27.50
1886........(4,290)	4,290						27.50
1887 87 over 86.............							115.00
1887 All Kinds(2,960)	7,961	12.50	16.00	19.00	27.50	60.00	87.50
1888........(4,582)	41,083	3.25	4.00	5.25	9.00	15.00	22.00
1889........(3,436)	21,561	3.50	4.35	5.75	9.00	17.00	23.00

NICKEL FIVE-CENT PIECES—Shield Type 1866-1883

The shield type nickel was made possible by the act of May 16, 1866. Its weight was set at 77-16/100 grains with the same composition as the nickel three-cent piece which was authorized in 1865. In 1866 the coin was designed with rays between the stars on the reverse. Some of the pieces minted in 1867 have the same details, but later the rays were eliminated creating two varieties for that year. There was no further change in the type until it was replaced by the Liberty head device in 1883.

Proofs only were struck in 1877 and 1878.

With Rays Without Rays

Good — All letters in Motto readable.

V. Good—Motto stands out clearly. Rims worn slightly but even. Part of shield lines visible.

Fine — Half of each olive leaf is smooth.

Ex. Fine — Leaf tips show slight wear. Cross over shield slightly worn.

		Good	V.G.	Fine	E.F.	Unc.	Proof
1866.............	14,742,500	4.25	6.00	10.00	25.00	50.00	600.00
1867 Rays All K.	30,909,500	5.50	10.50	17.50	40.00	95.00	———
1867 Without Rays.........		1.50	2.00	3.00	5.25	14.00	42.50
1868.............	28,817,000	1.50	2.00	3.00	5.25	14.00	40.00
1869.............	16,395,000	2.50	3.25	4.25	7.50	16.00	47.50
1870.............	4,806,000	2.75	4.00	6.00	9.50	20.00	48.50
1871.............	561,000	29.50	35.00	47.50	75.00	142.50	195.00
1872.............	6,036,000	3.50	4.50	6.25	10.50	22.50	39.00
1873(Clos.3)All Kds.	4,550,000	3.50	5.25	7.50	12.00	23.50	32.50
1873 (Open 3).............		3.00	4.25	6.00	10.00	20.00	
1874.............	3,538,000	6.00	7.50	10.00	14.00	25.00	55.00
1875.............	2,097,000	11.00	14.00	19.00	40.00	80.00	110.00

NICKEL FIVE-CENT PIECES

	Quan. Minted	Good	V.G.	Fine	E.F.	Unc.	Proof
1876	2,530,000	$ 6.00	$ 7.25	$ 9.00	$14.00	$ 27.50	$ 37.50
1877 Est. Issued...(500)	500						775.00
1878 (2,350)	2,350						160.00
1879 (3,200)	29,100	10.00	12.00	14.00	21.00	37.50	55.00
1880 (3,955)	19,955	13.50	15.00	19.00	26.00	45.00	55.00
1881 (3,575)	72,375	10.00	12.00	14.00	21.00	40.00	45.00
1882 (3,100)	11,476,600	1.75	2.50	3.75	6.50	14.00	30.00
1883 All K. (5,419)	1,456,919	2.00	3.00	4.00	6.50	14.00	25.00
1883 over 2						125.00	

LIBERTY HEAD TYPE 1883-1913

In 1883 the type was changed to the familiar "Liberty head." This type first appeared without the word CENTS on the coin, merely a large letter "V." These "centless" coins were goldplated and passed for five dollars. Later in that year the word CENTS was added.

It has been reported that five 1913 Liberty head nickels were originally owned by Col. Green (the deceased son of the famous Hetty Green). These have since been dispersed and are now held in the collections of several individuals. These were not a regular mint issue and were never placed in circulation.

Without CENTS

Good — No detail in head.
LIBERTY obliterated.
V. Good —At least 3 letters in LIBERTY readable.
Fine — All letters in LIBERTY show.
Ex. Fine — LIBERTY sharp.
Corn grains at bottom of wreath show, on reverse.

1883 Without CENTS							
(6,609)	5,479,519	.50	.70	1.25	2.00	4.50	21.00

 With CENTS

1883 With CENTS						
All Kinds (2,543) 16,032,983	4.00	5.75	8.00	11.50	20.00	30.00
1884 (3,942) 11,273,942	4.50	6.00	8.50	14.00	25.00	35.00
1885 (3,790) 1,476,490	47.50	55.00	75.00	105.00	160.00	180.00
1886 (4,290) 3,330,290	23.50	30.00	45.00	60.00	80.00	97.50
1887 (2,960) 15,263,652	2.25	3.25	5.25	9.50	22.50	27.00
1888 (4,582) 10,720,483	4.50	5.50	9.50	16.00	24.00	30.00
1889 (3,336) 15,881,362	2.25	3.25	5.00	8.25	24.00	30.00
1890 (2,740) 16,259,271	3.25	4.00	6.00	12.50	25.00	30.00
1891 (2,350) 16,834,350	2.00	2.75	4.25	8.50	20.00	31.00
1892 (2,745) 11,699,642	2.50	3.00	5.50	8.50	20.00	30.00
1893 (2,195) 13,370,195	2.00	2.75	3.75	8.00	20.00	31.00

NICKEL FIVE-CENT PIECES

	Quan. Minted	Good	V.G.	Fine	E.F.	Unc.	Proof
1894......(2,632)	5,413,132	$ 4.00	$ 5.75	$ 9.00	$15.00	$ 26.00	$ 35.00
1895......(2,062)	9,979,884	1.50	2.50	4.50	8.00	21.50	36.00
1896......(1,862)	8,842,920	2.00	4.00	9.00	16.00	40.00	67.50
1897......(1,938)	20,428,735	1.10	2.00	3.50	7.00	18.00	31.00
1898......(1,795)	12,532,087	1.10	2.00	3.50	7.00	18.00	31.00
1899......(2,031)	26,029,031	1.00	1.75	3.00	6.50	17.50	29.50
1900......(2,262)	27,255,995	.60	1.40	2.50	5.50	16.00	27.50
1901......(1,985)	26,480,213	.50	1.10	2.25	4.50	14.50	26.00
1902......(2,018)	31,480,579	.50	1.10	2.25	4.50	14.00	24.00
1903......(1,790)	28,006,725	.50	1.10	2.25	4.50	12.00	24.00
1904......(1,817)	21,404,984	.50	1.10	2.25	4.50	12.00	23.00
1905......(2,152)	29,827,276	.50	1.10	2.25	4.50	13.50	22.50
1906......(1,725)	38,613,725	.50	1.10	2.25	4.50	12.50	23.00
1907......(1,475)	39,214,800	.50	1.10	2.25	4.50	12.50	32.50
1908......(1,620)	22,686,177	.50	1.10	2.25	4.50	12.00	23.50
1909......(4,763)	11,590,526	.50	1.10	2.25	4.50	12.00	23.50
1910......(2,405)	30,169,353	.50	1.10	2.25	4.50	12.00	23.50
1911......(1,733)	39,559,372	.50	1.10	2.25	4.50	11.00	25.00
1912......(2,145)	26,236,714	.50	1.10	2.25	4.50	11.00	37.50
1912D............8,474,000		1.50	4.00	9.50	40.00	150.00	
1912S.............238,000		20.00	30.00	45.00	75.00	250.00	
1913 Liberty Hd. (5 Known)							

INDIAN HEAD OR BUFFALO TYPE 1913-1938

These pieces are known as Buffalo, Bison or Indian head nickels. In the first
year of issue, 1913, there were two distinct varieties; the first showing the bison
on a mound, and the second with the base redesigned to a thinner straight line.

James E. Fraser designed this nickel employing three different Indians as
models. His initial (F) is beneath the date. The bison was modeled after
"Black Diamond" in the New York Zoological Gardens.

Variety 1   Variety 2

Good — Legends and
date readable.
Horn worn off.
V. Good — Half horn
shows.
Fine — Two-thirds
horn shows.
Obv. rim intact.

Ex. Fine — Full horn. Some wear on Indian's braids.

		Good	V.G.	Fine	E.F.	Unc.	Matte Proof
1913 Var. 1							
.....(*2,594)	30,993,520	.70	.95	1.50	2.10	5.50	100.00
1913D Var. 1......5,337,000		1.95	2.75	3.50	8.00	17.00	
1913S Var. 1......2,105,000		3.75	5.50	7.50	14.50	27.50	
1913 Var. 2......29,858,700		.75	1.10	1.60	2.75	7.00	110.00
1913D Var. 2......4,156,000		12.50	16.00	22.00	35.00	60.00	
1913S Var. 2......1,209,000		25.00	32.50	45.00	65.00	97.50	
1914......(1,275)	20,665,738	.95	1.60	2.65	5.25	11.00	110.00
1914D............3,912,000		11.00	14.50	21.00	37.50	85.00	
1914S............3,470,000		2.50	4.75	8.25	21.00	47.50	
1915......(1,050)	20,987,270	.85	1.25	2.25	4.75	11.00	110.00

*Both Varieties.

INDIAN HEAD OR BUFFALO NICKELS

	Quan. Minted	Good	V.G.	Fine	E.F.	Unc.	Matte Proof
1915D	7,569,500	$ 2.25	$ 4.50	$ 7.50	$19.00	$ 47.50	
1915S	1,505,000	7.00	9.00	15.00	32.50	85.00	
1916	(600) 63,498,066	.35	.70	1.25	4.00	9.00	$125.00
1916D	13,333,000	1.50	2.65	4.50	12.50	45.00	
1916S	11,860,000	1.60	3.00	5.50	14.00	47.50	
1917	51,424,029	.35	.55	.85	2.75	8.50	
1917D	9,910,800	2.50	5.00	8.50	29.00	60.00	
1917S	4,193,000	2.75	5.25	9.00	30.00	75.00	
1918	32,086,314	.40	.90	1.75	4.25	25.00	

1918D over 7 Variety

1938D over S Variety

	Quan. Minted	Good	V.G.	Fine	E.F.	Unc.
1918D over 7 All K.	8,362,000	100.00	160.00	275.00	850.00	2,800.00
1918D Normal Date		2.75	4.50	7.50	37.50	90.00
1918S	4,882,000	2.75	4.75	8.50	40.00	90.00
1919	60,868,000	.30	.55	1.00	2.75	14.00
1919D	8,006,000	2.75	5.50	10.00	60.00	110.00
1919S	7,521,000	2.75	6.00	12.00	70.00	125.00
1920	63,093,000	.30	.50	.75	2.75	12.00
1920D	9,418,000	2.25	4.00	7.50	45.00	120.00
1920S	9,689,000	2.25	4.00	7.50	45.00	105.00
1921	10,663,000	.55	1.00	1.75	5.00	22.50
1921S	1,557,000	9.00	14.00	20.00	65.00	175.00
1923	35,715,000	.35	.55	1.00	3.00	11.00
1923S	6,142,000	1.75	4.00	7.00	42.50	110.00
1924	21,620,000	.35	.55	.90	2.75	12.50
1924D	5,258,000	1.75	3.00	5.00	35.00	100.00
1924S	1,437,000	5.00	8.50	15.00	70.00	175.00
1925	35,565,100	.30	.50	.85	3.25	13.50
1925D	4,450,000	5.00	8.00	12.50	35.00	70.00
1925S	6,256,000	3.75	7.00	10.00	37.50	155.00
1926	44,693,000	.25	.40	.65	1.75	10.00
1926D	5,638,000	2.25	3.50	6.00	27.50	190.00
1926S	970,000	3.50	9.25	19.50	95.00	275.00
1927	37,981,000	.25	.40	.60	1.75	9.00
1927D	5,730,000	.75	1.25	2.00	9.00	25.00
1927S	3,430,000	2.25	5.75	12.00	50.00	210.00
1928	23,411,000	.15	.25	.40	1.40	8.00
1928D	6,436,000	.20	.40	.70	2.00	9.00
1928S	6,936,000	.30	.75	1.50	9.50	37.50
1929	36,446,000	.15	.20	.30	1.25	5.50
1929D	8,370,000	.25	.40	.60	3.00	9.00
1929S	7,754,000	.25	.40	.60	3.00	9.00
1930	22,849,000	.15	.20	.30	1.50	7.50
1930S	5,435,000	.60	1.25	2.50	5.50	27.50
1931S	1,200,000	2.50	3.50	4.50	11.00	40.00
1934	20,213,003	.15	.20	.30	.90	7.00

NICKEL FIVE-CENT PIECES

	Quan. Minted	Good	V.G.	Fine	E.F.	Unc.	Proof
1934D	7,480,000	$ .20	$ .35	$ .50	$2.00	$ 8.00	
1935	58,264,000			.20	.60	2.50	
1935D	12,092,000			.30	1.25	7.00	
1935S	10,300,000			.35	1.40	6.50	
1936 (4,420)	119,001,420				.50	2.25	$100.00
1936D	24,418,000				.70	2.75	
1936S	14,930,000				.75	3.50	
1937 (5,769)	79,485,769				.50	2.00	45.00
1937D All Kinds	17,826,000				.50	4.00	
*1937D 3-Legged Var		20.00	25.00	35.00	55.00	125.00	
1937S	5,635,000				.55	3.00	
1938D All Kinds	7,020,000				.65	2.00	
1938D over S (See illustration on page 95.)					———	———	

*Beware of removed leg.

JEFFERSON TYPE 1938 TO DATE

This nickel was designed by Felix Schlag. He won an award of $1000 in a competition with some 390 artists. It established the definite public approval of portrait and pictorial rather than symbolic devices on our coinage.

Fine — Cheekbone worn flat. Hairlines faint or missing from ear upward. Eyebrow faint.

Ex. Fine — Cheekbone slightly worn. Hair lines worn but defined. Eyebrow sharp, slightly worn.

		Fine	E.F.	Unc.	Proof
1938 (19,365)	19,515,365	.20	.40	1.60	9.00
1938D	5,376,000	.75	2.00	6.50	
1938S	4,105,000	1.50	3.50	10.00	
1939 (12,535)	120,627,535	.15	.60	3.00	8.00
1939D	3,514,000	3.25	11.00	40.00	
1939S	6,630,000	1.25	4.25	16.00	
1940 (14,158)	176,499,158			1.00	8.75
1940D	43,540,000			1.75	
1940S	39,690,000			2.75	
1941 (18,720)	203,283,720			1.00	6.00
1941D	53,432,000			1.00	
1941S	43,445,000			2.00	
1942 (29,600)	49,818,600			1.10	4.00
1942D	13,938,000	.75	3.25	15.00	

On October 8, 1942, the wartime five-cent piece composed of copper (56%), silver (35%) and manganese (9%) made its first appearance. The mint mark was made larger and placed above the dome of Monticello. The letter P for the Philadelphia Mint was used for the first time on this piece to indicate the change of alloy. Nickel, a critical war material, was entirely eliminated.

		Fine	E.F.	Unc.	Proof
1942P (27,600)	57,900,600		1.25	3.50	5.50
1942S	32,900,000		.75	2.00	

JEFFERSON NICKELS

	Quan. Minted	E.F.	Unc.	Proof
1943P	271,165,000	$ .45	$1.50	
1943D	15,294,000	.65	2.25	
1943S	104,060,000	.65	1.50	
*1944P	119,150,000	.45	1.50	
1944D	32,309,000	.45	1.50	
1944S	21,640,000	.45	1.50	
1945P	119,408,100	.45	1.35	
1945D	37,158,000	.45	1.25	
1945S	58,939,000	.45	1.25	

*1944 Nickels without mint marks are counterfeits.

REGULAR COPPER-NICKEL COMPOSITION
(Small Mint Mark at Right of Building)

	Quan. Minted	E.F.	Unc.	Proof
1946	161,116,000		.60	
1946D	45,292,200		.60	
1946S	13,560,000		1.35	
1947	95,000,000		.60	
1947D	37,822,000		.60	
1947S	24,720,000		1.00	
1948	89,348,000		.75	
1948D	44,734,000		.75	
1948S	11,300,000		1.75	
1949	60,652,000		1.50	
1949D	35,238,000		1.50	
1949S	9,716,000		3.00	
1950 (51,386)	9,847,386		2.50	$23.00
1950D	2,630,030	10.00	15.00	
1951 (57,500)	28,689,500		.65	10.00
1951D	20,460,000		1.75	
1951S	7,776,000	1.10	4.50	
1952 (81,980)	64,069,980		.75	8.00
1952D	30,638,000		3.50	
1952S	20,572,000		1.25	
1953 (128,800)	46,772,800		.50	5.50
1953D	59,878,600		.55	
1953S	19,210,900		.85	
1954 (233,300)	47,917,350		.50	3.50
1954D	117,183,060		.50	
1954S	29,384,000		.60	
1955 (378,200)	8,266,200		2.00	3.00
1955D	74,464,100		.40	
1956 (669,384)	35,885,384		.30	2.00
1956D	67,222,040		.30	
1957 (1,247,952)	39,655,952		.30	1.25
1957D	136,828,900		.30	
1958 (875,652)	17,963,652		.60	2.75
1958D	168,249,120		.30	
1959 (1,149,291)	28,397,291		.25	1.25
1959D	160,738,240		.25	
1960 (1,691,602)	57,107,602		.15	1.25
1960D	192,582,180		.15	

JEFFERSON NICKELS

	Quan. Minted	Unc.	Proof
1961	(3,028,244) 76,668,244	$ .15	$ .75
1961D	229,342,760	.15	
1962	(3,218,019)100,602,019	.15	.75
1962D	280,195,720	.15	
1963		.15	.75
1963D		.15	

SILVER THREE-CENT PIECES
1851-1873

This smallest of United States coins was authorized by Congress March 3, 1851. The first three-cent silver pieces had no lines bordering the six-pointed star. From 1854 through 1858 there were three lines, while issues of the last fifteen years show only two lines. Issues from 1854 through 1873 have an olive sprig over the III and a bundle of three arrows beneath.

The original weight of this piece was $12\frac{3}{8}$ grains, .750 fine, which was changed by the law of March 3, 1853, to 11.52 grains, .900 fine.

 Type 1

mint mark
o

Good — Star worn smooth. Legend and date readable.

V. Good — Outline of shield defined. Legend and date clear.

Fine — Only star points worn smooth.

V. Fine — Only partial wear on star ridges.

	Quan. Minted	Good	V.G.	Fine	V.F.	Unc.	Proof
1851 Type 1	5,447,400	$ 4.00	$ 5.00	$ 7.00	$12.00	$ 25.00	
1851O	720,000	8.50	13.50	22.50	35.00	75.00	
1852	18,663,500	2.25	3.50	6.50	10.00	17.50	
1853	11,400,000	2.00	3.25	6.50	10.00	17.50	

 Type 2

 Type 3

1854 Three outlines to star.							
Type 2	671,000	6.00	8.00	12.00	16.00	27.50	
1855	139,000	10.00	15.00	27.50	40.00	95.00	385.00
1856	1,458,000	6.00	7.50	10.00	20.00	40.00	200.00
1857	1,042,000	5.50	7.25	10.00	18.50	37.50	225.00
1858	1,604,000	5.00	6.75	9.50	16.00	30.00	250.00
1859 Two outlines to star.							
Type 3	365,000	6.00	6.75	8.00	15.00	22.50	60.00
1860	287,000	6.00	6.75	8.00	15.00	22.50	60.00
1861	498,000	5.00	6.25	8.50	14.00	22.00	47.50
1862	363,550	5.00	6.25	8.50	14.00	22.00	47.50
1863	(460) 21,460					95.00	120.00
1864	(470) 470					120.00	140.00

SILVER THREE-CENT PIECES

		Quan. Minted			Proof
1865	(500)	8,500		....	$130.00
1866	(725)	22,725			70.00
1867	(625)	4,625	Circulated coins	....	72.50
1868	(600)	4,100	1863 to 1872 are	....	77.50
1869	(600)	5,100	rarely encountered.	....	77.50
1870	(1,000)	4,000	They were melted		62.50
1871	(960)	4,260	or exported.	....	63.50
1872	(950)	1,950		....	70.00
1873	(600)	600 (Closed 3 Only)			105.00

HALF DIMES

1794-1873

The half-dime types present the same general characteristics as larger United States silver coins. Authorized by the Act of April 2, 1792, they were not coined until 1794. At first the weight was 20.8 grains, and fineness 892.4. By the Act of January 18, 1837 the weight was slightly reduced to 20⅝ grains and the fineness changed to 900. Finally the weight was reduced to 19.2 grains by the Act of February 21, 1853. Both half dimes and dimes offer many varieties in the early dates. Until 1829 there was no indication of value on the half dimes.

Proofs prior to 1855 are known to exist of some dates and all are rare.

Note: Some early half dimes, while strictly uncirculated, bear file or adjustment marks.

Fair — *Details clear enough to identify.*

Good — *Eagle, wreath, bust outlined but lack details.*

V. Good — *Some details remain on face. All lettering readable.*

Fine — *Hair ends show. Hair at top smooth.*

V. Fine — *Hairlines at top show. Hair about ear defined.*

	Quan. Minted	Fair	Good	V.G.	Fine	V.F.	Unc.
1794	}86,416	$65.00	$125.00	$200.00	$275.00	$450.00	$900.00
1795		50.00	100.00	125.00	200.00	300.00	500.00

1796   1800

		Fair	Good	V.G.	Fine	V.F.	Unc.
1796 over 5 - All K.	10,230	125.00	250.00	350.00	425.00	600.00	1100.00
1796 Normal Date		50.00	100.00	145.00	200.00	300.00	650.00
1796 LIKERTY			200.00	275.00	400.00	———	———
1797 15 Stars All Kinds	44,527	35.00	70.00	100.00	160.00	240.00	500.00
1797 16 Stars		35.00	70.00	100.00	160.00	240.00	500.00
1797 13 Stars		40.00	80.00	110.00	175.00	265.00	550.00
1800 All Kinds	24,000	35.00	65.00	95.00	150.00	225.00	450.00

HALF DIMES

1796-1805

Fair — Details clear enough to identify.
Good—Date, stars, LIBERTY readable.
*   Bust outlined but no details.*
V. Good — Some details show.
Fine — Hair and drapery lines worn,
*   but visible.*
V. Fine—Only left of drapery indistinct.

1800 LIBEKTY Detail

1829-1837

Good — Bust outlined, no detail. Date and
*   legend readable.*
V. Good — Complete legend and date plain.
*   At least 3 letters of LIBERTY*
*   show clearly.*
Fine — All letters in LIBERTY show.
V. Fine — Full rim, both sides. Clasp on
*   shoulder and ear well defined.*

Draped Bust Liberty Cap
1829-1837

	Quan. Minted	Fair	Good	V.G.	Fine	V.F.	Unc.
1800 LIBEKTY........		$ 45.00	$ 72.50	$100.00	$150.00	$225.00	$500.00
1801.............33,910		42.50	70.00	110.00	215.00	350.00	725.00
1802......(Rare) 13,010		300.00	450.00	700.00	1250.00	2250.00	————
1803.............37,850		32.50	62.50	80.00	125.00	225.00	500.00
1805.............15,600		50.00	90.00	130.00	215.00	355.00	————

LIBERTY CAP TYPE

1829.........1,230,000		3.75	5.00	7.50	10.50	25.00
1830.........1,240,000		3.00	3.85	5.50	9.50	25.00
1831.........1,242,700		3.00	3.85	5.50	9.50	25.00
1832...........965,000		3.00	3.85	5.50	9.50	25.00
1833.........1,370,000		3.00	3.85	5.50	9.50	25.00
1834.........1,480,000		3.00	3.85	5.50	9.50	25.00
1835 Large Date Large 5c						
All Kinds..2,760,000		3.00	3.85	5.50	9.50	25.00
1835 Large Date Small 5c		3.00	3.85	5.50	9.50	25.00
1835 Small Date Large 5c		3.00	3.85	5.50	9.50	25.00
1835 Small Date Small 5c		3.00	3.85	5.50	9.50	25.00
1836 Small 5c						
All Kinds..1,900,000		3.00	3.85	5.50	9.50	25.00
1836 Large 5c..........		3.00	3.85	5.50	9.50	25.00
1837 Small 5c						
All Kinds..2,276,000		7.00	11.00	18.00	28.50	70.00
1837 Large 5c..........		3.00	3.85	5.50	9.50	25.00

LIBERTY SEATED TYPE

Good—LIBERTY on shield smooth. Date and
*   letters readable.*
V. Good—At least 3 letters in LIBERTY are
*   visible.*
Fine—Entire LIBERTY visible, weak spots.
V. Fine—Entire LIBERTY strong and even.

1837 No Stars, Sm. Date					
All Kinds..2,255,000	30.00	37.50	55.00	70.00	150.00
1837 No Stars, Lg. Date.	30.00	37.50	55.00	70.00	150.00
1838O No Stars..————	40.00	55.00	80.00	135.00	350.00

HALF DIMES

No Drapery from Elbow (Enlarged)   Drapery from Elbow (Enlarged)

	Quan. Minted	Good	V.G.	Fine	V.F.	Unc.	Proof
1838 No Drapery	2,255,000	$ 2.50	$ 3.40	$ 5.00	$ 9.00	$22.50	
1839 No Drapery	1,069,150	2.50	3.40	5.00	9.00	22.50	
1839O No Drapery	1,096,550	4.50	5.00	8.50	15.50	35.00	
1840 No Drpy.All K.	1,344,085	2.25	3.25	4.50	7.25	20.00	
1840O No Drpy.All K.	935,000	4.50	6.75	11.00	22.00	65.00	
1840 Drapery		2.25	3.25	5.00	10.50	35.00	
1840O Drapery		5.25	7.75	12.00	25.00	75.00	
1841	1,150,000	2.00	2.75	4.25	7.00	20.00	
1841O	815,000	3.00	4.65	7.50	12.00	60.00	
1842	815,000	2.00	2.75	4.00	6.50	17.50	
1842O	350,000	5.00	9.00	15.00	25.00	125.00	
1843	1,165,000	2.00	2.65	3.75	6.00	17.50	
1844	430,000	3.00	4.75	7.50	10.75	25.00	
1844O	220,000	5.75	10.00	17.50	33.00	90.00	
1845	1,564,000	2.00	2.65	3.75	6.00	17.50	
1846	27,000	42.50	60.00	75.00	100.00	200.00	
1847	1,274,000	2.00	2.65	3.75	6.00	16.00	
1848 Medium Date.	668,000	1.75	2.65	4.00	6.50	17.50	
1848 Large Date...		2.25	3.25	5.00	8.25	20.00	
1848O	600,000	4.25	6.75	11.00	22.00	65.00	
1849 over 48 All K.	1,309,000	2.50	3.75	5.75	9.25	22.50	
1849 over 46		2.50	3.75	5.75	9.00	22.00	
1849		1.75	2.50	3.75	6.50	17.50	
1849O	140,000	23.00	35.00	55.00	75.00	185.00	
1850	955,000	1.75	2.50	3.75	6.00	15.00	
1850O	690,000	3.00	4.50	7.00	17.00	65.00	
1851	781,000	1.75	2.40	3.50	5.75	15.50	
1851O	860,000	2.75	4.25	6.75	15.50	60.00	
1852	1,000,500	1.75	2.50	3.75	6.00	15.50	
1852O	260,000	4.75	7.75	13.00	28.00	80.00	
1853 No Arrows All Kinds	13,345,020	8.00	11.50	17.50	26.00	67.50	
1853O No Arrows All Kinds	2,360,000	57.50	72.50	110.00	150.00	300.00	

As on the dimes, quarters and halves, arrows were placed at the sides of the date for a short period starting in 1853. They were placed there to denote the reduction of weight under the terms of the Act of February 21, 1853.

1853 With Arrows	2.50	3.00	4.25	7.50	20.00

HALF DIMES

	Quan. Minted	Good	V.G.	Fine	V.F.	Unc.	Proof
1853O		$ 2.00	$ 2.65	$ 3.75	$ 6.75	$20.00	
1854	5,740,000	1.60	2.00	2.50	5.25	16.00	
1854O	1,560,000	2.00	2.75	3.75	7.00	22.50	
1855	1,750,000	1.50	1.85	2.50	5.50	17.50	$190.00
1855O	600,000	3.00	4.75	6.75	14.00	45.00	

Arrows At Date Removed

1856	4,880,000	1.00	1.35	2.00	4.00	14.00	175.00
1856O	1,100,000	2.00	2.75	4.00	7.00	20.00	
1857	7,280,000	1.00	1.35	2.00	4.00	14.00	125.00
1857O	1,380,000	1.75	2.50	3.60	6.50	22.50	
1858	3,500,000	.90	1.30	2.00	4.00	13.00	100.00
1858O	1,660,000	1.60	2.35	3.75	6.75	18.50	

New die 1859 Philadelphia Mint. Stars hollow in center. Arms slimmer.

1859	340,000	2.75	4.00	6.00	9.00	18.00	75.00
1859O	560,000	2.50	3.25	5.00	8.00	25.00	

In the years 1859 and 1860 a half-dime type was struck which does not bear our nation's identity. These coins are known as transitional patterns, and were struck at the time the inscription **UNITED STATES OF AMERICA** was being transferred from the reverse to the obverse side of the coin.

1859 Obv. of 59, Rev. of 60		1500.00
1860 Obv. of 59, Rev. of 60		
(With Stars)	100	750.00

Legend on Obverse

	Quan. Minted	Good	V.G.	Fine	V.F.	Unc.	Proof
1860 Legend	799,000	1.50	2.25	3.50	5.00	13.00	45.00
1860O Legend	1,060,000	2.75	3.75	5.00	7.75	22.50	
1861	3,281,000	1.50	2.00	2.75	4.50	12.50	45.00
1862	1,492,550	1.50	2.00	2.75	4.50	12.50	45.00
1863	(460) 18,460	9.00	11.00	16.00	25.00	50.00	90.00
1863S	100,000	8.25	11.25	16.50	30.00	60.00	
1864	(470) 470					———	170.00
1864S	90,000	9.50	14.50	23.00	38.50	90.00	
1865	(500) 13,500	9.00	12.00	17.00	26.00	55.00	80.00
1865S	120,000	6.50	9.50	14.00	25.00	60.00	
1866	(725) 10,725	6.00	7.00	12.00	20.00	50.00	55.00
1866S	120,000	5.00	5.35	9.00	20.00	55.00	
1867	(625) 8,625	5.00	5.35	9.00	20.00	50.00	60.00

HALF DIMES

	Quan. Minted	Good	V.G.	Fine	V.F.	Unc.	Proof
1867S	120,000	$4.25	$5.75	$8.50	$20.00	$50.00	
1868 (600)	85,900	3.00	4.00	6.00	10.00	22.50	$50.00
1868S	280,000	3.00	4.00	6.00	10.00	25.00	
1869 (600)	208,600	3.00	4.00	5.00	7.00	17.50	50.00
1869S	230,000	3.00	4.00	5.50	9.00	25.00	
1870 (1,000)	536,600	1.50	1.85	2.50	5.00	15.00	30.00
1871 (960)	1,488,860	1.50	1.85	2.50	5.00	15.00	27.50
1871S	161,000	9.00	13.00	19.00	31.00	70.00	
1872 (950)	2,947,950	1.50	2.10	3.00	5.25	15.50	35.00

Mint Mark Within Wreath, Reverse Side	Mint Mark Below Wreath, Reverse Side

		Good	V.G.	Fine	V.F.	Unc.	
1872S Mint Mark within Wreath							
All Kinds	837,000	1.50	2.25	3.50	5.75	16.00	
1872S Mt. M. below Wreath.		2.00	2.75	4.00	7.00	21.00	
1873 (Closed 3 only)							
(600)	712,600	1.25	1.65	2.50	5.00	16.00	50.00
1873S (Closed 3 only)	324,000	1.75	3.00	5.00	8.25	22.50	

BIBLIOGRAPHY

Newlin, H. P., Early Half Dimes. 1883.
Valentine, D. W., U. S. Half Dimes. 1931.
Breen, W., U. S. Half Dimes; A Supplement. 1958.

DIMES — 1796 To Date

The designs of the dimes, first coined in 1796, follow closely those of the half dimes up through the liberty seated type. The dimes in each instance weigh twice as much as the half dimes.

Note: File or adjustment marks as on half dimes.
Fair — Details clear enough to identify.
Good — Date readable. Bust outlined, but no detail.
V. Good — All but deepest drapery folds worn smooth. All hairlines, but curls lack detail.
Fine — All drapery lines visible. Hair partly worn.
V. Fine — Only left side of drapery is indistinct.

| | 1796 | 1797-16 Stars | | 1797-13 Stars | | |

	Quan. Minted	Fair	Good	V.G.	Fine	V.F.	Unc.
1796	22,135	125.00	200.00	300.00	500.00	750.00	1350.00
1797 16 Stars All K	25,261	95.00	185.00	250.00	450.00	650.00	1250.00
1797 13 Stars		85.00	175.00	225.00	350.00	525.00	1000.00

DIMES

Proofs prior to 1855 are known to exist of some dates, and all are rare.

	Quan. Minted	Fair	Good	V.G.	Fine	V.F.	Unc.
1798 over 97, 13 Stars on Reverse (Very Rare) All K.	27,550						
1798 over 97, 16 Stars on Rev.		$50.00	$75.00	$100.00	$130.00	$225.00	$500.00
1798		50.00	75.00	100.00	130.00	225.00	525.00
1798 Small 8							
1800	21,760	40.00	65.00	85.00	110.00	185.00	450.00
1801	34,640	52.50	92.50	115.00	170.00	275.00	590.00
1802	10,975	55.00	80.00	100.00	125.00	200.00	550.00
1803	33,040	47.50	77.50	90.00	110.00	175.00	475.00
1804 13 Stars on Reverse All Kinds	8,265	75.00	100.00	125.00	200.00	400.00	900.00
1804 14 Stars on Reverse		75.00	100.00	125.00	200.00	410.00	950.00
1805 4 Berries All K.	120,780	27.50	47.50	60.00	92.50	135.00	240.00
1805 5 Berries		27.50	47.50	60.00	97.50	140.00	250.00
1807	165,000	24.00	42.50	55.00	95.00	125.00	230.00

DRAPED BUST, LIBERTY CAP TYPE

Good — Date, letters and stars discernible. Bust outlined, no details.
V. Good — Legends and date plain. Minimum of 3 letters in LIBERTY show.
Fine — Full LIBERTY. Ear and shoulder clasp visible. Part of rim shows both sides.
V. Fine—LIBERTY distinct. Full rim. Ear and clasp plain and distinct.

1809	44,710	36.50	52.50	71.50	115.00	270.00
1811 over 9	65,180	21.00	32.50	44.00	68.00	150.00

1814 Sm. Date All K.	421,500	8.00	12.50	18.00	32.50	85.00
1814 Large Date		8.00	12.50	18.00	30.00	80.00
1820 Lg. O All Kinds	942,587	5.25	7.50	10.50	21.00	60.00
1820 Small O		4.75	7.25	10.00	20.00	55.00

DIMES

1821 Small Date — 1821 Large Date — 1822

	Quan. Minted	Good	V.G.	Fine	V.F.	Unc.
1821 Small Date						
All Kinds	1,186,512	$ 4.50	$ 7.00	$10.50	$22.50	$62.50
1821 Large Date		4.25	6.50	10.00	20.00	60.00
1822	100,000	32.50	37.50	77.50	165.00	425.00

1823 Over 22

Small E's — Large E's

		Good	V.G.	Fine	V.F.	Unc.
1823 over 22 Small E's						
All Kinds	440,000	6.50	10.00	17.50	32.50	85.00
1823 over 22 Large E's		6.50	10.00	17.50	32.50	85.00

1824 Over 22 — 1828 Small Date — 1828 Large Date

		Good	V.G.	Fine	V.F.	Unc.
1824 over 22	———	9.00	13.25	22.50	35.00	115.00
1825	510,000	6.50	8.25	11.50	22.50	60.00
1827	1,215,000	6.00	7.50	10.00	20.00	60.00
1828 Large Date						
All Kinds	125,000	16.00	25.00	45.00	60.00	120.00
1828 Small Date		9.00	12.00	18.50	35.00	95.00

1829 Small 10c — Large 10c

		Good	V.G.	Fine	V.F.	Unc.
1829 Sm. 10¢ All K.	770,000	2.75	3.75	5.75	10.00	25.00
1829 Medium 10¢		4.75	5.50	10.00	16.50	37.50
1829 Large 10¢		7.50	11.00	17.50	27.50	60.00
1830 Sm. 10¢ All K.	510,000	2.75	3.50	5.50	9.50	25.00
1830 Large 10¢		2.50	3.25	5.00	9.00	25.00
1831	771,350	2.50	3.25	5.00	9.00	25.00
1832	522,500	2.50	3.25	5.00	9.00	25.00
1833 All Kinds	485,000	2.75	3.75	5.50	9.50	25.00
1833 Last 3 High		2.75	3.75	5.50	9.50	25.00
1834 Sm. 4 All Kinds	635,000	2.75	3.75	5.50	9.50	30.00
1834 Large 4		2.50	3.50	5.00	8.50	24.50

DIMES

	Quan. Minted	Good	V.G.	Fine	V.F.	Unc.
1835	1,410,000	$2.50	$3.50	$5.00	$8.50	$24.50
1836	1,190,000	2.50	3.50	5.00	9.00	25.00
1837 All Kinds	1,042,000	3.00	4.00	6.00	11.00	30.00

LIBERTY SEATED TYPE

**No Drapery From Elbow
No Stars On Obverse**

*Good—LIBERTY on shield smooth. Date
and letters readable.*
*V. Good—At least 3 letters in LIBERTY
are visible.*
*Fine — Entire LIBERTY visible, weak
spots.*
*V. Fine — Entire LIBERTY strong and
even.*

		Good	V.G.	Fine	V.F.	Unc.
1837 Small Date		30.00	42.50	75.00	125.00	175.00
1837 Large Date		30.00	42.50	75.00	125.00	175.00
1838O	402,434	37.50	57.50	100.00	175.00	350.00

No Drapery From Elbow With Stars On Obverse

		Good	V.G.	Fine	V.F.	Unc.
1838 Small Stars						
All Kinds	1,992,500	8.50	12.50	21.00	30.00	60.00
1838 Large Stars		4.00	4.90	6.50	10.50	25.00
1838 with Partial Drapery		12.00	17.00	27.50	39.00	72.50
1839	1,053,115	2.75	3.65	5.50	9.50	25.00
1839O	1,243,272	4.00	6.25	10.00	14.50	35.00
1840 All Kinds	1,358,580	2.75	4.00	6.00	9.75	25.00
1840O	1,175,000	4.00	5.50	8.00	12.00	30.00
1841 All Kinds	1,622,500					

**Drapery From
Elbow**

		Good	V.G.	Fine	V.F.	Unc.
1840		5.00	7.50	11.00	17.00	40.00
1841		2.00	2.75	4.00	7.50	22.00
1841O	2,007,500	2.00	3.50	6.00	11.50	35.00
1842	1,887,500	2.00	2.75	4.00	7.75	24.00
1842O	2,020,000	4.00	5.50	7.50	15.25	40.00
1843	1,370,000	2.00	2.75	4.00	7.50	23.00
1843O	150,000	12.50	17.50	29.00	47.50	175.00
1844	72,500	18.00	30.00	50.00	77.50	180.00
1845	1,755,000	2.00	2.75	4.00	7.50	22.50

DIMES

	Quan. Minted	Good	V.G.	Fine	V.F.	Unc.	Proof
1845O	230,000	$ 6.50	$ 9.00	$12.50	$22.00	$55.00	
1846	31,300	12.00	16.00	25.00	40.00	85.00	
1847	245,000	4.00	5.50	8.00	15.00	42.50	
1848	451,500	3.00	4.50	5.50	10.00	30.00	
1849	839,000	2.00	2.75	4.00	7.75	22.50	
1849O	300,000	5.50	8.00	14.00	25.00	50.00	
1850	1,931,500	2.00	2.75	4.00	6.75	17.50	
1850O	510,000	4.75	7.00	11.00	20.00	50.00	
1851	1,026,500	2.00	2.75	4.00	7.00	19.50	
1851O	400,000	4.00	5.25	7.50	15.00	40.00	
1852	1,535,500	2.00	2.75	4.00	7.00	19.50	
1852O	430,000	4.00	6.00	9.00	18.00	50.00	
1853 (No Arrows) All Kinds	12,173,010	13.00	18.00	25.00	37.50	85.00	

Arrows At Date					Small Date Arrows Removed		

	Quan. Minted	Good	V.G.	Fine	V.F.	Unc.	Proof
1853 With Arrows		2.25	3.10	4.50	8.50	19.50	
1853O	1,100,000	4.00	5.00	6.75	10.00	22.50	
1854	4,470,000	2.00	2.75	4.00	6.75	17.50	
1854O	1,770,000	2.25	3.25	5.00	9.25	21.50	
1855	2,075,000	1.35	2.00	3.00	5.25	16.00	200.00
1856 Small Date All Kinds	5,780,000	1.50	2.10	3.25	5.75	16.00	210.00
1856 Large Date		2.25	3.10	4.50	7.50	30.00	
1856O	1,180,000	2.75	3.65	4.75	7.50	30.00	
1856S	70,000	25.00	40.00	60.00	100.00	240.00	
1857	5,580,000	1.75	2.75	3.75	5.50	18.50	225.00
1857O	1,540,000	2.25	3.10	4.50	8.00	20.00	
1858	1,540,000	1.25	2.25	4.00	6.50	20.00	180.00
1858O	290,000	4.00	5.50	7.75	13.25	30.00	
1858S	60,000	15.50	21.00	35.00	70.00	180.00	
1859	430,000	1.25	2.10	3.50	7.50	17.50	100.00
1859O	480,000	1.50	2.35	4.00	10.00	35.00	
1859S	60,000	14.00	18.50	25.00	42.50	100.00	
1860S	140,000	7.50	12.50	22.50	37.50	90.00	

TRANSITIONAL PATTERN—Same as Half Dimes 1859, 1860

Obverse of 1859   Reverse of 1860

1859 . . . .   2,750.00

DIMES

Legend Replaces Stars on Obverse

	Quan. Minted	Good	V.G.	Fine	V.F.	Unc.	Proof
1860	607,000	$ 1.75	$ 2.65	$ 3.75	$ 6.00	$12.50	$60.00
1860O	40,000	60.00	90.00	135.00	235.00	475.00	
1861	1,924,000	1.00	1.85	2.25	4.00	11.00	50.00
1861S	172,500	11.00	17.00	27.50	45.00	97.50	
1862	847,550	2.25	2.85	4.00	6.75	12.50	45.00
1862S	180,750	7.50	12.50	20.00	40.00	90.00	
1863	(460) 14,460	7.50	10.00	14.00	18.00	33.50	57.50
1863S	157,500	7.50	12.50	20.00	37.50	90.00	
1864	(470) 39,070	7.50	11.00	15.00	18.75	32.50	62.50
1864S	230,000	8.00	13.00	21.00	33.00	71.00	
1865	(500) 10,500	10.00	12.00	16.00	20.00	36.00	60.00
1865S	175,000	8.00	13.00	20.00	26.00	72.50	
1866	(725) 8,725	10.00	12.00	16.00	20.00	39.00	52.50
1866S	135,000	7.50	11.50	17.50	25.00	70.00	
1867	(625) 6,625	10.00	12.00	16.50	21.00	40.00	60.00
1867S	140,000	7.25	11.00	17.00	22.50	55.00	
1868	(600) 466,250	1.75	2.35	3.25	5.50	13.00	45.00
1868S	260,000	5.50	8.00	12.00	19.00	45.00	
1869	(600) 256,600	2.00	2.75	4.00	6.75	16.00	42.50
1869S	450,000	5.50	7.75	11.50	17.50	40.00	
1870	(1,000) 471,500	1.75	3.00	5.00	7.00	14.50	37.50
1870S	50,000	38.50	52.50	75.00	100.00	177.50	
1871	(960) 753,610	1.75	2.65	4.00	6.00	13.00	35.00
1871CC	20,100	120.00	170.00	260.00	435.00	———	
1871S	320,000	8.50	11.25	19.00	33.00	70.00	
1872	(950) 2,396,450	1.50	2.40	4.00	5.75	12.50	35.00
1872CC	24,000	80.00	110.00	160.00	290.00	380.00	
1872S	190,000	9.50	13.00	21.00	35.00	60.00	
1873 Closed 3							
All Kinds (600)	1,568,600	1.50	2.65	5.00	7.25	15.00	47.50
1873 Open 3		4.00	6.50	11.00	13.50	21.00	
1873CC (Unique)	12,400						

Arrows
At
Date

In 1873 the dime was increased in weight to 38.58 grains. Arrows at date in 1873 and 1874 indicate this change.

	Quan. Minted	Good	V.G.	Fine	V.F.	Unc.	Proof
1873	(800) 2,378,500	8.00	12.00	17.50	30.00	60.00	150.00
1873CC	18,791	300.00	400.00	575.00	685.00	1000.00	
1873S	455,000	14.00	20.00	30.00	40.00	90.00	
1874	(700) 2,940,700	8.00	12.00	17.50	35.00	70.00	125.00
1874CC	10,817	80.00	120.00	175.00	375.00	750.00	
1874S	240,000	14.00	20.00	30.00	50.00	110.00	

DIMES

	Quan. Minted	Good	V.G.	Fine	E.F.	Unc.	Proof
Arrows at Date Removed.							
1875.......(700)	10,350,700	$1.00	$ 1.65	$ 2.50	$ 4.25	$ 9.00	$37.50
1875CC Under Wreath							
All Kinds.....4,645,000		3.25	4.50	6.50	11.50	25.00	
1875CC In Wreath........		1.75	2.35	3.50	6.75	17.50	
1875S Under Wreath							
All Kinds.....9,070,000		1.50	2.10	3.00	5.25	12.50	
1875S In Wreath..........		1.50	2.10	3.00	5.25	12.50	
1876.....(1,150)	11,461,150	.85	1.10	1.50	3.65	9.00	30.00
1876CC...........8,270,000		1.75	2.35	3.50	6.00	13.50	
1876S...........10,420,000		1.50	2.25	3.25	5.75	11.00	
1877........(510)	7,310,510	1.00	1.35	2.00	5.00	9.00	90.00
1877CC...........7,700,000		1.50	1.85	2.50	5.50	13.00	
1877S...........2,340,000		1.50	1.85	2.50	5.50	12.50	
1878........(800)	1,678,800	1.50	1.85	2.50	5.50	11.50	30.00
1878CC...........200,000		11.00	15.00	23.50	34.50	57.50	
1879........(1,100)	15,100	8.00	10.50	13.00	15.00	25.00	45.00
1880........(1,355)	37,355	7.00	9.00	11.00	13.00	18.00	40.00
1881........(975)	24,975	7.50	9.50	12.00	14.00	19.00	42.50
1882.....(1,100)	3,911,100	1.00	1.35	2.00	3.75	8.50	30.00
1883.....(1,039)	7,675,712	1.00	1.35	2.00	3.75	8.50	30.00
1884.....(875)	3,366,380	1.00	1.35	2.00	4.00	9.50	30.00
1884S.............564,969		7.00	9.50	13.00	25.00	50.00	
1885.......(930)	2,533,427	1.00	1.35	2.00	4.00	9.00	27.50
1885S.............43,690		55.00	72.50	100.00	180.00	340.00	
1886........(886)	6,377,570	.90	1.30	2.00	4.00	9.00	26.50
1886S.............206,524		7.00	9.50	14.00	25.00	42.50	
1887......(710)	11,283,939	.90	1.30	2.00	3.50	8.00	30.00
1887S...........4,454,450		2.00	2.75	4.00	7.25	15.00	
1888........(832)	5,496,487	.90	1.35	2.00	4.00	10.00	27.50
1888S...........1,720,000		2.75	3.65	5.00	7.75	15.00	
1889........(711)	7,380,711	.90	1.35	2.00	4.00	9.00	27.50
1889S.............972,678		7.50	11.00	15.00	42.50	100.00	
1890.......(590)	9,911,541	.90	1.35	2.00	4.25	10.00	35.00
1890S...........1,423,076		2.75	3.65	5.00	7.75	17.50	
1891......(600)	15,310,600	.90	1.35	2.00	4.00	9.00	35.00
1891O...........4,540,000		2.25	3.10	4.50	13.00	30.00	
1891S...........3,196,116		1.75	2.35	3.25	7.50	18.00	

BARBER OR LIBERTY HEAD TYPE

Good — Date and letters plain. *LIBERTY*
over brow is obliterated.

V. Good — At least 3 letters visible in *LIB-
ERTY.*

Fine -- All letters in *L I B E R T Y* visible,
though some are weak.

Ex. Fine — All letters in *LIBERTY* are
sharp, distinct. Headband edges are distinct.

Designed by Charles E. Barber, Chief Engraver of the Mint. He also designed the 25 and 50-cent pieces. His initial (B) is at the truncation of the neck.

1892.....(1,245) 12,121,245	.65	1.25	2.25	4.50	10.00	35.00
1892O............3,841,700	1.75	2.85	5.00	11.00	30.00	
1892S.............990,710	16.00	20.00	30.00	50.00	75.00	

DIMES

	Quan. Minted	Good	V.G.	Fine	E.F.	Unc.	Proof
1893........(792)	3,340,792	$ 1.75	$ 2.35	$ 3.50	$ 6.00	$13.50	$47.50
1893O............	1,760,000	4.00	5.75	9.00	15.00	45.00	
1893S............	2,491,401	4.00	5.75	9.00	15.00	45.00	
1894........(972)	1,330,972	2.50	3.75	6.00	9.00	17.50	45.00
1894O............	720,000	30.00	45.00	75.00	125.00	275.00	
1894S............	24		Hydeman Sale 1961				$13,000.00
1895........(880)	690,880	20.00	28.00	42.50	60.00	110.00	190.00
1895O............	440,000	45.00	75.00	125.00	275.00	575.00	
1895S............	1,120,000	7.00	11.00	17.50	45.00	95.00	
1896........(762)	2,000,762	2.50	3.75	6.00	10.00	25.00	65.00
1896O............	610,000	17.50	27.00	42.50	90.00	170.00	
1896S............	575,056	25.00	32.50	50.00	110.00	220.00	
1897........(731)	10,869,264	.75	1.35	2.25	4.00	12.00	60.00
1897O............	666,000	17.50	27.00	42.50	85.00	170.00	
1897S............	1,342,844	6.00	10.50	17.50	40.00	90.00	
1898........(735)	16,320,735	.50	1.00	1.75	3.50	11.00	47.00
1898O............	2,130,000	3.25	5.75	9.50	40.00	100.00	
1898S............	1,702,507	3.00	4.75	7.50	30.00	65.00	
1899........(846)	19,580,846	.50	.90	1.60	3.50	11.50	42.50
1899O............	2,650,000	3.00	5.50	9.00	40.00	85.00	
1899S............	1,867,493	2.75	4.50	8.00	25.00	55.00	
1900........(912)	17,600,912	.40	.85	1.60	3.50	11.00	40.00
1900O............	2,010,000	2.75	5.50	9.50	30.00	90.00	
1900S............	5,168,270	2.00	3.75	6.50	16.50	50.00	
1901........(813)	18,860,478	.40	.85	1.60	3.50	11.00	40.00
1901O............	5,620,000	1.00	3.25	7.50	30.00	75.00	
1901S............	593,022	17.50	45.00	85.00	200.00	400.00	
1902........(777)	21,380,777	.40	.80	1.50	2.50	10.00	47.50
1902O............	4,500,000	1.00	2.75	5.50	25.00	55.00	
1902S............	2,070,000	3.00	5.50	9.00	30.00	70.00	
1903........(755)	19,500,755	.35	.60	1.00	2.50	10.00	45.00
1903O............	8,180,000	.75	2.35	5.50	15.00	45.00	
1903S............	613,300	7.50	11.00	15.00	37.50	105.00	
1904........(670)	14,601,027	.30	.55	1.00	2.50	10.00	50.00
1904S............	800,000	7.00	10.50	16.50	40.00	90.00	
1905........(727)	14,552,350	.35	.60	1.00	2.50	10.00	50.00
1905O............	3,400,000	1.25	2.65	5.00	13.50	50.00	
1905S............	6,855,199	.90	2.00	4.00	9.00	20.00	
1906........(675)	19,958,406	.25	.50	1.00	2.50	11.00	52.50
1906D............	4,060,000	.75	1.35	2.50	5.00	15.00	
1906O............	2,610,000	.75	1.85	3.75	7.50	25.00	
1906S............	3,136,640	.35	1.10	3.25	6.50	20.00	
1907........(575)	22,220,575	.25	.50	1.00	2.50	9.00	55.00
1907D............	4,080,000	.60	1.75	4.00	10.00	30.00	
1907O............	5,058,000	.55	1.25	2.25	5.50	20.00	
1907S............	3,178,470	.55	1.25	2.25	5.50	20.00	
1908........(545)	10,600,545	.30	.65	1.25	3.00	10.00	55.00
1908D............	7,490,000	.40	.90	1.75	4.50	12.00	
1908O............	1,789,000	.75	1.85	4.00	9.50	30.00	
1908S............	3,220,000	.75	1.85	3.25	9.00	25.00	
1909........(650)	10,240,650	.20	.50	1.00	3.00	10.00	50.00
1909D............	954,000	1.50	4.25	9.00	20.00	45.00	
1909O............	2,287,000	1.50	3.75	8.00	19.00	40.00	
1909S............	1,000,000	1.50	4.25	9.00	20.00	45.00	

DIMES

	Quan. Minted	Good	V.G.	Fine	E.F.	Unc.	Proof
1910......(551)	11,520,551	$ .25	$ .50	$1.00	$3.00	$11.00	$65.00
1910D............	3,490,000	.50	.95	1.75	5.00	12.50	
1910S............	1,240,000	1.25	2.25	4.00	10.00	32.50	
1911......(543)	18,870,543	.25	.50	1.00	3.00	10.00	70.00
1911D...........	11,209,000	.50	.95	1.75	5.00	12.50	
1911S............	3,520,000	1.00	1.75	3.00	9.00	22.50	
1912......(700)	19,350,700	.25	.50	1.00	3.00	10.00	65.00
1912D...........	11,760,000	.50	.95	1.75	5.00	12.50	
1912S............	3,420,000	1.00	1.75	3.00	9.00	22.50	
1913......(622)	19,760,622	.25	.50	1.00	3.00	10.00	90.00
1913S............	510,000	5.50	13.50	26.00	70.00	160.00	
1914......(425)	17,360,655	.25	.50	1.00	3.00	10.00	190.00
1914D...........	11,908,000	.50	.95	1.75	5.00	12.50	
1914S............	2,100,000	.75	2.00	4.00	10.00	32.50	
1915.......(450)	5,620,450	.25	.65	1.25	3.00	12.50	200.00
1915S............	960,000	1.50	2.75	5.00	10.00	27.50	
1916............	18,490,000	.25	.50	1.00	2.00	10.00	
1916S............	5,820,000	.30	.95	2.00	4.00	11.00	

WINGED HEAD OF LIBERTY OR "MERCURY" TYPE

This dime was designed by A. A. Weinman. Although it is commonly called the "Mercury Dime" the main device is in fact a representation of Liberty. The wings crowning her cap are intended to symbolize liberty of thought. The designer's initials AW are found back of the neck.

Good — Letters and dates clear. Lines and diagonal bands in fasces are obliterated.

V. Good — One-third of sticks discernible in fasces.

Fine — All sticks in fasces are defined. Diagonal bands worn at center high points only.

Ex. Fine — Diagonal bands complete, with only slight wear. Hair braids and hair before ear show clearly.

1916............	22,180,080	.30	.45	.65	1.50	5.50
1916D............	264,000	60.00	85.00	150.00	290.00	500.00
1916S............	10,450,000	.50	.85	1.25	4.25	9.50
1917............	55,230,000	.35	.55	.95	1.75	6.00
1917D...........	9,402,000	1.00	1.75	4.00	13.00	47.50
1917S...........	27,330,000	.50	.85	1.25	4.25	15.00
1918............	26,680,000	.50	.85	1.25	5.50	22.50
1918D..........	22,674,800	.65	1.40	2.25	8.50	32.50
1918S...........	19,300,000	.50	1.00	2.00	7.50	25.00
1919............	35,740,000	.40	.65	1.30	7.00	25.00
1919D..........	9,939,000	1.35	2.50	4.50	35.00	80.00
1919S...........	8,850,000	1.35	2.50	4.50	35.00	95.00
1920............	59,030,000	.35	.60	1.00	2.25	9.50
1920D..........	19,171,000	.60	1.00	1.75	9.00	27.50

DIMES

	Quan. Minted	Good	V.G.	Fine	E.F.	Unc.	Proof
1920S	13,820,000	$ .60	$ 1.00	$ 1.75	$ 9.00	$30.00	
1921	1,230,000	7.00	15.00	30.00	65.00	230.00	
1921D	1,080,000	8.00	17.50	37.50	77.50	175.00	
*1923	50,130,000	.35	.55	.80	1.85	10.50	
1923S	6,440,000	1.00	2.10	3.50	17.50	72.50	
1924	24,010,000	.35	.55	.95	2.50	13.00	
1924D	6,810,000	.60	1.25	2.00	8.00	32.50	
1924S	7,120,000	.65	1.35	2.50	15.00	60.00	
1925	25,610,000	.35	.55	.95	2.50	13.00	
1925D	5,117,000	1.25	2.50	4.75	35.00	250.00	
1925S	5,850,000	.65	1.35	3.00	20.00	75.00	
1926	32,160,000	.35	.55	.95	2.00	9.00	
1926D	6,828,000	.60	1.00	1.50	8.00	35.00	
1926S	1,520,000	2.75	5.00	8.00	37.50	95.00	
1927	28,080,000	.35	.45	.65	1.50	8.00	
1927D	4,812,000	.75	1.75	3.50	35.00	175.00	
1927S	4,770,000	.50	1.10	2.25	19.00	75.00	
1928	19,480,000	.25	.40	.55	1.50	8.00	
1928D	4,161,000	.50	1.10	2.25	17.00	80.00	
1928S	7,400,000	.40	1.00	1.75	12.50	50.00	
1929	25,970,000	.25	.40	.55	1.50	5.00	
1929D	5,034,000	.45	.65	1.25	3.00	10.00	
1929S	4,730,000	.55	.75	1.50	5.00	14.00	
1930	6,770,000	.45	.60	1.00	2.25	9.00	
1930S	1,843,000	1.50	2.25	3.00	8.50	35.00	
1931	3,150,000	.85	1.25	1.60	2.75	15.00	
1931D	1,260,000	2.50	3.25	5.00	10.00	45.00	
1931S	1,800,000	1.50	2.25	3.00	9.00	37.50	
1934	24,080,000	.25	.35	.50	1.00	5.00	
1934D	6,772,000	.45	.60	1.00	2.25	8.00	
1935	58,830,000	.20	.35	.50	.75	3.00	
1935D	10,477,000	.30	.45	.65	2.50	14.00	
1935S	15,840,000	.25	.40	.60	1.35	7.50	
1936 (4,130)	87,504,130					1.50	$42.50
1936D	16,132,000				2.50	9.50	
1936S	9,210,000				2.50	7.50	
1937 (5,756)	56,865,756					1.50	35.00
1937D	14,146,000				1.25	4.25	
1937S	9,740,000				1.25	5.00	
1938 (8,728)	22,198,728					2.00	11.00
1938D	5,537,000				1.25	3.50	
1938S	8,090,000				1.50	4.50	
1939 (9,321)	67,749,321					1.50	10.00
1939D	24,394,000					2.00	
1939S	10,540,000				1.25	4.50	
1940 (11,827)	65,361,827					1.25	9.00
1940D	21,198,000					1.50	
1940S	21,560,000					1.75	
1941 (16,557)	175,106,557					1.00	8.00
1941D	45,634,000					1.50	
1941S	43,090,000					1.75	

*Dimes dated 1923D are counterfeit.

DIMES

Enlarged Detail of 1942
over 41 Dime

	Quan. Minted	Good	V.G.	Fine	E.F.	Unc.	Proof
1942 over 41		$50.00	$65.00	$80.00	$125.00	$275.00	
1942 All(22,329)	205,432,329					.70	$7.50
1942D	60,740,000					.90	
1942S	49,300,000					1.60	
1943	191,710,000					.65	
1943D	71,949,000					.85	
1943S	60,400,000					1.10	
1944	231,410,000					.60	
1944D	62,224,000					.70	
1944S	49,490,000					.95	
1945	159,130,000					.60	
1945D	40,245,000					.70	
1945S	41,920,000					.90	
1945S Micro S				1.50	3.50	15.00	

ROOSEVELT TYPE

John R. Sinnock (whose initials JS are at the truncation of the neck) designed
this dime showing a portrait of Franklin D. Roosevelt. The design has
heavier lettering and a more modernistic character than preceding types.
The reverse displays the torch of liberty between sprays of laurel and oak.

Quan. Minted	Unc.	Proof
1946....255,250,000	.65	
1946D....61,043,500	.70	
1946S....27,900,000	1.00	
1947....121,520,000	2.00	
1947D....46,835,000	1.40	
1947S....34,840,000	1.75	
1948....74,950,000	2.75	
1948D....52,841,000	1.50	
1948S....35,520,000	2.00	
1949....30,940,000	6.00	
1949D...26,034,000	1.75	
1949S....13,510,000	7.00	
1950 (51,386)		
.....50,181,500	2.75	12.00
1950D....46,803,000	1.25	
1950S....20,440,000	6.50	
1951 (57,500)		
....103,937,602	.65	7.00

Quan. Minted	Unc.	Proof
1951D....52,191,800	.65	
1951S....31,630,000	5.75	
1952 (81,980)		
.....99,122,073	.65	4.00
1952D...122,100,000	.65	
1952S....44,419,500	2.00	
1953 (128,800)		
.....53,618,920	.60	2.50
1953D...136,433,000	.60	
1953S...39,180,000	.65	
1954 (233,300)		
....114,243,503	.50	2.50
1954D...106,397,000	.50	
1954S....22,860,000	.60	
1955 (378,200)		
.....12,828,381	1.25	2.00
1955D....13,959,000	1.00	
1955S....18,510,000	.95	
1956 (669,384)		
....109,309,384	.35	1.25
1956D...108,015,100	.35	
1957 (1,247,952)		
....161,407,952	.35	.75
1957D...113,354,330	.35	
1958 (875,652)		
.....32,785,652	.50	1.75
1958D...136,564,600	.30	

Bibliography, U.S. Dimes—A. Kosoff.

DIMES

Quan. Minted	Unc.	Proof	Quan. Minted	Unc.	Proof
1959 (1,149,291)			1961D...209,146,550	$ .25	
....86,929,291	$ .30	$ .75	1962 (3,218,019)		
1959D...164,919,790	.25		75,668,019	.20	$ .50
1960 (1,691,602)			1962D...334,948,380	.20	
....72,081,602	.25	.60	1963.............	.20	.50
1960D...200,160,400	.25		1963D.............	.20	
1961 (3,028,244)					
....96,758,244	.25	.50			

TWENTY-CENT PIECES — 1875-1878

This short-lived coin was authorized by the Act of March 3, 1875. Soon after the appearance of the first twenty-cent pieces, the people complained about the similarity in design and size with the quarter-dollar. The eagle is very similar to that used on the Trade Dollar. The edge of the coin is plain. Most of the 1876CC coins were melted at the mint and never released.

Good — LIBERTY on shield obliterated. Letters and date legible.
V. Good — At least 3 letters of LIBERTY show.
Fine — LIBERTY completely readable, but partly weak.
Very Fine — All letters of LIBERTY bold.
Ex. Fine — LIBERTY sharp. Only slight wear on high points of coin.

Quan. Minted	Good	V.G.	Fine	V.F.	E.F.	Unc.	Proof
1875..(1,200) 39,700	$12.50	$17.50	$25.00	$30.00	$37.50	$70.00	$100.00
1875CC.....133,290	12.50	17.50	27.50	40.00	62.50	90.00	
1875S......1,155,000	10.00	12.50	17.50	22.50	32.50	55.00	
1876..(1,150) 15,900	15.00	18.00	22.50	32.50	42.50	75.00	120.00
1876CC......10,000	(14 Known) Hydeman Sale 1961					6,900.00	
1877......(510) 510	....						375.00
1878......(600) 600	....						275.00

QUARTER DOLLARS 1796 To Date

The first date, 1796, follows the pattern of the early half-dimes and dimes by the absence of a mark of value. In 1804 25C was added to the reverse. Figures were used until 1838 when QUAR. DOL. appeared. It was not until 1892 that the value was spelled out entirely.

Authorized in 1792 it was not issued until four years later followed by a lapse of about eight years. The first type weighed 104 grains which remained standard until modified by the Act of January 18, 1837 to 103⅛ grains. As with the dime and half-dime, the weight was reduced and arrows placed at the date in 1853, and rays were placed in the field of the reverse during that year only.

The law of 1873 also affected the quarter, for the weight was slightly increased and arrows again placed at the date.

Proofs prior to 1855 are known to exist of some dates, and all are rare.

QUARTER DOLLARS

Fair — Details clear enough to identify.
Good — Date readable. Bust outlined, but no detail.
V. Good — All but deepest drapery folds worn smooth. All hairlines but curls lack detail.
Fine — All drapery lines visible. Hair partly worn.
V. Fine — Only left side of drapery is indistinct.

Quan. Minted	Fair	Good	V.G.	Fine	V.F.	Unc.
1796.....5,894	$350.00	$500.00	$900.00	$1,700.00	$1965.00	$2,750.00
1804.....6,738	75.00	125.00	165.00	275.00	485.00	———
1805...121,394	35.00	45.00	60.00	100.00	200.00	500.00

1806 Over 5   Reverse   1806 Normal Date

	Fair	Good	V.G.	Fine	V.F.	Unc.
1806 over 5 All Kinds.206,124	$25.00	$40.00	$60.00	$92.50	$185.00	$500.00
1806....................	25.00	37.50	55.00	75.00	155.00	450.00
1807..............220,643	25.00	37.50	55.00	75.00	160.00	475.00

LIBERTY HEAD FACING LEFT

Fair — Details clear enough to identify.
Good — Date, letters and stars readable. Hair under headband smooth. Cap lines worn smooth.
V. Good — Rim well defined. Main details visible. Full LIBERTY on cap. Hair above eye nearly smooth.
Fine — All hairlines show but drapery has only part details. Shoulder clasp distinct.
V. Fine — All details show, but some wear. Clasp and ear sharp.

1818 Over 15

1815

1815...............69,232	11.50	14.50	23.00	37.50	92.50	250.00
1818 over 15 All K...361,174	11.50	14.50	23.00	37.50	95.00	275.00
1818....................	10.50	12.75	18.50	28.00	50.00	150.00
1819 Sm. 9 All Kinds.144,000	10.50	12.75	19.00	29.00	51.50	150.00
1819 Large 9.............	10.50	12.75	19.00	29.00	51.50	150.00

QUARTER DOLLARS

1820 Small O		1820 Large O			1822, 25 Over 50c		
Quan. Minted	Fair	Good	V.G.	Fine	V.F.	Unc.	Proof

1820 Small O All Kinds..127,440	$ 9.25	$11.50	$16.50	$26.00	$47.50	$135.00	
1820 Large O.......	8.75	11.00	16.00	24.50	42.00	125.00	
1821........216,850	8.75	11.00	16.00	24.50	42.00	125.00	
1822 All Kds..64,084	10.50	14.00	22.00	34.50	70.00	200.00	
1822 25 over 50c....	115.00	125.00	180.00	270.00	425.00	1000.00	

1823 over 22..17,801	350.00	500.00	650.00	900.00	1750.00	
1824......... ———	14.00	21.00	29.00	45.00	77.50	200.00

1825 Over 22		1825 Over 23				

1825 over 22 All Kinds..168,000	11.50	15.50	20.00	29.00	39.50	130.00
1825 over 23........	11.50	15.50	20.00	29.00	39.50	130.00
1825 over 24........	11.50	15.50	20.00	29.00	39.50	130.00
1827 Original (Curled base 2 in 25c) (6 or 7 known) 4,000 Minted.....———						
1827 Restrike (Square base 2 in 25c)............................———						
1828 All Kds.102,000	9.25	12.75	17.50	25.00	47.50	150.00
1828 25 over 50c....	25.00	40.00	50.00	65.00	115.00	350.00

Reduced Size — No Motto On Reverse

Good — Bust is well defined. Hair under headband is smooth. Date letters, stars readable. Scant rims.

V. Good — Details apparent but worn on high spots. Rims strong. Full LIBERTY.

Fine—All hairlines visible. Drapery partly worn. Shoulder clasp distinct.

V. Fine — Only top spots worn. Clasp sharp. Ear distinct.

QUARTER DOLLARS

1831   Small   Large
            Letters   Letters

	Quan. Minted	Good	V.G.	Fine	V.F.	Unc.	Proof
1831 Small Letters							
All Kinds......398,000		$ 5.00	$ 6.50	$10.00	$20.00	$70.00	
1831 Large Letters.........		5.00	6.50	10.00	20.00	70.00	
1832...............320,000		4.00	6.00	9.50	19.00	65.00	
1833...............156,000		4.00	6.00	9.50	19.00	65.00	
1834...............286,000		4.00	6.00	9.50	19.00	65.00	
1835.............1,952,000		4.00	6.00	9.50	19.00	65.00	
1836...............472,000		4.00	6.00	9.50	19.00	65.00	
1837...............252,400		4.00	6.00	9.50	19.00	65.00	
1838 All Kinds......832,000		4.00	6.00	9.50	19.00	65.00	

LIBERTY SEATED TYPE

Good — Scant rim. LIBERTY on shield worn off. Date and letters readable.
V. Good — Rim fairly defined, at least 3 letters in LIBERTY evident.
Fine — LIBERTY complete, but partly weak.
V. Fine — LIBERTY strong.

No Drapery From Elbow   Drapery From Elbow

1838 No Drapery..........		4.50	8.00	13.50	21.50	50.00
1839 No Drapery....491,146	4.00	6.50	11.00	17.75	45.00
1840O No Drapery					
All Kinds......425,200	4.25	6.75	11.00	18.25	50.00
1840 Drapery.......188,127	5.50	8.25	13.00	19.75	50.00
1840O Drapery............	4.50	6.75	11.00	19.00	50.00
1841.............120,000	12.50	16.50	22.50	33.50	80.00
1841O.............452,000	4.00	5.25	7.50	15.75	40.00

Small Date   Large Date

1842 Sm. Date All K..88,000				Proofs Only ———	
1842 Large Date...........	4.00	5.50	7.75	14.00	40.00
1842O Sm. Date All.769,000	12.50	16.50	22.50	24.50	80.00
1842O Large Date..........	4.50	5.65	9.50	16.75	45.00

QUARTER DOLLARS

	Quan. Minted	Good	V.G.	Fine	V.F.	Unc.	Proof
1843	645,600	$ 3.50	$ 5.00	$ 7.50	$12.25	$33.00	
1843O	968,000	3.50	5.00	7.50	12.50	35.00	
1844	421,200	3.50	5.00	7.50	12.50	35.00	
1844O	740,000	4.00	5.50	5.75	13.75	37.50	
1845	922,000	3.25	4.50	7.00	11.00	30.00	
1846	510,000	3.50	4.75	7.25	11.50	30.00	
1847	734,000	3.50	4.75	7.00	9.00	27.50	
1847O	368,000	4.00	5.50	8.00	11.25	30.00	
1848	146,000	4.00	5.50	8.00	11.25	30.00	
1849	340,000	3.25	4.50	7.00	9.75	30.00	
1849O	——	60.00	77.50	110.00	162.50	350.00	
1850	190,800	4.00	5.75	8.50	14.50	40.00	
1850O	412,000	3.50	4.75	7.00	12.75	40.00	
1851	160,000	3.50	4.75	7.00	13.00	40.00	
1851O	88,000	3.50	5.50	9.00	20.00	65.00	
1852	177,060	3.50	5.50	9.00	16.75	47.50	
1852O	96,000	6.50	8.75	13.00	25.00	60.00	

No Arrows   No Rays   Arrows at Date   Rays Around Eagle

1853 over 52

No Arrows or Rays....		45.00	50.00	87.50	130.00	300.00

The reduction in weight is indicated by the arrows at the date. Rays were added on the reverse side in the field around the eagle. The arrows were retained until 1856, but the rays were omitted after 1853.

1853	15,254,220	4.00	5.25	7.50	12.75	40.00
1853O	1,332,000	6.50	9.00	13.50	21.00	45.00

Arrows At Date — Rays Removed From Reverse

1854	12,380,000	3.00	3.85	5.50	7.50	32.50	
1854O	1,484,000	3.25	4.25	6.00	11.50	32.50	
1855	2,857,000	3.00	4.00	5.75	9.75	25.00	$300.00
1855O	176,000	35.00	47.50	67.50	120.00	300.00	
1855S	396,400	40.00	50.00	70.00	120.00	300.00	

Arrows At Date Removed

1856	7,264,000	2.75	3.25	4.00	6.25	15.00	260.00
1856O	968,000	3.00	3.75	5.00	8.00	17.50	
1856S	286,000	15.50	23.00	34.00	67.50	175.00	
1857	9,644,000	2.50	2.65	3.00	5.25	14.50	240.00
1857O	1,180,000	3.00	3.75	5.00	8.00	20.00	
1857S	82,000	15.00	21.50	32.50	75.00	210.00	
1858	7,368,000	3.00	3.75	5.00	7.00	15.00	235.00

QUARTER DOLLARS

	Quan. Minted	Good	V.G.	Fine	V.F.	Unc.	Proof
1858O	520,000	$ 4.00	$ 5.50	$ 6.50	$ 9.75	$22.50	
1858S	121,000	24.00	28.50	37.00	70.00	175.00	
1859	1,344,000	3.00	3.65	4.50	6.75	15.50	$80.00
1859O	260,000	3.50	4.25	5.50	8.00	18.00	
1859S	80,000	24.00	28.50	37.00	75.00	200.00	
1860	805,400	2.50	3.25	4.25	7.00	18.00	70.00
1860O	388,000	3.00	3.85	5.25	8.00	19.00	
1860S	56,000	15.00	18.00	25.00	59.00	190.00	
1861	4,854,600	2.50	3.25	4.25	7.00	17.50	60.00
1861S	96,000	15.00	18.00	25.00	55.00	140.00	
1862	932,550	2.50	3.00	4.00	6.50	17.50	55.00
1862S	67,000	11.00	13.00	16.00	45.00	140.00	
1863	(460) 192,060	3.25	4.25	6.00	9.00	22.50	60.00
1864	(470) 94,070	3.00	3.75	5.00	8.50	23.00	60.00
1864S	20,000	12.00	14.25	18.50	47.00	140.00	
1865	(500) 59,300	4.00	5.25	7.00	10.00	25.00	60.00
1865S	41,000	9.00	11.50	15.00	39.00	110.00	
1866 One Known (proof) Hydeman Sale 1961							$24,500.00

MOTTO ABOVE EAGLE

The motto **IN GOD WE TRUST** was added to the reverse side in 1866. As on the half-dollar and silver dollar the motto has been retained since that time.

		Good	V.G.	Fine	V.F.	Unc.	Proof
1866	(725) 17,525	4.00	5.00	6.00	10.00	25.00	62.50
1866S	28,000	11.00	12.50	15.00	40.00	130.00	
1867	(625) 20,625	3.25	4.25	5.75	8.50	19.00	55.00
1867S	48,000	10.00	11.50	14.00	38.50	115.00	
1868	(600) 30,000	4.00	5.00	6.00	9.25	22.00	55.00
1868S	96,000	9.00	11.00	13.50	33.00	90.00	
1869	(600) 16,600	4.50	5.50	8.00	12.50	23.00	55.00
1869S	76,000	9.00	11.00	13.50	33.00	90.00	
1870	(1,000) 87,400	3.00	3.65	4.50	7.00	17.50	45.00
1870CC	8,340	120.00	140.00	175.00	300.00	650.00	
1871	(960) 171,232	2.50	2.85	3.50	5.50	14.00	37.50
1871CC	10,890	100.00	120.00	150.00	260.00	600.00	
1871S	30,900	7.50	11.00	17.50	38.00	100.00	
1872	(950) 182,950	2.50	3.10	4.00	6.00	14.50	37.50
1872CC	9,100	150.00	180.00	225.00	420.00	1000.00	
1872S	103,000	15.00	18.50	25.00	45.00	100.00	
1873 Closed 3 All Kinds							
	(600) 220,600	7.00	10.00	15.00	18.75	36.00	52.50
1873 Open 3		6.00	8.25	12.00	15.75	35.00	
1873CC	4,000	350.00	465.00	650.00	900.00	———	

Arrows were placed at the date in the years 1873 and 1874 to denote the change of weight from 96 to 96.45 grains.

QUARTER DOLLARS

Arrows at Date   **Arrows Removed Starting 1875**

	Quan. Minted	Good	V.G.	Fine	V.F.	Unc.	Proof
1873........(540)	1,263,700	$16.00	$19.50	$25.00	$40.00	$105.00	$215.00
1873CC.............	12,462	300.00	390.00	550.00	765.00	1400.00	
1873S.............	156,000	20.00	25.00	32.50	50.00	110.00	
1874........(700)	471,900	16.00	19.50	25.00	38.00	95.00	180.00
1874S.............	392,000	23.00	27.50	35.00	54.00	120.00	

Arrows Removed

	Quan. Minted	Good	V.G.	Fine	V.F.	Unc.	Proof
1875........(700)	4,293,500	2.50	3.00	3.75	5.50	13.50	50.00
1875CC............	140,000	5.00	6.25	8.00	12.25	30.00	
1875S.............	680,000	7.50	9.00	13.00	27.50	75.00	
1876.....(1,150)	17,817,150	2.50	3.00	3.75	5.50	12.00	35.00
1876CC...........	4,944,000	2.75	3.40	4.50	7.75	20.00	
1876S.............	8,596,000	2.50	3.10	4.25	6.00	13.50	
1877........(510)	10,911,710	2.50	3.00	4.00	5.50	12.00	65.00
1877CC...........	4,192,000	3.00	3.35	5.00	8.00	22.50	
1877S All Kinds...8,996,000		2.50	3.00	4.00	5.75	13.50	
1877S (Over Horizontal S)				85.00	110.00	180.00	
1878........(800)	2,260,800	2.50	3.10	4.25	6.00	13.50	42.50
1878CC...........	996,000	5.00	6.00	7.50	12.50	29.00	
1878S.............	140,000	115.00	155.00	225.00	330.00	700.00	
1879..........(250)	14,700	13.50	15.00	18.00	22.00	40.00	77.50
1880........(1,355)	14,955	12.00	12.75	14.00	17.00	30.00	40.00
1881........(975)	12,975	13.00	14.75	17.50	20.00	32.50	45.00
1882........(1,100)	16,300	12.00	13.50	16.00	18.50	31.50	45.00
1883........(1,039)	15,439	12.00	13.75	16.50	19.50	32.50	50.00
1884..........(875)	8,875	17.50	18.50	20.00	25.00	45.00	65.00
1885..........(930)	14,530	13.00	14.75	17.50	21.00	35.00	55.00
1886..........(886)	5,886	25.00	28.50	35.00	44.00	77.50	110.00
1887..........(710)	10,710	13.00	14.75	17.50	21.00	35.00	55.00
1888..........(832)	10,833	13.00	14.75	17.50	21.00	35.00	45.00
1888S.............	1,216,000	2.50	3.00	4.00	7.25	20.00	
1889........(711)	12,711	13.00	14.50	17.00	20.00	32.50	55.00
1890........(590)	80,590	3.00	3.75	5.00	7.75	20.00	60.00
1891........(600)	3,920,600	2.50	3.25	4.50	6.50	15.00	50.00
1891O.............	68,000	75.00	85.00	100.00	175.00	400.00	
1891S.............	2,216,000	2.50	3.50	4.75	7.25	20.00	

BARBER OR LIBERTY HEAD TYPE

Like other silver coins of this type the quarter dollars minted from 1892 to 1916 were designed by Charles E. Barber. His initial B is found at the base of the neck of Liberty.

QUARTER DOLLARS

	Quan. Minted	Good	V.G.	Fine	E.F.	Unc.	Proof
1892......(1,245)	8,237,245	$ .90	$ 1.35	$ 2.25	$ 5.00	$15.00	$50.00
1892O............	2,640,000	3.00	4.50	7.50	15.00	40.00	
1892S............	964,079	9.00	14.50	25.00	65.00	132.50	
1893........(792)	5,444,815	.90	1.30	2.00	4.00	14.50	50.00
1893O............	3,396,000	1.75	3.10	5.50	15.00	42.50	
1893S............	1,454,535	2.75	4.25	7.50	16.00	52.50	
1894........(972)	3,432,972	.90	1.45	2.35	5.00	15.50	50.00
1894O............	2,852,000	1.75	3.50	7.00	15.00	52.50	
1894S............	2,648,821	1.50	3.00	6.00	14.00	50.00	
1895........(880)	4,440,880	.85	1.30	2.00	5.00	15.50	57.50
1895O............	2,816,000	2.00	3.65	6.50	30.00	100.00	
1895S............	1,764,681	2.50	4.25	7.00	15.00	65.00	
1896........(762)	3,874,762	1.00	1.65	2.50	5.50	20.00	55.00
1896O............	1,484,000	3.50	7.50	15.00	55.00	200.00	
1896S............	188,039	65.00	110.00	200.00	400.00	1200.00	
1897........(731)	8,140,731	.85	1.30	2.00	5.00	16.00	60.00
1897O............	1,414,800	6.50	10.00	16.00	45.00	130.00	
1897S............	542,229	7.50	11.00	17.50	50.00	150.00	
1898......(735)	11,100,735	.75	1.10	1.75	4.00	16.00	55.00
1898O............	1,868,000	1.90	3.75	7.00	30.00	90.00	
1898S............	1,020,592	1.90	3.75	7.00	30.00	90.00	
1899......(846)	12,624,846	.75	1.10	1.75	4.00	15.00	52.50
1899O............	2,644,000	1.75	3.50	6.50	20.00	72.50	
1899S............	708,000	5.50	7.25	10.00	25.00	82.50	
1900......(912)	10,016,912	.65	1.10	1.75	4.00	15.00	47.50
1900O............	3,416,000	2.00	3.75	7.00	21.00	72.50	
1900S............	1,858,585	1.35	3.25	6.50	35.00	90.00	
1901........(813)	8,892,813	.60	1.00	1.75	4.00	15.00	45.00
1901O............	1,612,000	8.00	17.00	32.50	100.00	315.00	
1901S............	72,664	190.00	275.00	375.00	800.00	1600.00	
1902......(777)	12,197,744	.50	1.00	1.75	3.50	15.00	50.00
1902O............	4,748,000	2.00	4.25	8.50	25.00	70.00	
1902S............	1,524,612	2.50	5.00	9.50	37.50	95.00	
1903........(755)	9,670,064	.50	1.00	1.75	3.50	15.00	55.00
1903O............	3,500,000	2.75	5.25	10.50	60.00	162.50	
1903S............	1,036,000	2.75	5.25	10.50	60.00	155.00	
1904........(670)	9,588,813	.50	1.00	1.75	3.50	15.00	52.50
1904O............	2,456,000	5.50	9.00	15.00	65.00	275.00	
1905........(727)	4,968,250	.50	1.00	1.75	3.50	15.00	52.50
1905O............	1,230,000	4.50	7.75	13.50	40.00	160.00	
1905S............	1,884,000	2.25	4.25	7.00	25.00	70.00	
1906........(675)	3,656,435	.50	1.00	1.75	3.50	15.00	52.50
1906D............	3,280,000	1.25	2.00	3.25	6.00	20.00	

QUARTER DOLLARS

	Quan. Minted	Good	V.G.	Fine	E.F.	Unc.	Proof
1906O	2,056,000	$ 1.25	$ 2.25	$ 4.00	$ 8.50	$40.00	
1907 (575)	7,192,575	.50	1.00	1.75	3.50	15.00	$60.00
1907D	2,484,000	1.25	2.00	3.00	6.00	22.50	
1907O	4,560,000	1.25	2.00	3.00	6.00	20.00	
1907S	1,360,000	1.75	3.00	5.00	20.00	60.00	
1908 (545)	4,232,545	.50	1.00	1.75	3.50	15.00	62.50
1908D	5,788,000	.60	1.10	2.00	5.00	18.00	
1908O	6,244,000	.60	1.10	2.00	5.00	18.00	
1908S	784,000	4.00	5.75	8.50	25.00	75.00	
1909 (650)	9,268,650	.50	1.00	1.75	3.50	15.00	62.50
1909D	5,114,000	.60	1.10	2.00	5.00	17.50	
1909O	712,000	10.00	18.50	32.50	90.00	330.00	
1909S	1,348,000	1.00	2.50	5.50	15.00	52.50	
1910 (551)	2,244,551	.75	1.65	3.25	6.00	20.00	67.50
1910D	1,500,000	1.50	2.25	3.50	6.50	21.00	
1911 (543)	3,720,543	.50	1.00	1.75	3.50	15.00	75.00
1911D	933,600	1.50	3.00	5.50	15.00	47.50	
1911S	988,000	1.50	3.00	5.50	15.00	47.50	
1912 (700)	4,400,700	.50	1.00	1.75	3.50	15.00	67.50
1912S	708,000	2.00	4.50	9.00	35.00	110.00	
1913 (613)	484,613	1.75	3.75	6.00	10.00	67.50	130.00
1913D	1,450,800	1.25	2.65	5.00	8.50	30.00	
1913S	40,000	75.00	125.00	195.00	450.00	1200.00	
1914 (380)	6,244,610	.50	1.00	1.75	6.00	20.00	225.00
1914D	3,046,000	.50	1.00	1.75	5.50	18.00	
1914S	264,000	3.50	8.00	16.00	80.00	275.00	
1915 (450)	3,480,450	.50	1.25	2.00	6.00	20.00	215.00
1915D	3,694,000	.50	1.00	1.75	3.50	15.00	
1915S	704,000	1.50	2.75	3.00	15.00	42.50	
1916	1,788,000	.50	1.65	3.50	8.00	27.50	
1916D	6,540,800	.50	1.25	2.50	4.25	15.00	

STANDING LIBERTY TYPE

This type quarter was designed by Herman A. MacNeil. The left arm of Liberty is upraised bearing a shield in the attitude of protection, from which the cover is being drawn. The right hand bears the olive branch of peace. The designer's initial M is located above and to the right of the date.

There was a modification in 1917. The reverse has a new arrangement of the stars and the eagle is higher.

In 1925 a depression was made in the pedestal on which Liberty stands, and which bears the date. On the first issues the dates wore off easily because they were too high and were not protected by other features of the coin. The new "recessed" dates proved more durable as a result of this change.

Good — Date and lettering readable. Top of date worn. Liberty's right leg and toes worn off. Left leg and drapery lines show much wear.

V. Good — Distinct date. Toes show faintly. Drapery lines visible above her left leg.

Fine — High curve of her right leg flat from thigh to ankle. Left leg shows only slight wear. Drapery lines over right knee seen only at sides of leg.

Ex. Fine — Flattened only at high spots. Her toes are sharp. Drapery lines across right leg are evident.

(Some modifications must be made for grading variety 2.)

QUARTER DOLLARS

Uncirculated Standing Liberty Quarters with full head are worth more than prices listed below.

Variety 1

	Quan. Minted	Good	V.G.	Fine	E.F.	Unc.
1916	52,000	$175.00	$275.00	$350.00	$500.00	$900.00
1917 Variety 1	8,792,000	2.75	3.75	5.00	11.00	21.00
1917D Variety 1	1,509,200	4.00	6.00	9.00	22.50	37.50
1917S Variety 1	1,952,000	4.50	6.50	11.00	25.00	47.50

Variety 2   1918S Over 7

	Quan. Minted	Good	V.G.	Fine	E.F.	Unc.
1917 Variety 2	13,880,000	2.75	3.75	7.00	13.00	20.00
1917D Variety 2	6,224,400	5.25	8.00	13.50	27.50	55.00
1917S Variety 2	5,552,000	5.25	8.50	13.75	30.00	57.50
1918	12,240,000	2.75	4.50	8.00	27.00	52.50
1918D	7,380,000	4.25	6.50	9.50	31.00	60.00
1918S All Kinds	11,072,000	3.00	4.75	8.50	22.00	47.50
1918S over 7		200.00	300.00	450.00	800.00	2500.00
1919	11,324,000	3.50	5.50	9.00	27.50	45.00
1919D	1,944,000	20.00	27.50	40.00	90.00	200.00
1919S	1,836,000	22.50	37.50	55.00	110.00	250.00
1920	27,860,000	2.00	2.50	4.50	8.75	17.00
1920D	3,586,400	9.00	14.00	21.50	48.00	95.00
1920S	6,380,000	4.50	7.00	10.00	25.00	57.50
1921	1,916,000	20.00	27.50	35.00	75.00	165.00
1923	9,716,000	2.00	3.00	4.50	8.25	15.00
*1923S	1,360,000	27.00	35.00	50.00	100.00	165.00
1924	10,920,000	2.00	3.00	4.50	8.25	20.00
1924D	3,112,000	4.00	6.00	9.00	12.50	25.00
1924S	2,860,000	7.00	9.00	13.50	27.50	67.50
1925	12,280,000			3.00	6.50	15.00
1926	11,316,000			3.00	6.50	15.00
1926D	1,716,000			2.75	5.00	11.00
1926S	2,700,000	3.75	6.75	13.00	60.00	120.00
1927	11,912,000			2.75	5.50	17.50
1927D	976,400			3.00	6.50	42.50
1927S	396,000	7.50	12.00	20.00	135.00	550.00
1928	6,336,000			2.00	5.50	16.00
1928D	1,627,600			2.00	5.50	15.00
1928S	2,644,000			2.00	5.50	15.00

*Beware Altered Date.

QUARTER DOLLARS

	Quan. Minted	Fine	E.F.	Unc.
1929	11,140,000	$1.85	$5.25	$13.00
1929D	1,358,000	1.85	5.25	20.00
1929S	1,764,000	1.85	5.25	16.50
1930	5,632,000	1.85	5.25	12.50
1930S	1,556,000	1.85	5.25	16.00

Washington Head Type

This type was intended to be a commemorative issue marking the two-hundredth anniversary of Washington's birth. John Flanagan, a New York sculptor, was the designer. The initials JF are found at the base of the neck.

Good — *Letters and date flat, but separated from rim. No hairlines near face.*

V. Good — *Wing-tips outlined. Rims on both sides are fine and even. Tops of letters at rim are flattened.*

Fine — *Hairlines about ear are visible. Tiny feathers on eagle's breast are faintly visible.*

Ex. Fine — *Hairlines sharp. Wear spots confined to top of eagle's legs and center of breast.*

	Quan. Minted	Good	V.G.	Fine	E.F.	Unc.	Proof
1932	5,404,000			$1.25	$2.25	$ 7.00	
1932D	436,800	$8.50	14.00	21.00	55.00	150.00	
1932S	408,000	7.00	11.00	15.00	25.00	60.00	
1934	31,912,052			1.25	2.90	10.00	
1934D	3,527,200			2.50	7.50	42.50	
1935	32,484,000				2.25	8.00	
1935D	5,780,000			1.65	6.00	30.00	
1935S	5,660,000			1.65	6.25	31.00	
1936 (3,837)	41,303,837				1.45	7.00	$100.00
1936D	5,374,000	2.50	3.75	7.00	40.00	160.00	
1936S	3,828,000				4.25	26.00	
1937 (5,542)	19,701,542				1.50	7.00	45.00
1937D	7,189,600				1.50	10.00	
1937S	1,652,000			3.00	6.00	50.00	
1938 (8,045)	9,480,045			2.00	5.00	45.00	45.00
1938S	2,832,000				2.75	19.00	
1939 (8,795)	33,548,795				1.50	8.50	30.00
1939D	7,092,000				1.50	8.50	
1939S	2,628,000				3.50	24.00	
1940 (11,246)	35,715,246				2.25	11.00	20.00
1940D	2,797,600				4.00	27.50	
1940S	8,244,000					6.00	
1941 (15,287)	79,047,287					3.00	17.50
1941D	16,714,800					4.00	
1941S	16,080,000					5.00	
1942 (21,123)	102,117,123					3.00	16.00
1942D	17,487,200					2.50	
1942S	19,384,000					8.00	
1943	99,700,000					1.35	
1943D	16,095,600					2.00	

QUARTER DOLLARS

Quan. Minted	Unc.	Proof
1943S..........21,700,000........................	$4.00	
1944..........104,956,000........................	1.50	
1944D..........14,600,000........................	1.50	
1944S..........12,560,000........................	2.60	
1945..........74,372,000........................	1.35	
1945D..........12,341,600........................	1.35	
1945S..........17,004,001........................	1.75	
1946..........53,436,000........................	1.35	
1946D..........9,072,800........................	1.10	
1946S..........4,204,000........................	2.75	
1947..........22,556,000........................	1.10	
1947D..........15,338,400........................	1.35	
1947S..........5,532,000........................	2.00	
1948..........35,196,000........................	1.25	
1948D..........16,766,800........................	1.25	
1948S..........15,960,000........................	1.60	
1949..........9,312,000........................	5.50	
1949D..........10,068,400........................	2.00	
1950....(51,386) 24,971,512........................	1.50	$14.00
1950D..........21,075,600........................	1.25	
1950S..........10,284,004........................	2.60	
1951....(57,500) 43,505,602........................	1.10	7.00
1951D..........35,354,800........................	1.10	
1951S..........8,948,000........................	3.50	
1952....(81,980) 38,862,073........................	1.00	4.00
1952D..........49,795,200........................	1.00	
1952S..........13,707,800........................	2.25	
1953...(128,800) 18,664,920........................	1.25	2.50
1953D..........56,112,400........................	1.00	
1953S..........14,016,000........................	1.10	
1954...(233,300) 54,645,503........................	.75	2.50
1954D..........46,305,500........................	.75	
1954S..........11,834,722........................	.95	
1955...(378,200) 18,558,381........................	1.10	2.00
1955D..........3,182,400........................	2.00	
1956...(669,384) 44,813,384........................	.70	1.25
1956D..........32,334,500........................	.70	
1957..(1,247,952) 47,779,952........................	.60	1.00
1957D..........77,924,160........................	.60	
1958....(875,652) 7,235,652........................	.75	1.75
1958D..........78,124,900........................	.60	
1959..(1,149,291) 25,533,291........................	.60	1.00
1959D..........62,054,232........................	.60	
1960..(1,691,602) 30,855,602........................	.55	1.00
1960D..........63,000,324........................	.55	
1961..(3,028,244) 40,064,244........................	.50	.90
1961D..........83,656,928........................	.50	
1962..(3,218,019) 39,374,019........................	.50	.90
1962D..........127,554,756........................	.50	
1963..	.50	.90
1963D...	.50	

BIBLIOGRAPHY

Browning, A. W., Early Quarter Dollars of the U. S. (1796-1838). 1925.
Haseltine, J. W., Type Table of U. S. Dollars, Half and Quarter Dollars. 1881.
Reprint 1933.

HALF DOLLARS 1794 To Date

The half-dollar, authorized by the Act of April 2, 1792, was not minted until 1794. This is a series that has been extensively collected by varieties and many dates contain both rare and common varieties. Valuations are for the most common varieties. Scarcer varieties, as listed by Beistle (See page 141, Bibliography), command higher prices.

The weight of the half-dollar was 208 grains and its fineness 892.4 when first issued. This standard was not changed until 1837 when the law of January 18, 1837 specified 206¼ grains, .900 fine.

Arrows at the date in 1853 indicate the reduction of weight to 192 grains in conformity with the Act of February 21, 1853. During that year only, rays were added to the field on the reverse side. Arrows remained in 1854 and 1855.

In 1873 the weight was raised by law to 192.9 grains and arrows were again placed at the date, to be removed in 1875.

The half-dollars had **FIFTY CENTS OR HALF A DOLLAR** lettered on the edge until 1836 after which the edge of the coins was reeded.

Proofs prior to 1855 are known to exist of some dates, and all are rare.

Fair — Clear enough to identify.

Good — Date and letters sufficient to be readable. Main devices outlined, but lack details.

V. Good — Major details discernible. Letters well formed but worn.

Fine — Hair ends distinguishable. Top hairlines show, but otherwise worn smooth.

V. Fine — Hair in center shows some detail. Other details more bold.

1794   3 Leaves
Under Wings

	Quan. Minted	Fair	Good	V.G.	Fine	V.F.
1794	5,300	$125.00	$200.00	$300.00	$400.00	$800.00
1795 All Kinds	317,844	72.50	90.00	110.00	150.00	350.00
1795 3 leaves under each wing	125.00	275.00	450.00	600.00	900.00

Grading same as above for Fair to Fine.

V. Fine — Right side of drapery slightly worn. Left side to curls is smooth.

1796, 15 Stars

1796 Fifteen Stars (No mint report)

650.00   900.00   1,350.00   2,200.00   3,100.00

HALF DOLLARS

1796 - 16 Stars   1797

	Quan. Minted	Fair	Good	V.G.	Fine	V.F.
1796 16 Stars............		$675.00	$1,000.00	$1,500.00	$2,250.00	$3,250.00
1797...............	3,918	575.00	900.00	1,200.00	2,000.00	3,000.00

1801   1803 Large 3

Good — Letters and date readable. E. PLURIBUS UNUM obliterated.
V. Good — Motto partially readable. Only deepest drapery details visible. All other lines smooth.
Fine — All drapery lines distinguishable. Hairlines near cheek and neck show some detail.
V. Fine — Left side of drapery worn smooth.

		Good	V.G	Fine	V.F	Unc.
1801......................	30,289	$60.00	$95.00	$160.00	$300.00	$800.00
1802......................	29,890	57.50	82.50	130.00	225.00	460.00
1803 Small 3 All Kinds.......	31,715	50.00	70.00	85.00	150.00	400.00
1803 Large 3....................		30.00	37.50	55.00	115.00	325.00

1805
Over
4

1806
Over
5

1805 over 4 All Kinds.......	211,722	47.50	60.00	90.00	150.00	325.00

HALF DOLLARS

	Quan. Minted	Good	V.G.	Fine	V.F.	Unc.
1805		$17.50	$25.00	$35.00	$70.00	$200.00
1806 over 5 All Kinds	839,576	30.00	35.00	47.50	95.00	250.00
1806 over inverted 6		52.50	70.00	105.00	210.00	475.00

Round Top 6 Large Stars

Branch Stem Through Claw

Pointed Top 6

Branch Stem Not Through Claw

	Good	V.G.	Fine	V.F.	Unc.
1806 Round top 6, Large stars	16.00	23.00	35.00	60.00	150.00
1806 Round top 6, Small stars	16.00	23.00	35.00	60.00	150.00
1806 Pointed top 6, Stem through claw	16.00	23.00	35.00	60.00	150.00
1806 Ptd. top 6, Stem not thru claw.	16.00	23.00	35.00	60.00	150.00
1807 301,076	16.00	23.00	35.00	60.00	150.00

TURBAN HEAD TYPE

John Reich designed the first Turban Head concept of Liberty. The head of Liberty facing left was used on all U.S. coin denominations for the next thirty years. Reich was the first artist to consistently include the denomination on our gold and silver coins. He was from Germany and a bondman freed from servitude by a mint official.

Good — Date and letters readable. Bust worn smooth with outline distinct.

V. Good — LIBERTY visible but faint. Legends distinguishable. Clasp at shoulder visible. Curl above it nearly smooth.

Fine — Clasp and adjacent curl clearly outlined with slight details.

V. Fine — Clasp at shoulder clear. Curl has wear only on highest point. Hair over brow distinguishable.

Ex. Fine — Clasp and adjacent curl fairly sharp. Brow and hair above distinct. Curls well defined.

[128]

HALF DOLLARS

Small Stars	Large Stars	50 Over 20c

	Quan. Minted	Good	V.G.	Fine	V.F.	E.F.	Unc.
1807 Sm. stars All K.	750,500	$11.50	$15.50	$22.50	$55.00	$97.50	$250.00
1807 Large stars...........		10.00	13.50	20.00	37.50	69.00	140.00
1807 50 over 20............		10.50	16.00	28.50	40.00	82.50	165.00

1808
Over
7

		Good	V.G.	Fine	V.F.	E.F.	Unc.
1808 over 7 All K.	1,368,600	7.50	11.50	17.50	25.00	39.00	70.00
1808.....................		5.00	6.50	9.50	16.50	29.00	62.50
1809.............	1,405,810	4.75	6.25	8.50	16.00	27.50	62.50
1810.............	1,276,276	4.75	6.25	8.50	15.00	26.00	55.00

1811 Small 8	(18.11) Punctuated Date	1814 Over 13

		Good	V.G.	Fine	V.F.	E.F.	Unc.
1811 Sm. 8 All K.	1,203,644	3.75	5.50	7.50	12.50	20.00	45.00
1811 Large 8.............		5.00	7.50	12.50	19.00	40.00	85.00
1811 Date 18.11............		6.50	10.00	15.00	22.50	45.00	85.00
1812 over 11 All K.	1,628,059	9.50	12.00	17.50	45.00	75.00	122.50
1812.....................		4.25	5.75	8.00	13.00	20.00	42.50
1813.............	1,241,903	4.25	5.75	8.00	13.00	20.00	45.00

HALF DOLLARS

	Quan. Minted	Good	V.G.	Fine	V.F.	E.F.	Unc.
1814 over 13 All K.	1,039,075	$10.50	$14.50	$20.00	$35.00	$57.50	$110.00
1814		5.25	6.50	9.50	13.00	17.50	50.00

1815
(Mint Report for
1816 — 47,150.)

All have 1815 over 12.
Good..........$ 60.00
V. Good...... 70.00
Fine......... 120.00
V. Fine....... 150.00
Ex. Fine..... 200.00
Unc.......... 400.00

1817
Over
13

1819
Over
18
Small
9

	Quan. Minted	Good	V.G.	Fine	V.F.	E.F.	Unc.
1817 over 13 All K.	1,215,567	12.00	16.00	25.00	40.00	57.50	110.00
1817 over 14..... (Ex. Rare)							
1817 Dated 181.7		9.50	15.00	24.00	37.50	55.00	100.00
1817		4.00	5.50	8.00	14.00	20.00	45.00
1818 over 17 All K.	1,960,322	4.00	5.50	8.00	14.00	20.00	45.00
1818		3.00	4.25	6.00	10.00	14.00	30.00
1819 over 18. Small 9 All Kinds	2,208,000	3.50	4.75	6.50	13.00	19.00	40.00
1819 over 18. Large 9		3.50	4.75	6.50	13.00	19.00	40.00
1819		3.50	4.50	6.00	12.00	18.00	35.00
1820 over 19 All K.	751,122	7.00	9.00	12.00	20.00	30.00	60.00
1820 Small Date		6.50	8.00	10.00	20.00	30.00	60.00
1820 Large Date		6.50	8.00	10.00	20.00	30.00	60.00
1821	1,305,797	3.25	4.00	5.50	9.00	11.00	25.00
1822 All Kinds	1,559,573	3.00	3.75	5.00	9.00	11.00	25.00
1822 over 1		30.00	42.50	65.00	80.00	100.00	200.00
1823 over 22 Broken 3 All Kinds	1,694,200	30.00	41.00	60.00	75.00	90.00	160.00
1823 over 22 Patched		12.00	19.00	30.00	35.00	45.00	70.00
1823 over 22 Ugly 3		6.00	10.00	16.00	25.00	30.00	45.00
1823		3.50	4.50	6.00	9.00	11.00	25.00
1824 over 21 All K.	3,504,954	4.00	5.25	7.50	12.00	16.00	35.00
1824 over Various Dates		4.50	6.25	9.00	13.00	17.50	35.00
1824		3.50	4.25	5.50	8.00	10.00	22.50
1825	2,943,166	3.50	4.25	5.50	7.50	9.75	20.00
1826	4,004,180	3.50	4.25	5.50	7.50	9.75	20.00

HALF DOLLARS

1827 Over 6

1828 Small 8's Square-base 2

	Quan. Minted	Good	V.G.	Fine	V.F.	E.F.	Unc.
1827 over 6 All K	5,493,400	$ 9.50	$13.00	$18.50	$35.00	$50.00	$80.00
1827 Square-base 2		2.75	3.75	5.50	7.00	9.00	19.00
1827 Curled 2		8.00	11.00	15.00	37.50	55.00	90.00
1828 Curled-base w/out knobbed 2							
All Kinds	3,075,200	5.00	5.75	7.00	12.00	18.00	35.00
1828 Curled-base knobbed 2		27.50	35.00	47.50	72.50	82.50	135.00
1828 Lg. 8's Square-base 2		5.00	5.75	7.00	12.00	18.00	35.00
1828 Sm. 8's Sq-base 2 Lg. let.		4.00	4.75	5.50	7.00	9.00	19.00
1829 over 21 All K	3,712,156	4.50	5.25	9.00	14.00	20.00	50.00
1829		4.00	4.75	5.50	7.00	9.00	20.00
1830 Small O in Date							
All Kinds	4,764,800	3.00	3.50	4.50	7.00	9.00	20.00
1830 Large O in Date		4.00	4.75	6.00	7.50	11.00	20.00
1831	5,873,660	2.50	3.25	4.50	7.00	9.00	20.00
1832 Sm. Let. All	4,797,000	2.50	3.25	4.50	7.00	9.00	20.00
1832 Large letters		3.50	6.00	10.00	14.00	20.00	40.00
1833	5,206,000	3.00	3.50	4.50	7.00	9.00	20.00

1828 Large 8 Curled-base Knobbed 2

1834 Small Date Small Stars

	Quan. Minted	Good	V.G.	Fine	V.F.	E.F.	Unc.
1834 Small date. Large stars, Small letters-All K	6,412,004	2.50	3.25	4.50	7.00	9.00	16.00
1834 Small date-stars-letters		2.50	3.25	4.50	7.00	9.00	16.00
1834 Lg. date. Sm. letters		2.50	3.25	4.50	7.00	9.00	16.00
1834 Lg. date. Lg. letters		3.50	4.75	6.50	10.00	17.00	35.00
1835	5,352,006	2.50	3.25	4.50	7.00	9.00	16.00
1836 (Lettered edge)							
All Kinds	6,546,200	2.50	3.25	4.50	7.00	9.00	16.00
1836 (Ltd. edge) 50 over 00		25.00	32.50	45.00	60.00	80.00	140.00

HALF DOLLARS

Reeded Edge —

Good—LIBERTY discernible on headband.
V. Gd.—Minimum of 3 letters in LIBERTY must be clear.
Fine—LIBERTY complete.
V.F.—LIBERTY is sharp. Shoulder clasp is clear.
E.F.—LIBERTY sharp and strong. Hair details show.

50 CENTS On Reverse

	Quan. Minted	Good	V.G.	Fine	V.F.	E.F.	Unc.
1836		$37.50	$50.00	$70.00	$110.00	$135.00	$200.00
1837	3,629,820	8.00	15.00	25.00	32.50	45.00	75.00

1838-O

HALF DOL.

1838	3,546,000	8.00	12.50	20.00	27.50	40.00	65.00
1838O	(20)						

1838O Not mentioned in Director's report. (Rufus Tyler, coiner of New Orleans Mint, stated that only 20 were coined.)

First branch mint half-dollar. This and following year mint mark appears on Obv. All other years (except 1916-17) mint mark is on Rev.

1839 All Kinds	3,334,560	7.00	9.50	14.00	27.50	40.00	65.00
1839O	162,976	45.00	65.00	100.00	120.00	160.00	300.00

LIBERTY SEATED TYPE

Gd.—Scant rim. LIBERTY on shield worn off. Date and letters readable.
V.G.—Rim fairly defined. At least 3 letters in LIBERTY are evident.
Fine—LIBERTY complete, but weak.
V. Fine—LIBERTY mostly sharp.

E.F.—LIBERTY entirely sharp. Scroll edges, and clasp distinct.

1839 No Drapery from Elbow	21.00	29.00	50.00	60.00	85.00	175.00

HALF DOLLARS

Drapery
From
Elbow

Small
Letters
in Legend

	Quan. Minted	Good	V.G.	Fine	V.F.	Unc.
1839		$7.00	$9.00	$12.00	$20.00	$50.00
1840 All Kinds	1,435,008	4.00	5.50	8.00	12.00	40.00
1840O	855,100	3.50	4.35	6.00	10.00	30.00
1841	310,000	5.00	7.00	10.00	18.00	50.00
1841O	401,000	4.00	4.75	6.00	10.00	40.00
1842O Small Date All Kinds	957,000	50.00	65.00	100.00	125.00	225.00

Letters
on
Reverse
Larger
Than
Previous
Type

		Good	V.G.	Fine	V.F.	Unc.
1840 Similar reverse to 1838. Large letters		20.00	32.50	50.00	90.00	160.00

| Small Date | | Large Date | | Larger Letters Than on 1840 Reverse | |

	Quan. Minted	Good	V.G.	Fine	V.F.	Unc.
1842 Small Date All Kinds	2,012,764	3.25	4.00	5.50	10.00	30.00
1842 Large Date		3.25	4.00	5.50	10.00	30.00
1842O Large Date		3.25	4.00	5.50	10.00	35.00
1843	3,844,000	3.25	4.00	5.50	10.00	35.00
1843O	2,268,000	3.25	4.00	5.50	9.50	30.00
1844	1,766,000	3.25	4.00	5.50	9.50	30.00
1844O	2,005,000	3.25	4.00	5.50	9.50	30.00

HALF DOLLARS

	Quan. Minted	Good	V.G.	Fine	V.F.	Unc.	Proof
1845	589,000	$ 3.25	$ 4.00	$ 5.50	$ 9.50	$30.00	
1845O All Kinds	2,094,000	3.25	4.00	5.50	9.50	30.00	
1845O No Drapery		18.00	27.00	40.00	75.00	112.50	
1846 Sm. Date All	2,110,000	3.25	4.00	5.50	9.50	30.00	
1846 Tall Date		4.00	5.00	6.50	10.00	30.00	
1846 over horizontal 6 (error)		32.50	47.50	72.50	125.00	180.00	
1846O Small Date							
All Kinds	2,304,000	3.00	3.75	5.00	9.50	30.00	
1846O Tall Date		21.00	28.00	40.00	110.00	152.50	
1847 over 46 All K.	1,156,000	125.00	170.00	240.00	500.00	700.00	
1847		3.00	4.25	6.00	11.00	35.00	
1847O	2,584,000	3.00	4.25	6.00	11.00	35.00	
1848	580,000	3.00	4.25	6.00	11.00	35.00	
1848O	3,180,000	2.50	3.75	5.50	11.00	35.00	
1849	1,252,000	3.00	4.25	6.00	11.00	30.00	
1849O	2,310,000	3.00	3.75	5.00	9.00	27.50	
1850	227,000	22.50	29.00	40.00	70.00	100.00	
1850O	2,456,000	4.50	5.50	8.00	11.00	35.00	
1851	200,750	7.50	10.00	16.00	50.00	90.00	
1851O	402,000	3.25	4.00	6.00	10.00	27.50	
1852	77,130	22.50	30.00	45.00	135.00	175.00	
1852O	144,000	16.00	21.00	30.00	72.50	125.00	
1853O	(Ex. Rare)	—	—	—	—	—	

Arrows
at
Date

Rays
Around
Eagle

1853	3,532,708	4.50	7.50	12.50	20.00	70.00
1853O All Kinds	1,328,000	4.50	9.00	15.00	22.50	75.00

Arrows At Date — No Rays on Reverse

1854	2,982,000	3.00	4.50	6.50	10.00	35.00	
1854O	5,240,000	3.00	4.50	6.50	10.00	35.00	
1855	759,500	4.00	5.25	7.50	11.00	40.00	500.00
1855O	3,688,000	2.50	4.25	7.00	10.50	35.00	
1855S	129,950	32.50	52.50	85.00	175.00	300.00	

No Arrows At Date

1856	938,000	1.75	2.75	4.50	8.00	20.00	415.00
1856O	2,658,000	1.75	2.75	4.50	8.00	20.00	
1856S	211,000	10.00	15.00	22.00	75.00	130.00	
1857	1,988,000	1.75	2.75	4.50	8.00	20.00	345.00
1857O	818,000	3.00	3.90	5.50	10.00	25.00	
1857S	158,000	15.00	22.00	35.00	75.00	160.00	
1858	4,226,000	1.60	2.50	4.00	7.00	18.00	230.00

HALF DOLLARS

	Quan. Minted	Good	V.G.	Fine	V.F.	Unc.	Proof
1858O	7,294,000	$ 1.60	$ 2.50	$ 4.00	$ 7.00	$18.00	
1858S	476,000	6.00	11.00	17.50	30.00	70.00	
1859	748,000	1.60	2.50	4.00	7.50	20.00	$145.00
1859O	2,834,000	1.60	2.50	4.00	7.50	20.00	
1859S	566,000	8.00	11.50	18.00	30.00	70.00	
1860	303,700	1.60	2.50	4.00	7.50	20.00	90.00
1860O	1,290,000	1.60	2.50	4.00	7.50	20.00	
1860S	472,000	4.00	6.25	10.00	19.00	45.00	
1861	2,888,400	1.60	2.50	4.00	7.00	18.00	90.00
*1861O		2.00	3.00	5.00	10.00	25.00	
1861S	939,500	3.00	4.75	8.00	15.00	40.00	
1862	252,350	2.50	3.75	6.00	9.00	25.00	90.00
1862S	1,352,000	2.50	3.75	6.00	19.00	45.00	
1863 (460)	503,660	2.50	3.75	6.00	8.50	24.00	90.00
1863S	916,000	2.50	3.75	6.00	11.00	30.00	
1864 (470)	379,570	2.50	3.75	6.00	9.00	25.00	90.00
1864S	658,000	2.50	3.75	6.00	11.00	30.00	
1865 (500)	511,900	2.50	3.75	6.00	11.00	30.00	90.00
1865S	675,000	2.50	3.75	6.00	11.00	30.00	
1866 Unique Proof — Hydeman Sale 1961							$15,500.00
1866S		35.00	55.00	90.00	165.00	275.00	

*1861O Struck by
    U.S. Govt...330,000
1861O For
    Louisiana...1,240,000
1861O For
    Confed......962,633

Motto Above Eagle

	Quan. Minted	Good	V.G.	Fine	V.F.	Unc.	Proof
1866 (725)	745,625	3.50	5.00	8.00	12.00	31.00	85.00
1866S All Kinds	1,054,000	3.50	5.00	8.00	15.00	40.00	
1867 (625)	424,325	3.25	4.25	6.00	11.00	35.00	80.00
1867S	1,196,000	2.25	3.25	5.00	12.50	37.00	
1868 (600)	378,200	3.25	4.25	6.00	11.00	35.00	80.00
1868S	1,160,000	2.25	3.25	5.00	9.00	30.00	
1869 (600)	795,900	2.75	3.50	5.00	9.00	24.00	80.00
1869S	656,000	2.25	3.25	5.00	9.00	25.00	
1870 (1,000)	600,900	2.25	3.25	5.00	9.00	25.00	65.00
1870CC	54,617	50.00	67.50	100.00	200.00	450.00	
1870S	1,004,000	3.00	4.50	7.00	20.00	50.00	
1871 (960)	1,165,360	2.25	3.25	5.00	8.00	20.00	62.50
1871CC	139,950	40.00	62.50	100.00	200.00	375.00	
1871S	2,178,000	2.25	3.25	5.00	9.00	36.00	
1872 (950)	881,550	2.25	3.25	5.00	8.00	20.00	62.50
1872CC	272,000	27.50	42.50	70.00	100.00	220.00	
1872S	580,000	3.25	6.50	15.00	20.00	45.00	
1873 Closed 3 All Kinds (600)	801,800	3.00	4.50	7.00	10.00	28.00	70.00
1873 Open 3		12.00	19.00	30.00	42.50	65.00	
1873CC	122,500	30.00	52.50	90.00	130.00	250.00	

1873S No Arrows (Rare) Quan. Minted 5,000. Unknown in any collection.

HALF DOLLARS

Arrows
At
Date

	Quan. Minted	Good	V.G.	Fine	V.F.	Unc.	Proof
1873........(550)	1,815,700	$13.00	$21.00	$32.00	$50.00	$120.00	$250.00
1873CC..........	214,560	20.00	30.00	55.00	72.50	180.00	
1873S...........	228,000	18.00	26.00	40.00	60.00	150.00	
1874........(700)	2,360,300	13.00	28.50	35.00	55.00	120.00	225.00
1874CC..........	59,000	30.00	50.00	90.00	150.00	275.00	
1874S...........	394,000	22.50	30.00	50.00	80.00	150.00	

No Arrows At Date

	Quan. Minted	Good	V.G.	Fine	V.F.	Unc.	Proof
1875........(700)	6,027,500	2.25	3.25	5.00	7.50	18.00	65.00
1875CC..........	1,008,000	5.00	6.00	8.00	20.00	50.00	
1875S...........	3,200,000	2.25	3.25	5.00	7.50	18.00	
1876......(1,150)	8,419,150	2.00	2.75	4.50	7.00	18.00	50.00
1876CC..........	1,956,000	4.00	5.50	7.00	15.00	35.00	
1876S...........	4,528,000	2.00	2.75	4.50	7.00	17.50	
1877........(510)	8,304,510	2.00	2.75	4.50	7.00	17.50	95.00
1877CC..........	1,420,000	4.00	5.50	7.00	15.00	35.00	
1877S...........	5,356,000	2.00	2.75	4.50	6.00	14.00	
1878........(800)	1,378,400	2.00	2.75	4.50	7.00	17.50	90.00
1878CC..........	62,000	80.00	100.00	135.00	220.00	450.00	
1878S...........	12,000	275.00	375.00	550.00	1150.00	2500.00	
1879..:.......(1,100)	5,900	40.00	45.00	50.00	55.00	60.00	65.00
1880..........(1,355)	9,755	35.00	40.00	45.00	50.00	55.00	65.00
1881..........(975)	10,975	35.00	40.00	45.00	50.00	55.00	65.00
1882..........(1,100)	5,500	35.00	40.00	45.00	50.00	55.00	65.00
1883..........(1,039)	9,039	35.00	40.00	45.00	50.00	55.00	65.00
1884..........(875)	5,275	30.00	35.00	40.00	45.00	50.00	75.00
1885..........(930)	6,130	30.00	35.00	40.00	45.00	50.00	75.00
1886..........(886)	5,886	65.00	70.00	75.00	80.00	85.00	105.00
1887..........(710)	5,710	40.00	45.00	50.00	55.00	60.00	95.00
1888..........(832)	12,833	30.00	35.00	40.00	45.00	50.00	75.00
1889..........(711)	12,711	35.00	40.00	45.00	50.00	55.00	85.00
1890..........(590)	12,590	40.00	45.00	50.00	55.00	60.00	100.00
1891........(600)	200,600	4.00	4.75	6.00	11.00	30.00	80.00

BARBER OR LIBERTY HEAD TYPE

Like the dime and quarter dollar, this type was designed by Charles E. Barber whose initial B is at the base of the neck.

Good — Date and legends readable. LIBERTY worn off on headband.
V. Good — Minimum of 3 letters readable in LIBERTY.
Fine — LIBERTY completely readable, but not sharp.
Ex. Fine — LIBERTY bold, and its ribbon distinct.

HALF DOLLARS

	Quan. Minted	Good	V.G.	Fine	E.F.	Unc.	Proof
1892........(1,245)	935,245	$1.50	$3.25	$6.00	$10.00	$20.00	$65.00
1892O.............	390,000	20.00	27.50	40.00	65.00	85.00	
1892S.............	1,029,028	20.00	29.00	45.00	80.00	150.00	
1893........(792)	1,826,792	1.50	2.65	5.50	10.00	17.50	85.00
1893O.............	1,389,000	5.00	8.00	17.50	40.00	70.00	
1893S.............	740,000	19.00	26.50	40.00	75.00	100.00	
1894........(972)	1,148,972	2.00	3.75	7.50	13.50	22.50	75.00
1894O.............	2,138,000	2.50	6.75	15.00	50.00	100.00	
1894S.............	4,048,690	2.75	7.00	15.00	50.00	100.00	
1895........(880)	1,835,218	1.50	3.25	6.00	10.00	21.00	85.00
1895O.............	1,766,000	2.00	5.50	12.00	40.00	90.00	
1895S.............	1,108,086	5.00	8.50	15.00	50.00	110.00	
1896........(762)	950,762	1.50	3.25	6.00	11.00	25.00	85.00
1896O.............	924,000	5.00	11.00	20.00	90.00	185.00	
1896S.............	1,140,948	20.00	32.00	50.00	125.00	290.00	
1897........(731)	2,480,731	1.50	3.25	6.00	11.00	25.00	85.00
1897O.............	632,000	20.00	32.00	50.00	110.00	275.00	
1897S.............	933,900	20.00	32.00	50.00	115.00	300.00	
1898........(735)	2,956,735	1.25	2.25	4.00	10.00	25.00	85.00
1898O.............	874,000	2.50	5.25	10.00	40.00	100.00	
1898S.............	2,358,550	2.50	5.25	10.00	40.00	100.00	
1899........(846)	5,538,846	1.25	2.15	3.75	9.00	22.50	80.00
1899O.............	1,724,000	2.00	4.25	8.00	40.00	100.00	
1899S.............	1,686,411	1.75	4.00	8.00	40.00	100.00	
1900........(912)	4,762,912	1.25	2.15	3.75	9.00	22.50	65.00
1900O.............	2,744,000	1.25	3.25	7.00	40.00	95.00	
1900S.............	2,560,322	1.75	3.25	6.00	35.00	80.00	
1901........(813)	4,268,813	1.25	2.10	3.50	8.00	20.00	75.00
1901O.............	1,124,000	2.50	9.00	20.00	125.00	300.00	
1901S.............	847,044	6.00	22.50	50.00	200.00	700.00	
1902........(777)	4,922,777	1.00	2.00	3.50	8.00	19.00	75.00
1902O.............	2,526,000	1.75	4.00	8.00	35.00	85.00	
1902S.............	1,460,670	1.75	4.25	8.50	75.00	200.00	
1903........(755)	2,278,755	1.25	2.10	3.50	8.00	18.50	70.00
1903O.............	2,100,000	1.25	3.50	7.50	55.00	150.00	
1903S.............	1,920,772	2.50	7.00	15.00	100.00	395.00	
1904........(670)	2,992,670	1.00	1.90	3.50	8.00	17.50	80.00
1904O.............	1,117,600	1.75	4.25	8.00	35.00	110.00	
1904S.............	553,038	6.00	16.00	35.00	100 00	350.00	
1905........(727)	662,727	1.25	3.25	7.00	15.00	25.00	80.00
1905O.............	505,000	2.50	7.00	15.00	50.00	150.00	

HALF DOLLARS

	Quan. Minted	Good	V.G.	Fine	E.F.	Unc.	Proof
1905S.............2,494,000		$1.75	$3.00	$6.50	$25.00	$80.00	
1906.......(675) 2,638,675		1.00	1.85	3.25	8.00	18.00	$85.00
1906D...........4,028,000		1.25	2.25	4.00	10.00	21.00	
1906O...........2,446,000		1.25	2.75	6.50	17.50	43.00	
1906S.............1,740,154		1.75	3.75	8.00	25.00	85.00	
1907.......(575) 2,598,575		1.00	1.75	3.25	8.00	17.50	90.00
1907D...........3,856,000		1.25	2.25	3.75	10.00	22.50	
1907O...........3,946,600		1.40	2.30	3.75	10.00	23.50	
1907S.............1,250,000		1.40	3.75	8.00	30.00	120.00	
1908.......(545) 1,354,545		1.00	1.75	3.25	8.00	20.00	90.00
1908D...........3,280,000		1.00	1.85	3.50	8.50	21.00	
1908O...........5,360,000		1.25	2.00	3.50	10.00	22.50	
1908S.............1,644,828		1.40	3.50	7.00	25.00	80.00	
1909.......(650) 2,368,650		1.00	1.75	3.00	8.00	19.00	80.00
1909O..............925,400		1.75	4.00	8.50	30.00	80.00	
1909S.............1,764,000		1.50	3.25	6.50	25.00	70.00	
1910.........(551) 418,551		2.00	3.75	7.50	15.00	32.50	130.00
1910S.............1,948,000		1.25	3.25	6.50	25.00	60.00	
1911.......(543) 1,406,543		1.00	1.75	3.00	7.00	18.00	130.00
1911D..............695,080		1.25	3.00	6.00	15.00	45.00	
1911S.............1,272,000		1.40	3.00	6.00	22.50	55.00	
1912.......(700) 1,550,700		1.00	1.75	3.00	7.00	18.00	100.00
1912D...........2,300,800		1.00	1.85	3.50	10.00	24.00	
1912S.............1,370,000		1.40	2.75	5.00	17.50	55.00	
1913........(627) 188,627		7.50	15.00	27.50	55.00	110.00	275.00
1913D..............534,000		1.40	3.00	6.00	15.00	37.50	
1913S..............604,000		1.75	5.50	12.50	50.00	140.00	
1914........(380) 124,610		7.50	21.00	45.00	75.00	190.00	550.00
1914S..............992,000		1.50	4.00	8.50	30.00	75.00	
1915........(450) 138,450		9.00	26.00	47.50	95.00	200.00	550.00
1915D...........1,170,400		1.40	2.75	5.00	10.00	25.00	
1915S.............1,604,000		1.40	3.25	6.50	25.00	75.00	

LIBERTY WALKING TYPE

This type was designed by A. A. Weinman. The designer's monogram **AW** appears under the tip of the wing feathers. On the 1916 coins and some of the 1917 coins the mint mark is located on the obverse below the motto.

Good — Rims are defined. Motto IN GOD WE TRUST readable.
V. Good — Motto is distinct. About half of skirt lines at left are clear.
Fine — All skirt lines evident, but worn in spots. Details in sandal above date are clear.
Ex. Fine — All skirt lines bold.

Uncirculated, well-struck specimens worth 25 % to 50 % above prices listed.

HALF DOLLARS

	Quan. Minted	Good	V.G.	Fine	E.F.	Unc.	Proof
1916	608,000	$2.25	$ 3.65	$ 6.00	$10.00	$30.00	
1916D on Obv	1,014,400	2.50	4.25	7.00	12.50	30.00	
1916S on Obv	508,000	7.50	11.25	17.50	37.50	95.00	
1917	12,292,000			1.00	5.00	10.50	
1917D on Obv	765,400	1.50	3.75	8.00	15.00	47.50	
1917D on Rev	1,940,000	1.75	4.25	9.00	45.00	95.00	
1917S on Obv	952,000	4.50	16.00	35.00	100.00	385.00	
1917S on Rev	5,554,000	1.25	3.25	6.50	15.00	70.00	
1918	6,634,000	1.00	2.00	3.50	25.00	65.00	
1918D	3,853,040	1.00	2.50	5.00	30.00	82.50	
1918S	10,282,000	1.00	2.50	5.00	30.00	85.00	
1919	962,000	1.50	3.75	7.50	35.00	100.00	
1919D	1,165,000	2.00	4.50	9.00	100.00	310.00	
1919S	1,552,000	2.00	11.00	25.00	125.00	465.00	
1920	6,372,000	1.00	1.50	2.50	7.50	32.50	
1920D	1,551,000	1.50	3.25	6.50	65.00	225.00	
1920S	4,624,000	1.50	3.00	6.00	65.00	195.00	
1921	246,000	6.50	16.50	35.00	95.00	250.00	
1921D	208,000	6.50	16.50	35.00	110.00	250.00	
1921S	548,000	2.00	6.50	14.00	75.00	290.00	
1923S	2,178,000	1.00	2.25	4.50	50.00	175.00	
1927S	2,392,000	1.00	1.75	3.00	10.00	65.00	
1928S	1,940,000	1.00	1.75	3.00	10.00	75.00	
1929D	1,001,200	1.00	2.00	2.50	7.50	35.00	
1929S	1,902,000	1.00	2.10	2.75	7.50	35.00	
1933S	1,786,000	1.00	2.10	2.75	10.00	50.00	
1934	6,964,000				1.00	5.50	
1934D	2,361,400				1.50	12.50	
1934S	3,652,000			1.00	10.00	42.50	
1935	9,162,000				1.00	5.50	
1935D	3,003,800			1.00	5.00	22.50	
1935S	3,854,000			1.00	9.00	40.00	
1936 (3,901)	12,617,901				1.00	4.50	$140.00
1936D	4,252,400				1.00	6.50	
1936S	3,884,000			1.00	7.50	22.50	
1937 (5,728)	9,527,728				1.00	6.00	70.00
1937D	1,760,001			1.00	6.00	25.00	
1937S	2,090,000			1.00	6.00	22.50	
1938 (8,152)	4,118,152				1.00	7.50	45.00
1938D	491,600			4.00	13.50	60.00	
1939 (8,808)	6,820,808				1.00	8.00	40.00
1939D	4,267,800				1.00	5.00	
1939S	2,552,000			1.00	4.00	15.00	
1940 (11,279)	9,167,279				1.00	4.00	29.00
1940S	4,550,000				1.00	8.00	
1941 (15,412)	24,207,412					3.00	*27.50
1941D	11,248,400				1.00	3.00	
1941S	8,098,000				1.00	5.00	
1942 (21,120)	47,839,120					2.50	23.00
1942D	10,973,800				1.00	3.50	
1942S	12,708,000				1.00	5.00	
1943	53,190,000					2.00	

*Proofs struck with or without designer's initials.

HALF DOLLARS

	Quan. Minted	Good	V.G.	Fine	E.F.	Unc.	Proof
1943D	11,346,000					$3.50	
1943S	13,450,000				$1.00	4.50	
1944	28,206,000					2.00	
1944D	9,769,000					2.00	
1944S	8,904,000					3.75	
1945	31,502,000					1.75	
1945D	9,966,800					2.00	
1945S	10,156,000					2.50	
1946	12,118,000					1.75	
1946D	2,151,000					2.00	
1946S	3,724,000					3.00	
1947	4,094,000					2.00	
1947D	3,900,000					2.25	

FRANKLIN-LIBERTY BELL TYPE

Select, well-struck
uncirculated halves
command higher
prices.

The designer was John R. Sinnock, and his initials appear under the shoulder.

Ex. Fine — Wear spots appear at top of end curls and hair back of ears.
On reverse, Liberty Bell will show wear at top.

	Quan. Minted	Good	V.G.	Fine	E.F.	Unc.	Proof
1948	3,006,814				.95	4.50	
1948D	4,028,600					4.50	
1949	5,714,000				3.00	16.00	
1949D	4,120,600					5.00	
1949S	3,744,000					6.50	
1950 (51,386)	7,793,509					7.00	$18.00
1950D	8,031,600					6.00	
1951 (57,500)	16,859,602					2.75	11.00
1951D	9,475,200					2.75	
1951S	13,696,000					4.75	
1952 (81,980)	21,274,073					2.25	8.00
1952D	25,395,600					2.25	
1952S	5,526,000					2.75	
1953 (128,800)	2,796,920					2.75	6.00
1953D	20,900,400					1.75	
1953S	4,148,000					2.00	
1954 (233,300)	13,421,503					1.50	4.50
1954D	25,445,580					1.50	
1954S	4,993,400					1.75	
1955 (378,200)	2,876,381					1.50	3.75
1956 (669,384)	4,701,384					1.25	2.75
1957 (1,247,952)	6,361,952					1.25	1.75
1957D	19,966,850					1.25	

HALF DOLLARS

	Quan. Minted	Good	V.G.	Fine	E.F.	Unc.	Proof
1958.....(875,652)	4,917,652					$1.10	$3.25
1958D..........23,962,412						1.10	
1959...(1,149,291)	7,349,291					1.00	1.50
1959D..........13,053,750						1.00	
1960...(1,691,602)	7,715,602					1.00	1.50
1960D..........18,215,812						1.00	
1961...(3,028,244)11,318,244						1.00	1.25
1961D..........20,276,442						1.00	
1962...(3,218,019)12,932,019						1.00	1.25
1962D..........35,473,281						1.00	
1963						1.00	1.25
1963D						1.00	

BIBLIOGRAPHY

Beistle, M.L., Register of U. S. Half Dollar Die Varieties. 1929.
Haseltine J. W., Type Table of U. S. Dollars, Half and Quarter Dollars.
1881. Reprint 1933.

SILVER DOLLARS
1794-1935

The silver dollar was authorized by Congress April 2, 1792. Weight and fineness were specified at 416 grains and 892.4 fine. The first issues appeared in 1794 and until 1804 all silver dollars had the value stamped on the edge: HUNDRED CENTS, ONE DOLLAR OR UNIT. After a lapse in coinage of the silver dollar covering the period 1804 to 1840 these coins had reeded edges and the value was placed on the reverse side.

There were several interesting pattern dollars produced by Christian Gobrecht from 1836 to 1839. The seated figure of Liberty was the resulting type, becoming a regular coinage issue starting in 1840. Thenceforth the edge was reeded.

The weight was changed by the law of January 18, 1837 to 412½ grains fineness .900. The coinage was discontinued by the act of February 12, 1873 and reauthorized by the Act of February 28, 1878. The dollar was again discontinued after 1935.

ORIGIN OF THE DOLLAR

The word Dollar evolves from German Taler, the name given to the first large-sized European silver coin. Designed as a substitute for the gold Florin, the coin originated in the Tirol in 1484. So popular did these large silver coins become during the 16th century that many other countries struck similar pieces, giving them names derived from taler. In the Netherlands the coin was called Rijksdalder, in Denmark Rigsdaler, in Italy Tallero, in Poland Talar, in France Jocandale, in Russia Jefimok. All these names are abbreviations of "Joachimsthaler." Until the discovery of the great silver deposits in Mexican and South American mines, the mint with the greatest output of large silver coins was that of Joachimsthal in the Bohemian Erzgebirge.

The Spanish Dollar, or piece-of-eight was widely used and familiar to everyone in the English-American colonies. It was only natural therefore that the word "dollar" was adopted officially as the standard monetary unit of the United States by Congress on July 6, 1785.

REGARDING DOLLARS REPORTED FOR 1805

The 321 silver dollars reported for 1805 were not dated 1805. An entry in Bullion Journal dated June 28, 1805, mentions these 321 pieces as "being

SILVER DOLLARS

found amongst Spanish Dollars brought to the Mint." They were of earlier coinage and instead of being melted they were transferred to the Director.

Fair — Clear enough to identify.
Good — Date and letters readable. Main devices outlined, but lack
  details.
V. Good — Major details discernible. Letters well formed but worn.
Fine — Hair ends distinguishable. Top hairlines show, but otherwise
  worn smooth.
V. Fine — Hair in center shows some detail. Other details more bold.

Quan. Minted	Fair	Good	V.G.	Fine	V. Fine	Unc.
1794.....1,758	$600.00	$1,000.00	$1,500.00	$2,500.00	$5,000.00	$12,500.00

**Two Leaves Beneath
Each Wing (11 Varieties)**

1795 All Kinds ...184,013						
Two Leaves	65.00	100.00	125.00	150.00	250.00	750.00

**Three Leaves Beneath
Each Wing**

1795 Three Leaves ...	65.00	100.00	125.00	150.00	250.00	850.00

SILVER DOLLARS
BUST TYPE

Fair — Clear enough to identify.
Good — Bust outlined, no detail. Date readable, some leaves evident.
V. Good — Drapery worn except deepest folds. Hairlines smooth.
Fine — All drapery lines distinguishable. Hairlines near cheek and
neck show some detail.
V. Fine — Left side of drapery worn smooth.

	Quan. Minted	Fair	Good	V.G.	Fine	V. Fine	Unc.
1795 (Two Varieties)		$55.00	$80.00	$100.00	$135.00	$185.00	$700.00

Small Date · Large Date

Small Letters · Large Letters

1796 Sm. Date, Sm. Let. (3 Var.)						
All Kinds	72,920	45.00	65.00	85.00	115.00	175.00	500.00
1796 Sm. Date Lg. Let		45.00	65.00	85.00	115.00	175.00	550.00
1796 Lg. Date Sm. Let		45.00	65.00	85.00	140.00	225.00	550.00
1797 9 Stars Left, 7 Right							
Sm. Let. A Kinds	7,776	100.00	125.00	195.00	250.00	600.00	1100.00
1797 9 Stars L., 7 R. Lg. L.		55.00	85.00	120.00	175.00	275.00	850.00
1797 10 Stars Left, 6 Right		55.00	85.00	120.00	175.00	275.00	850.00
1798 15 Stars (Small Eagle)		50.00	75.00	110.00	150.00	250.00	750.00
1798 13 Stars (Small Eagle)							
All Kinds	327,536	45.00	65.00	90.00	125.00	200.00	500.00

SILVER DOLLARS

HERALDIC EAGLE

Good — *Letters and date readable. E.
PLURIBUS UNUM obliterated.*

V. Gd. — *Motto partially readable. Only
deepest drapery details visible.
All other lines smooth.*

Fine — *All drapery lines distinguishable.
Hairlines near cheek and neck
show some detail.*

V.F. — *Left side of drapery worn smooth.*

Heraldic Eagle Reverse

	Quan. Minted	Good	V.G.	Fine	V. Fine	Unc.
1798 Large Heraldic Eagle, Knob 9 (5 Varieties)		$35.00	$45.00	$75.00	$115.00	$325.00
1798 Lg. Eagle, 10 Arrows (5 Var.)		30.00	40.00	70.00	100.00	300.00
1798 Close Date, 4 Berries in Branch		35.00	45.00	75.00	110.00	325.00
1798 Close Date, 5 Berries, 12 Arrows		35.00	45.00	75.00	110.00	325.00
1798 Close Date, High 8 (6 Var.)		30.00	40.00	70.00	110.00	300.00
1798 Wide Date, 13 Arrows (11 Var.)		25.00	30.00	65.00	100.00	300.00

1799
Over
98,
Stars
7 & 6

Stars
8 & 5

	Quan. Minted	Good	V.G.	Fine	V. Fine	Unc.
1799 over 98 Rev. with 15 Stars All Kinds	423,515	50.00	65.00	85.00	160.00	325.00
1799 over 98 Rev. with 13 Stars		35.00	50.00	75.00	125.00	275.00
1799 Irregular Date, 15-Star Rev		40.00	55.00	75.00	135.00	300.00
1799 Irregular Date, 13-Star Rev		40.00	55.00	75.00	125.00	275.00
1799 Perfect Date, No Berries in Br.		35.00	50.00	65.00	115.00	250.00
1799 Perfect Date, Small Berries		35.00	50.00	65.00	110.00	210.00
1799 Perfect Date, Medium Large Berries (15 Varieties)		30.00	45.00	60.00	110.00	225.00
1799 Perfect Date, Ex. Lg. Berries		35.00	50.00	65.00	110.00	230.00
1799 Stars 8 Left, 5 Right		35.00	60.00	85.00	185.00	400.00
1800 LIBERTY with R Double Cut All Kinds	220,920	35.00	55.00	70.00	120.00	200.00
1800 First T in STATES Double Cut		35.00	55.00	70.00	120.00	250.00
1800 Both R in LIBERTY and First T in STATES Double Cut		40.00	55.00	75.00	120.00	240.00
1800 Let. T in UNITED Double Cut		35.00	45.00	60.00	100.00	225.00
1800 Very Wide Date, Low 8		40.00	55.00	75.00	110.00	225.00

SILVER DOLLARS

	Quan. Minted	Good	V.G.	Fine	V. Fine	Unc.
1800 Small Berries in Branch.......		$35.00	$45.00	$65.00	$110.00	$225.00
1800 "Dotted Date" from Die Breaks		35.00	45.00	65.00	125.00	250.00
1800 Only 12 Arrows..............		35.00	45.00	60.00	100.00	200.00
1800 Only 10 Arrows..............		35.00	45.00	70.00	110.00	210.00
1800 AMERICAI (2 Varieties).....		45.00	55.00	85.00	150.00	300.00
1801 Four Varieties All Kinds.	54,454	45.00	60.00	80.00	125.00	250.00
1801 Proof Restrike (Rev. Struck from First Die of 1804 Dollar)......				(Proof)	———	

1802 Over 1

		Good	V.G.	Fine	V. Fine	Unc.
1802 over 1, Close Overdate All Kinds..............	41,650	40.00	50.00	75.00	100.00	250.00
1802 over 1, Wide Overdate.......		35.00	40.00	60.00	90.00	225.00
1802 Close, Perfect Date..........		35.00	40.00	50.00	80.00	200.00
1802 Wide, Perfect Date..........		40.00	50.00	65.00	110.00	240.00
1802 Proof Restrike..............					(Proof)	———

Small 3

Large 3

		Good	V.G.	Fine	V. Fine	Unc.
1803 Large 3 (1 Variety) All..	66,064	35.00	40.00	50.00	80.00	175.00
1803 Small 3 (5 Varieties).........		40.00	50.00	70.00	100.00	210.00
1803 Proof Restrike..............					(Proof)	———

THE 1804 DOLLAR

This piece is one of the most publicized rarities in the United States series. There are specimens known as originals (type 1) of which eight are known, and restrikes (type 2) of which seven are known.

Opinion has long been divided regarding the origin, date of issue and authenticity of this coin. Those who have stated that these coins were struck in 1804 point to such evidence as the letter written by Robert Patterson, Director of the Mint, to President Thomas Jefferson. This letter stated that no dollars had been minted "during the last two years." Inasmuch as the letter was dated April 2, 1807, they infer that dollars were struck during 1804.

Mint records show that 19,570 silver dollars were coined in 1804 and that these coins were struck before March 28, 1804. Years later a die with the date 1804 was found at the mint among discarded dies. It is a matter of record that Director Boudinot stopped the coinage of silver dollars in 1804 to prevent their exportation because their face value was less than their bullion value.

Numismatists now know that the 1804 "original" dollars were struck at the mint between 1834 and 1835, for use in presentation proof sets. The first known specimen, a proof, was obtained from a mint officer by Mr. Stickney on May 9, 1843, in exchange for an "Immune Columbia" piece of gold. Later, in 1859, the pieces known as restrikes were made at the mint to supply the needs of collectors who wanted specimens of these dollars.

SILVER DOLLARS

Evidence that these pieces were struck during the later period is based on the fact that the 1804 dollars differ from issues of 1803 or earlier and conform more closely to those struck after 1836 — their edges or borders having beaded segments and raised rim, not elongated denticles such as are found on the earlier dates.

Although the mint records state that 19,570 dollars were coined in 1804, in no place does it mention that they were dated 1804. It was the practice in those days to use old dies as long as they were serviceable with no regard in the annual reports for the dating of the coins. It is probable that the 1804 total for dollars actually covered coins which were dated 1803.

The 1804 dollar has been and probably will continue to be a subject of much discussion. Its existence or disappearance may always be a matter of speculation for the numismatic fraternity.

TYPE 1

Note Position of Words STATES OF With Relation to Clouds

1804 Type 1, Original (Stickney specimen sold for $10,500.00 in 1946.)
(Dexter specimen sold for $10,000.00 in 1950.)

TYPE 2

Compare With Type 1 Above

1804 Type 2, Restrike (Idler Specimen sold for $29,000.00 in 1961).
(Davis-Hale Specimen sold for $28,000.00 in 1960.)

BIBLIOGRAPHY

Bolender, M. H., The UNITED STATES EARLY SILVER DOLLARS from 1794 to 1803. 1950.
Newman-Bressett — THE FANTASTIC 1804 DOLLAR. 1962.

SILVER DOLLARS

CHRISTIAN GOBRECHT

Christian Gobrecht was born December 23, 1785. He went to Philadelphia in 1811 and became an engraver of bank notes, seals, calico printers' rolls, bookbinders' dies, etc. He was appointed assistant to Mint Engraver William Kneass in 1836. According to Edgar H. Adams, he prepared a series of dies for pattern dollars, after designs by Sully, exquisite in design and character. The first pattern shows the familiar seated figure of Liberty on the obverse. The name C. Gobrecht F. (F.=Fecit=made it) was placed just under the figure of Liberty and over the date. In the field on the reverse was a large eagle in full flight surrounded by twenty-six stars and the legend UNITED STATES OF AMERICA ONE DOLLAR.

In response to criticism Gobrecht removed his name from the die after a few specimens had been struck, some in silver and some in copper.

Director Patterson ordered the name replaced, this time on the base. Patterns were also made in 1836 with the stars omitted from the field of the reverse.

In 1838 the engraver's name was omitted altogether from the design and thirteen stars were placed around the seated figure of Liberty on the obverse. Stars were omitted from the reverse on one pattern and retained on another. Similar pieces were struck in 1839.

1836 C. Gobrecht F. in field between base and date. Rev. Eagle   Proof
    flying left amid stars. Plain edge (Rare.) (18)..............$2,500.00
1836 Obv. as above. Rev. Eagle flying in plain field.
    Plain edge (Very rare.) (5)................................ 2,750.00

1836 C. Gobrecht on base. Rev. Eagle flying left in field containing stars.

[147]

SILVER DOLLARS

	Very Fine	Proof
Plain edge. Although scarce, this is the most common variety. (1,000)	$550.00	$1,250.00
1836 As above, reeded edge. (Very rare.) (3)		2,000.00

Proof

1838 As above, reeded edge. Generally considered to be very rare. 25 Struck. Also unknown quantity of restrikes	2,500.00
1838 Obv. as above. Rev. Eagle in plain field. Plain edge. (Very rare.) (3)	3,000.00
1838 Seated Liberty. Obv. name of designer is left off and stars added around obverse border. Rev. Eagle flying left surrounded by stars. Plain edge. (Very rare.) (3)	3,000.00
1839 Obv. same as 1838. Rev. Eagle in plain field. Plain edge. (Very rare.) (3)	2,750.00
1839 Obv. as above. Rev. Eagle amid stars. Plain edge. (Very rare.) (3)	2,750.00
1839 Obv. as above. Rev. Eagle in plain field. Reeded edge. Most common 1839 variety. (Rare) (300)	1,750.00

Quantities shown for the above patterns are probably inaccurate as restrikes of many are known to have been made.

When in 1840 silver dollars were again issued for general circulation the seated figure of Liberty device was adopted for the obverse. For some mysterious reason the flying eagle design was rejected, and the more familiar form with olive branch and arrows was used.

SILVER DOLLARS

Beware of early strike Philadelphia mint uncirculated dollars being offered as proofs.

8 Tail Feathers
1878 Philadelphia Only

Most uncirculated silver dollars have scratches or nicks because of handling of mint bags. Perfect coins without blemishes are generally worth 50% more than listed values.

7 Tail Feathers
1878 and Later Dates

	Quan. Minted	Ex. Fine	Unc.	Proof
1878 8 Tail Feathers...(700) 416,000...........		$ 3.00	$ 6.00	$85.00
1878 7 Tail Feathers over 8 Tail Feathers.......		3.00	10.00	
1878 7 Tail Feathers.(300)10,093,550.................			3.00	115.00
1878CC.................2,212,000............		2.00	7.50	
1878S....................9,774,000...................			3.00	
1879....(1,100) 14,807,100...................			3.00	70.00
1879CC...................756,000...........		25.00	95.00	
1879O.................2,887,000............		2.00	9.50	
1879S....................9,110,000.................			3.75	
1880....(1,355) 12,601,355...................			2.75	75.00
1880CC...................591,000...........		10.00	30.00	
1880O.................5,305,000............		1.75	7.50	
1880S....................8,900,000.................			3.00	
1881....(975) 9,163,975...................			2.75	75.00
1881CC...................296,000...........		10.00	35.00	
1881O.................5,708,000............			4.00	
1881S....................12,760,000.................			3.25	
1882....(1,100) 11,101,100...................			2.75	70.00
1882CC.................1,133,000............		6.00	15.00	
1882O.................6,090,000............		1.75	7.50	
1882S....................9,250,000.................			3.00	
1883...........(1,039) 12,291,039...................			3.00	72.50

SILVER DOLLARS

	Quan. Minted	Ex. Fine	Unc.	Proof
1883CC	1,204,000	$6.00	$15.00	
1883O	8,725,000		4.50	
1883S	6,250,000	3.50	12.50	
1884	(875) 14,070,875		3.50	$72.50
1884CC	1,136,000	5.50	17.50	
1884O	9,730,000		4.00	
1884S	3,200,000	3.50	20.00	
1885	(930) 17,787,767		3.50	70.00
1885CC	228,000	15.00	25.00	
1885O	9,185,000		4.00	
1885S	1,497,000		6.00	
1886	(886) 19,963,886		3.50	75.00
1886O	10,710,000	3.50	15.00	
1886S	750,000		20.00	
1887	(710) 20,290,710		3.50	85.00
1887O	11,550,000	3.00	9.50	
1887S	1,771,000	3.00	12.00	
1888	(832) 19,183,833		4.00	80.00
1888O	12,150,000	1.75	6.50	
1888S	657,000		20.00	
1889	(811) 21,726,811		2.50	80.00
1889CC	350,000	150.00	350.00	
1889O	11,875,000	2.50	4.00	
1889S	700,000	10.00	20.00	
1890	(590) 16,802,590		3.50	110.00
1890CC	2,309,041		10.00	
1890O	10,701,000		4.00	
1890S	8,230,373		5.00	
1891	(650) 8,694,206		4.00	80.00
1891CC	1,618,000		10.00	
1891O	7,954,529	2.50	6.00	
1891S	5,296,000		6.00	
1892	(1,245) 1,037,245	3.50	12.50	60.00
1892CC	1,352,000	10.00	30.00	
1892O	2,744,000	3.50	12.00	
1892S	1,200,000	40.00	175.00	
1893	(792) 378,792	4.00	15.00	75.00
1893CC	677,000	15.00	75.00	
1893O	300,000	6.00	65.00	
1893S	100,000	150.00	1,500.00	
1894	(972) 110,972	25.00	75.00	75.00
1894O	1,723,000	4.50	15.00	
1894S	1,260,000	10.00	25.00	
*1895	(880) 12,880			2,500.00
1895O	450,000	20.00	75.00	
1895S	400,000	35.00	150.00	
1896	(762) 9,976,762		2.50	75.00
1896O	4,900,000	4.50	15.00	
1896S	5,000,000	20.00	65.00	
1897	(731) 2,822,731		3.00	72.50
1897O	4,004,000	3.00	15.00	
1897S	5,825,000		7.50	

*Beware removed mint letter.

SILVER DOLLARS

	Quan. Minted	Ex. Fine	Unc.	Proof
1898	(735) 5,884,735		$4.50	$75.00
1898O	4,440,000		5.00	
1898S	4,102,000	$7.50	15.00	
1899	(846) 330,846		10.00	70.00
1899O	12,290,000		3.00	
1899S	2,562,000	7.50	15.00	
1900	(912) 8,830,912		3.50	70.00
1900O	12,590,000		3.50	
1900S	3,540,000	5.00	15.00	
1901	(813) 6,962,813	7.50	37.50	75.00
1901O	13,320,000		4.00	
1901S	2,284,000	7.50	22.50	
1902	(777) 7,994,777		3.50	75.00
1902O	8,636,000		3.00	
1902S	1,530,000	10.00	27.50	
1903	(755) 4,652,755		3.00	80.00
1903O	4,450,000	15.00	30.00	
1903S	1,241,000	12.50	75.00	
1904	(650) 2,788,650	4.00	10.00	92.50
1904O	3,720,000		3.50	
1904S	2,304,000	7.50	55.00	

270,232,722 silver dollars were melted under the Pittman Act of April, 1918. 259,121,554 for export to India, and 11,111,168 for domestic subsidiary coins.

1921	44,690,000		2.25	190.00
1921D	20,345,000		2.50	
1921S	21,695,000		2.50	

BIBLIOGRAPHY

Haseltine, J. W., Type Table of U. S. Dollars, Half and Quarter Dollars. 1881. Reprint 1933.

PEACE TYPE

Anthony De Francisci, a medalist, designed this dollar. His monogram is located in the field of the coin under the neck of Liberty.

The new Peace Dollar was placed in circulation January 3, 1922. 1,006,473 pieces were struck in December, 1921.

The high relief of the 1921 design was found impractical for coinage and was slightly modified in 1922.

Ex. Fine — *Hairlines over brow and ear are strong though slightly worn. Outside wing feathers at right and those at top are visible but faint.*

[153]

SILVER DOLLARS

Most uncirculated silver dollars have scratches or nicks because of handling of mint bags. Perfect coins without blemishes are generally worth 50% more than listed values.

	Quan. Minted	Ex. Fine	Unc.	Matte Proof
1921	1,006,473	$9.00	$22.50	———
1922 Type of 1921				———
1922 All Kinds	51,737,000		2.50	
1922D	15,063,000		7.50	
1922S	17,475,000		4.50	
1923	30,800,000		2.50	
1923D	6,811,000	4.00	8.50	
1923S	19,020,000		5.00	
1924	11,811,000		3.00	
1924S	1,728,000	5.00	20.00	
1925	10,198,000		2.50	
1925S	1,610,000	5.00	16.00	
1926	1,939,000	5.00	10.00	
1926D	2,348,700	4.00	14.00	
1926S	6,980,000		10.00	
1927	848,000	5.00	25.00	
1927D	1,268,900	3.00	20.00	
1927S	866,000	3.00	20.00	
1928	360,649	32.50	45.00	
1928S	1,632,000	3.00	22.50	
1934	954,057	5.00	22.50	
1934D	1,569,500	3.00	15.00	
1934S	1,011,000	9.00	140.00	
1935	1,576,000	2.00	15.00	
1935S	1,964,000	4.00	20.00	

TRADE DOLLARS 1873 - 1885

This coin was issued for circulation in the Orient to compete with the Mexican peso. It is 420 grains in weight compared to 412½ grains which is the standard weight of the regular silver dollars.

When first coined they were legal tender in the United States to the extent of $5.00 but with the decline in price of silver bullion Congress repealed the legal tender provision in 1876 and authorized the Treasury to limit coinage to export demand. In 1887 a law was passed authorizing the Treasury to redeem all Trade dollars which were not mutilated. U. S. Trade dollars are

TRADE DOLLARS

no longer circulating in the Orient. Those struck in the last few years of coinage were undoubtedly all specimen proof strikings.

The trade dollars of 1884 and 1885 were unknown to collectors generally until 1908. None is listed in the Director's report and numismatists believe that they are not a part of the regular mint issue. The law authorizing Trade Dollars was repealed in February, 1887.

V. Good — About half of mottoes IN GOD WE TRUST and E. PLURI-BUS UNUM will show. Rim on both sides well defined.

Fine — Mottoes and LIBERTY readable but worn.

Ex. Fine — Mottoes and LIBERTY are sharp. Only slight wear on rims.

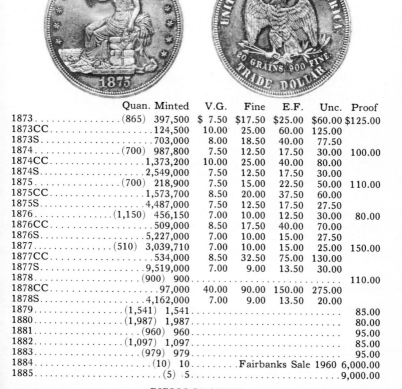

	Quan. Minted	V.G.	Fine	E.F.	Unc.	Proof
1873	(865) 397,500	$ 7.50	$17.50	$25.00	$60.00	$125.00
1873CC	124,500	10.00	25.00	60.00	125.00	
1873S	703,000	8.00	18.50	40.00	77.50	
1874	(700) 987,800	7.50	12.50	17.50	30.00	100.00
1874CC	1,373,200	10.00	25.00	40.00	80.00	
1874S	2,549,000	7.50	12.50	17.50	30.00	
1875	(700) 218,900	7.50	15.00	22.50	50.00	110.00
1875CC	1,573,700	8.50	20.00	37.50	60.00	
1875S	4,487,000	7.50	12.50	17.50	27.50	
1876	(1,150) 456,150	7.00	10.00	12.50	30.00	80.00
1876CC	509,000	8.50	17.50	40.00	70.00	
1876S	5,227,000	7.00	10.00	15.00	27.50	
1877	(510) 3,039,710	7.00	10.00	15.00	25.00	150.00
1877CC	534,000	8.50	32.50	75.00	130.00	
1877S	9,519,000	7.00	9.00	13.50	30.00	
1878	(900) 900					110.00
1878CC	97,000	40.00	90.00	150.00	275.00	
1878S	4,162,000	7.00	9.00	13.50	20.00	
1879	(1,541) 1,541					85.00
1880	(1,987) 1,987					80.00
1881	(960) 960					95.00
1882	(1,097) 1,097					85.00
1883	(979) 979					95.00
1884	(10) 10			Fairbanks Sale 1960	6,000.00	
1885	(5) 5					9,000.00

BIBLIOGRAPHY

John M. Willem, Jr., *The United States Trade Dollar,* 1959.

GOLD

Gold, the earliest known and most beautiful of all metallic substances, has been and remains of the greatest commercial consequence. Of the precious metals, gold particularly has for ages been the chief material used for coins.

Gold is common to most nations as a standard for measurement of all other values. In our own country paper currency and token coins now serve exclusively as money. Gold continues to serve as the yardstick of money values, although it is no longer used for actual coinage. The gold possessed by the United States treasury is held as a reserve to back up our token or representative money.

The amount of money in circulation in the United States is tied to the amount of gold reserves. Our money will remain stable so long as we adhere to the gold standard with a fixed weight of gold as the dollar (now 13.71 grains of pure gold).

Since gold has not circulated as money since 1933 it has been stored in bullion form thus saving the expense of coinage. Being a standard of value its worth is the same whether in the shape of coins or in bars.

As a result of the gold surrender order, United States gold coins have become scarce, and the small remaining supply of these beautiful and respected representatives of our monetary past is being legally and carefully preserved by the Numismatic fraternity.

GOLD DOLLARS

1849-1889

Coinage of the gold dollar was authorized by the Act of March 3, 1849. The weight was 25.8 grains fineness .900. The first type, struck until 1854, is known as the Liberty Head or small-sized type. In 1854 the piece was made larger in diameter and thinner. The design was changed to a feather headdress on a female generally referred to as the Indian Head or Large-sized type. In 1856 the type was changed slightly by enlarging the size of the head.

The Type 1 dollars after 1849 all have a closed wreath on the reverse.

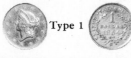 Type 1

V. Fine — LIBERTY on headband complete and readable. Knobs on coronet are defined.

	Quan. Minted	V. Fine	Unc.
1849 Open Wreath - All Kinds	688,567	$ 37.50	$ 75.00
1849 Closed Wreath (wreath ends closer to Figure 1)		35.00	65.00
1849C Closed Wreath - All Kinds	11,634	140.00	490.00
1849C Open Wreath (2 known) (1956 A.N.A. Sale $6,000.00)			
1849D Open Wreath	21,588	200.00	350.00
1849O Open Wreath	215,000	42.50	60.00
1850	481,953	35.00	55.00
1850C	6,966	200.00	615.00
1850D	8,382	160.00	350.00
1850O	14,000	40.00	75.00
1851	3,317,671	35.00	45.00
1851C	41,267	125.00	190.00
1851D	9,882	150.00	260.00
1851O	290,000	40.00	55.00

GOLD DOLLARS

	Quan. Minted	V. Fine	Unc.	Proof
1852	2,045,351	$ 33.50	$ 47.50	
1852C	9,434	140.00	250.00	
1852D	6,360	165.00	275.00	
1852O	140,000	37.50	60.00	
1853	4,076,051	35.00	47.50	
1853C	11,515	125.00	250.00	
1853D	6,583	165.00	350.00	
1853O	290,000	37.50	50.00	
1854 All Kinds	1,639,445	37.50	55.00	
1854D	2,935	250.00	600.00	
1854S	14,632	100.00	225.00	

 Type 2

V. Fine — Feather curl tips outlined but details worn.

	Quan. Minted	V. Fine	Unc.	Proof
1854		100.00	200.00	
1854C (Unknown)	4			
1855	758,269	100.00	200.00	
1855C	9,803	160.00	325.00	
1855D	1,811	900.00	1,750.00	
1855O	55,000	110.00	210.00	
1856S	24,600	125.00	250.00	

 Type 3

V. Fine — Curled feathers have slight detail. Details worn smooth at eyebrow, hair under headdress and behind ear and bottom curl.

	Quan. Minted	V. Fine	Unc.	Proof
1856 Slant 5 - All Kinds	1,762,936	37.50	55.00	700.00
1856 Upright 5		40.00	60.00	
1856D	1,460	900.00	2,200.00	
1857	774,789	40.00	55.00	650.00
1857C	13,280	125.00	300.00	
1857D	3,533	325.00	600.00	
1857S	10,000	80.00	155.00	
1858	117,995	42.50	55.00	650.00
1858D	3,477	300.00	650.00	
1858S	10,000	100.00	170.00	
1859	168,244	40.00	60.00	400.00
1859C	5,235	160.00	350.00	
1859D	4,952	200.00	400.00	
1859S	15,000	100.00	150.00	
1860	36,668	40.00	62.50	400.00
1860D	1,566	1,400.00	3,000.00	
1860S	13,000	100.00	170.00	
1861	527,499	37.50	60.00	275.00
1861D		3,500.00	5,750.00	
1862	1,326,865	40.00	57.50	350.00
1863	6,250	150.00	350.00	650.00

GOLD DOLLARS

	Quan. Minted	V. Fine	Unc.	Proof
1864	5,950	$100.00	$300.00	$850.00
1865	(25) 3,725	155.00	300.00	450.00
1866	(30) 7,180	90.00	185.00	450.00
1867	(50) 5,250	110.00	200.00	400.00
1868	(25) 10,525	100.00	180.00	400.00
1869	(25) 5,925	100.00	180.00	400.00
1870	(35) 6,335	75.00	175.00	375.00
1870S	3,000	300.00	800.00	
1871	(30) 3,930	75.00	175.00	375.00
1872	(30) 3,530	95.00	175.00	375.00
1873 (Closed 3) All Kinds	(25) 125,125	42.50	75.00	275.00
1873 (Open 3)		42.50	75.00	
1874	(20) 198,820	40.00	60.00	350.00
1875	(20) 420	625.00	1,100.00	2,000.00
1876	(45) 3,245	80.00	150.00	300.00
1877	(20) 3,920	75.00	140.00	350.00
1878	(20) 3,020	75.00	150.00	350.00
1879	(30) 3,030	75.00	150.00	350.00
1880	(36) 1,636	100.00	175.00	325.00
1881	(40) 7,660	65.00	105.00	240.00
1882	(40) 5,040	65.00	105.00	240.00
1883	(40) 10,840	65.00	105.00	240.00
1884	(976) 6,206	57.50	90.00	150.00
1885	(1,049) 12,205	57.50	90.00	150.00
1886	(1,016) 6,016	57.50	90.00	150.00
1887	(1,043) 8,543	57.50	90.00	150.00
1888	(457) 16,080	57.50	90.00	150.00
1889	(1,779) 30,729	57.50	90.00	150.00

QUARTER EAGLES

($2.50 GOLD PIECES)

Authorized by the Act of April 2, 1792 they weighed 67.5 grains, 916⅔ fine until the weight was changed to 64.5 grains fineness 899.225 by the Act of June 28, 1834. The Act of January 18, 1837 established fineness at .900. Most dates before 1834 are rare. The first issue was struck in 1796, most of which had no stars on the obverse.

Proofs prior to 1855 are known to exist of some dates, and all are rare.

Fine — Hair worn smooth on high spots. E.PLURIBUS UNUM weak but readable.

V. Fine — Some wear on high spots.

	Quan. Minted	Fine	V. Fine	Unc.
1796 No Stars	897	$2,000.00	$4,000.00	$6,750.00

QUARTER EAGLES

1796
with
Stars

1797

	Quan. Minted	Fine	V. Fine	Unc.
1796 Stars	66	$2,000.00	$4,000.00	$6,750.00
1797	1,756	850.00	1,600.00	2,750.00
1798	614	1,000.00	1,600.00	4,500.00

1802
over
1

1806
over
4

1806
over
5

1802 over 1	2,612	450.00	850.00	2,100.00
1804	3,327	400.00	700.00	1,400.00
1805	1,781	400.00	700.00	1,400.00
1806 over 4 - All Kinds	1,616	450.00	1,200.00	2,100.00
1806 over 5		550.00	1,300.00	2,200.00
1807	6,812	400.00	650.00	1,250.00

BUST TYPE — FACING LEFT — ROUND CAP

Fine — *E. PLURIBUS UNUM and LIB-ERTY on headband readable but weak.*

V. Fine — *Motto and LIBERTY clear.*

1808	2,710	1,450.00	3,500.00	6,000.00

REDUCED SIZE

1821

1826
over
25

1821	6,448	350.00	500.00	2,000.00
1824 over 21	2,600	350.00	800.00	2,000.00
1825	4,434	300.00	450.00	1,250.00
1826 over 25	760	500.00	1,000.00	2,200.00
1827	2,800	400.00	650.00	1,750.00
1829	3,403	325.00	500.00	950.00

QUARTER EAGLES

	Quan. Minted	Fine	V. Fine	Unc.
1830	4,540	$300.00	$400.00	$700.00
1831	4,520	300.00	400.00	700.00
1832	4,400	300.00	400.00	700.00
1833	4,160	300.00	400.00	700.00
1834 (Motto)	4,000	475.00	725.00	1,500.00

LIBERTY CAP REMOVED — MOTTO REMOVED FROM REVERSE

In 1834 the quarter eagle was redesigned. A ribbon binding the hair, bearing the word LIBERTY, replaces the liberty cap. The motto was omitted from the reverse. In 1840 a coronet and smaller head were designed to conform in appearance with the larger gold coins.

Fine — *LIBERTY readable and complete. Curl under ear outlined but no detail.*

V. Fine — *LIBERTY plain. Hair curl has detail.*

1834 No Motto	112,234	45.00	52.50	100.00
1835	131,402	45.00	52.50	100.00
1836	547,986	45.00	52.50	100.00
1837	45,080	50.00	57.50	105.00
1838	47,030	50.00	57.50	105.00
1838C	7,908	110.00	150.00	260.00
1839	27,021	45.00	52.50	100.00
1839C	18,173	100.00	150.00	275.00
1839D	13,674	125.00	160.00	325.00
1839O	17,781	75.00	100.00	160.00

New Small Head

1840	18,859	42.50	55.00	75.00
1840C	12,838	75.00	110.00	250.00
1840D	3,532	80.00	145.00	300.00
1840O	26,200	40.00	50.00	80.00
1841 Proofs only				Ex. Rare
1841C	10,297	100.00	160.00	300.00
1841D	4,164	115.00	225.00	300.00
1841O (Unknown)	7,380			
1842	2,823	70.00	110.00	165.00
1842C	6,737	90.00	130.00	225.00
1842D	4,643	90.00	130.00	225.00
1842O	19,800	40.00	55.00	90.00
1843	100,546	37.50	47.50	70.00

QUARTER EAGLES

	Quan. Minted	Fine	V. Fine	Unc.
1843C Small Date - All Kinds........26,096		$ 85.00	$125.00	$600.00
1843C Large Date.......................		65.00	85.00	125.00
1843D Small Date...................36,209		65.00	85.00	125.00
1843O Small Date - All Kinds........368,002		37.50	45.00	75.00
1843O Large Date.......................		45.00	70.00	120.00
1844.................................6,784		75.00	110.00	165.00
1844C...............................11,622		65.00	90.00	160.00
1844D...............................17,332		65.00	90.00	160.00
1845................................91,051		37.50	50.00	80.00
1845D...............................19,460		60.00	85.00	175.00
1845O...............................4,000		80.00	120.00	175.00
1846................................21,598		40.00	50.00	75.00
1846C...............................4,808		80.00	110.00	165.00
1846D...............................19,303		65.00	85.00	155.00
1846O...............................66,000		40.00	47.50	80.00
1847................................29,814		45.00	55.00	75.00
1847C...............................23,226		60.00	80.00	160.00
1847D...............................15,784		65.00	100.00	165.00
1847O...............................124,000		40.00	50.00	70.00
1848................................8,886		125.00	400.00	700.00

CAL. above eagle on Reverse

CALIF. GOLD QUARTER EAGLE

In 1848 about two hundred and thirty ounces of gold were sent to Secretary of War Marcy by Col. R. B. Mason, Military governor of California. The gold was turned over to the mint and made into quarter eagles. The distinguishing mark "CAL." was punched above the eagle on the reverse side, while the coins were in the die.

	Quan. Minted	V. Fine	Unc.
1848 CAL above eagle (2 Proofs known)..........1,389		$1,850.00	$5,000.00
1848C...............................16,788		100.00	220.00
1848D...............................13,771		110.00	255.00
1849................................23,294		40.00	85.00
1849C...............................10,220		95.00	210.00
1849D...............................10,945		95.00	210.00
1850................................252,923		37.50	65.00
1850C...............................9,148		100.00	175.00
1850D...............................12,148		100.00	175.00
1850O...............................84,000		40.00	65.00
1851................................1,372,748		40.00	60.00
1851C...............................14,923		85.00	300.00
1851D...............................11,264		85.00	300.00
1851O...............................148,000		37.50	60.00
1852................................1,159,681		40.00	55.00
1852C...............................9,772		100.00	165.00
1852D...............................4,078		200.00	325.00
1852O...............................140,000		37.50	55.00
1853................................1,404,668		37.50	55.00

QUARTER EAGLES

	Quan. Minted	V. Fine	Unc.	Proof
1853D	3,178	$300.00	$600.00	
1854	596,258	37.50	57.50	
1854C	7,295	110.00	280.00	
1854D	1,760	750.00	1,300.00	
1854O	153,000	40.00	55.00	
1854S	246	3,000.00	5,000.00	
1855	235,480	40.00	55.00	$2,500.00
1855C	3,677	175.00	300.00	
1855D	1,123	575.00	1,700.00	
1856	384,240	37.50	55.00	1,800.00
1856C	7,913	110.00	225.00	
1856D	874	1,000.00	3,000.00	
1856O	21,100	40.00	62.50	
1856S	71,120	40.00	80.00	
1857	214,130	40.00	55.00	1,750.00
1857D	2,364	250.00	450.00	
1857O	34,000	40.00	60.00	
1857S	68,000	40.00	67.50	
1858	47,377	40.00	55.00	1,250.00
1858C	9,056	125.00	225.00	
1858S (Unknown)	1,200			
1859	39,444	40.00	55.00	800.00
1859D	2,244	200.00	425.00	
1859S	15,200	45.00	100.00	
1860	22,675	40.00	65.00	900.00
1860C	7,469	120.00	175.00	
1860S	35,600	50.00	100.00	
1861	1,272,518	42.50	55.00	900.00
1861S	24,000	40.00	65.00	
1862	112,353	40.00	55.00	900.00
1862 over 1				
1862S	8,000	55.00	100.00	
1863 Proofs only (30)	30			3,500.00
1863S	10,800	47.50	85.00	
1864	2,874	150.00	300.00	1,100.00
1865	(25) 1,545	175.00	375.00	1,100.00
1865S	23,376	40.00	70.00	
1866	(30) 3,110	135.00	250.00	650.00
1866S	38,960	40.00	65.00	
1867	(50) 3,250	100.00	175.00	600.00
1867S	28,000	50.00	75.00	
1868	(25) 3,625	90.00	160.00	550.00
1868S	34,000	47.50	72.50	
1869	(25) 4,345	60.00	110.00	600.00
1869S	29,500	40.00	67.50	
1870	(35) 4,555	70.00	120.00	500.00
1870S	16,000	40.00	75.00	
1871	(30) 5,350	65.00	105.00	500.00
1871S	22,000	52.50	72.50	
1872	(30) 3,030	55.00	95.00	500.00
1872S	18,000	50.00	75.00	
1873 (Closed 3) All Kinds	(25) 178,025	40.00	55.00	550.00
1873 (Open 3)		40.00	55.00	

QUARTER EAGLES

	Quan. Minted	V. Fine	Unc.	Proof
1873S	27,000	$ 40.00	$ 60.00	
1874	(20) 3,940	60.00	125.00	$ 725.00
1875	(20) 420	350.00	700.00	1,500.00
1875S	11,600	70.00	150.00	
1876	(45) 4,221	65.00	105.00	650.00
1876S	5,000	45.00	95.00	
1877	(20) 1,652	100.00	225.00	900.00
1877S	35,400	40.00	60.00	
1878	(20) 286,260	40.00	50.00	700.00
1878S	178,000	40.00	50.00	
1879	(30) 88,900	40.00	50.00	550.00
1879S	43,500	45.00	65.00	
1880	(36) 2,996	90.00	135.00	600.00
1881	(40) 680	240.00	425.00	900.00
1882	(40) 4,040	82.50	150.00	600.00
1883	(40) 1,960	100.00	165.00	550.00
1884	(43) 1,993	105.00	175.00	600.00
1885	(87) 887	250.00	400.00	800.00
1886	(88) 4,088	65.00	110.00	450.00
1887	(122) 6,282	55.00	95.00	400.00
1888	(92) 16,098	45.00	65.00	350.00
1889	(48) 17,648	45.00	60.00	400.00
1890	(93) 8,813	55.00	95.00	400.00
1891	(80) 11,040	45.00	65.00	350.00
1892	(105) 2,545	80.00	150.00	400.00
1893	(106) 30,106	40.00	65.00	375.00
1894	(122) 4,122	60.00	100.00	450.00
1895	(119) 6,119	50.00	75.00	350.00
1896	(132) 19,202	42.50	60.00	350.00
1897	(136) 29,904	40.00	55.00	300.00
1898	(165) 24,165	40.00	55.00	300.00
1899	(150) 27,350	40.00	55.00	275.00
1900	(205) 67,205	40.00	55.00	250.00
1901	(233) 91,323	40.00	55.00	250.00
1902	(193) 133,733	40.00	55.00	250.00
1903	(197) 201,257	40.00	55.00	250.00
1904	(170) 160,960	40.00	55.00	250.00
1905*	(144) 217,944	40.00	55.00	250.00
1906	(160) 176,490	40.00	55.00	250.00
1907	(154) 336,448	40.00	55.00	250.00

*Pieces dated 1905S are counterfeit.

INDIAN HEAD TYPE

The new type represents a departure from all preceding coin types in the United States series. Bela Lyon Pratt was the designer of this and the half eagle piece. The coin has no raised milling and the main devices and legends are incuse.

V. Fine — *Haircord knot distinct. Feathers at top of head clear. Cheek bone noticeably worn.*

Ex. Fine — *Cheek bone slightly worn. War-bonnet and headband feathers slightly worn.*

QUARTER EAGLES

	Quan.	Minted	V. Fine	Unc.	Matte Proof
1908	(236)	565,057	$ 23.50	$ 35.00	$500.00
1909	(139)	441,899	23.50	35.00	600.00
1910	(682)	492,682	23.50	35.00	450.00
1911	(191)	704,191	23.50	35.00	500.00
1911D		55,680	310.00	400.00	
1912	(197)	616,197	23.50	35.00	600.00
1913	(165)	722,165	24.00	32.00	600.00
1914	(117)	240,117	36.00	47.50	700.00
1914D		448,000	30.00	40.00	
1915	(100)	606,100	24.00	32.00	600.00
1925D		578,000	24.00	32.00	
1926		446,000	24.00	32.00	
1927		388,000	24.00	32.00	
1928		416,000	24.00	32.00	
1929		532,000	24.00	32.00	

THREE-DOLLAR GOLD PIECES

1854-1889

The three-dollar gold piece was authorized by Act of February 21, 1853. The coin was first struck in 1854. It was never popular and saw very little circulation.

The coin weighs 77.4 grains, .900 fine. The head on the obverse represents an Indian princess with hair tightly curling over the neck, head crowned with a circle of feathers, the band of which is inscribed LIBERTY. A wreath of tobacco, wheat, corn and cotton occupies the field of the reverse, with the denomination and date within it. No change of type was made during the life of this denomination.

In the year 1854 only, the word DOLLARS is in much smaller letters than in years 1855 through 1889.

V. Fine — Eyebrow, hair about forehead and ear and bottom curl are worn smooth. Curled feather-ends have faint details showing.

	Quan. Minted	V. Fine	Unc.	Proof
1854	138,618	180.00	245.00	2,000.00
1854D	1,120	1,500.00	2,100.00	
1854O	24,000	190.00	260.00	
1855	50,555	180.00	240.00	1,800.00
1855S	6,600	180.00	275.00	
1856	26,010	180.00	250.00	1,200.00
1856 Small S - All Kinds	34,500	190.00	260.00	
1856 Large S		190.00	260.00	
1857	20,891	190.00	260.00	2,500.00
1857S	14,000	200.00	300.00	
1858	2,133	275.00	600.00	1,500.00
1859	15,638	190.00	270.00	800.00

THREE-DOLLAR GOLD PIECES

	Quan. Minted	V. Fine	Unc.	Proof
1860	7,155	$180.00	$ 265.00	$ 800.00
1860S	7,000	180.00	265.00	
1861	6,072	180.00	265.00	1,500.00
1862	5,785	185.00	265.00	1,100.00
1863	5,039	195.00	300.00	1,200.00
1864	2,680	225.00	500.00	1,100.00
1865	(25) 1,165	260.00	500.00	1,200.00
1866	(30) 4,030	200.00	260.00	1,100.00
1867	(50) 2,650	200.00	275.00	1,100.00
1868	(25) 4,875	195.00	260.00	1,200.00
1869	(25) 2,525	210.00	275.00	1,200.00
1870	(35) 3,535	195.00	260.00	1,100.00
1870S (Unique)	2			
1871	(30) 1,330	250.00	350.00	1,300.00
1872	(30) 2,030	235.00	325.00	1,200.00
1873 (Open 3)	(25) 25			2,100.00
1873 (Closed 3) (All restrikes)			1,500.00	1,750.00
1874	(20) 41,820	180.00	230.00	1,200.00
1875 (Proofs Only)	(20) 20	Wolfson Sale $17,000.00		
1876 (Proofs Only)	(45) 45			7,000.00
1877	(20) 1,488	350.00	625.00	2,200.00
1878	(20) 82,324	180.00	240.00	1,100.00
1879	(30) 3,030	200.00	325.00	950.00
1880	(36) 1,036	235.00	400.00	1,000.00
1881	(54) 550	375.00	650.00	1,600.00
1882	(76) 1,540	225.00	375.00	1,000.00
1883	(89) 940	275.00	425.00	1,000.00
1884	(106) 1,106	235.00	425.00	1,000.00
1885	(110) 910	275.00	450.00	1,200.00
1886	(142) 1,142	240.00	400.00	1,000.00
1887	(160) 6,160	200.00	275.00	900.00
1888	(291) 5,291	210.00	275.00	800.00
1889	(129) 2,429	210.00	315.00	850.00

FOUR-DOLLAR GOLD OR "STELLA"

These pattern coins were first suggested by Hon. John A. Kasson, then U. S. Minister to Austria; and it was through the efforts of Dr. W. W. Hubbell who patented the goloid metal, used in making the goloid metric dollars, that we have these beautiful and interesting pieces.

There are two distinct types in both years of issue. Barber designed the flowing hair type, and Morgan the coiled hair. They were struck in gold, aluminum, copper and white metal. Only those struck in gold are listed.

	Proof		Proof
1879 Flowing hair (415)	$ 6,000.00	1880 Flowing hair (15)	$12,250.00
1879 Coiled hair (10)	14,500.00	1880 Coiled hair (10)	15,000.00

HALF EAGLES — 1795-1929
($5.00 GOLD PIECES)

The half-eagle was the first gold coin actually struck for the United States. The $5.00 piece was authorized to be coined by the Act of April 2, 1792 and the first type weighed 135 grains, 916⅔ fine. The weight was changed by Act of June 28, 1834 to 129 grains, 899.225 fine. Fineness became .900 by Act of January 18, 1837.

There are many varieties among the early dates caused by changes in the number of stars, style of eagle, over-dates, and differences in the size of figures in the dates. Those dated prior to 1807 do not bear any mark of value. The 1822 half-eagle is considered the most valuable regular issue coin of the entire United States series. Proofs prior to 1855 are known to exist of some dates, and all are rare.

Fine — Hair worn smooth but with distinct outline. After 1797 E. PLURIBUS UNUM is faint but readable.

V. Fine — Slight to noticeable wear on high spots such as hair, turban, eagle's head and wings.

	Small Eagle		Large Eagle	
	Quan. Minted	Fine	V. Fine	Unc.
1795 Small eagle - All Kinds	8,707	$ 600.00	$ 800.00	$1,400.00
1795 Large or heraldic eagle		800.00	1,350.00	2,750.00

1796 over 95 Small eagle	3,399	575.00	800.00	1,600.00

1797 over 95 Lg. or heraldic eagle - All	6,406	1,000.00	1,500.00	2,250.00

HALF EAGLES

1797 - 15 Stars   16 Stars   1799

	Quan. Minted	Fine	V. Fine	Unc.
1797 15 Stars, small eagle on rev............		$1,000.00	$1,500.00	$2,500.00
1797 16 Stars, small eagle on rev............		1,000.00	1,400.00	2,300.00
1798 Small eagle (5 known) All Kinds..24,867				
1798 Large or heraldic eagle, small 8 in date..		195.00	275.00	475.00
1798 Large eagle, lg. 8 in date, 13 star reverse.		235.00	375.00	700.00
1798 Large eagle, lg. 8 in date, 14 star reverse.		300.00	550.00	900.00
1799................................7,451		240.00	350.00	500.00

1802 over 1   1803 over 2   Small 8   Large 8

1800................................11,622	200.00	335.00	465.00
1802 over 1........................53,176	195.00	300.00	450.00
1803 over 2........................33,506	195.00	300.00	450.00
1804 Small 8 - All Kinds..............30,475	210.00	320.00	450.00
1804 Large 8...........................	200.00	325.00	450.00
1805................................33,183	200.00	325.00	450.00

Pointed         Round Top
6   6

1806 Pointed top 6 - All Kinds........64,093	225.00	300.00	450.00
1806 Round top 6......................	225.00	300.00	450.00
1807................................33,496	225.00	300.00	450.00

HALF EAGLES

LIBERTY FACING LEFT — ROUND CAP — SMALLER EAGLE
VALUE 5D. USED FOR FIRST TIME

Fine — LIBERTY readable but partly weak.

V.F.— Headband edges slightly worn. LIBERTY is bold.

	Quan. Minted	Fine	V. Fine	Unc.
1807	50,597	$210.00	$300.00	$460.00

1808 over 7	Normal Date	Small Date	Small 5

		Fine	V. Fine	Unc.
1808 over 7 - All Kinds	55,578	200.00	265.00	425.00
1808		200.00	265.00	425.00
1809 over 8 - All Kinds	33,875	200.00	265.00	425.00
1809		200.00	265.00	425.00
1810 Small date, small 5 - All Kinds	100,287	200.00	265.00	425.00
1810 Small date, tall 5		200.00	265.00	425.00

Large Date   Tall 5

		Fine	V. Fine	Unc.
1810 Large date		200.00	265.00	425.00
1811 Small 5 - All Kinds	99,581	200.00	265.00	425.00
1811 Large 5		200.00	265.00	425.00
1812	58,087	200.00	265.00	425.00

NEW TYPE — LARGER HEAD

		Fine	V. Fine	Unc.
1813	95,428	230.00	300.00	650.00
1814	15,454	230.00	325.00	675.00
1815	635			5,000.00
1818	48,588	225.00	290.00	600.00
1819	51,723	2,500.00	4,000.00	7,500.00

HALF EAGLES

Curve-Based 2

Square-Based 2

Small Letters

Large Letters

	Quan. Minted	Fine	V. Fine	Unc.
1820 Curve-based 2, small letters				
All Kinds	263,806	$325.00	$500.00	$ 875.00
1820 Curve-based 2, large letters		350.00	550.00	1,100.00
1820 Square-based 2		260.00	425.00	750.00
1821	34,641	820.00	1,200.00	2,400.00

1822

1825 over 21

1825 over 24

1822 (3 Known)	17,796	—	—	
1823	14,485	375.00	550.00	1,000.00
1824	17,340			5,000.00
1825 over 21 - All Kinds	29,060	700.00	1,100.00	1,850.00
1825 over 24		1,000.00	2,000.00	3,000.00
1826	18,069	875.00	1,400.00	2,500.00
1827	24,913	1,800.00	2,750.00	5,000.00

1828 over 27

Small Date

Large Date

1828 over 27 - All Kinds	28,029	Wolfson Sale $5,250.00		
1828		1,350.00	1,850.00	3,500.00
1829 Small date - All Kinds	57,442	1963 Florida Sale $21,500.00		
1829 Large date		—	—	—

[169]

HALF EAGLES

Small 5D	Large 5D	12 Stars, Curve-Based 2	13 Stars, Square-Based 2

	Quan. Minted	Fine	V. Fine	Unc.
1830 Small 5 D - All Kinds	126,351	$400.00	$650.00	$1,250.00
1830 Large 5 D		415.00	675.00	1,300.00
1831	140,594	450.00	700.00	1,350.00
1832 Curve-based 2, 12 stars - All K.	157,487			
1832 Square-based 2, 13 stars		1,150.00	1,900.00	3,500.00
1833	193,630	450.00	700.00	1,350.00

4

Plain 4

4

Crosslet 4

1834 Plain 4 - Both Kinds	50,141	500.00	725.00	1,500.00
1834 Crosslet 4		650.00	825.00	1,800.00

NO MOTTO ON REVERSE

As on the quarter dollar of 1831, the motto E PLURIBUS UNUM was omitted from the new, reduced size half-eagle in 1834, presumably for lack of space. The new motto IN GOD WE TRUST was nevertheless artistically added to the reverse in the form of a scroll in 1866.

1834 Plain 4 - Both Kinds	682,028	50.00	60.00	100.00
1834 Crosslet 4		125.00	160.00	310.00
1835	371,534	50.00	60.00	110.00
1836	553,147	55.00	65.00	110.00
1837	207,121	50.00	60.00	110.00
1838	286,588	52.50	65.00	125.00
1838C	12,913	140.00	235.00	400.00
1838D	20,583	140.00	235.00	400.00

NEW TYPE — SMALLER HEAD WITH CORONET

Fine — LIBERTY readable, but partly weak. Neck hair worn, but outlines clear.
V. Fine — LIBERTY bold. Major lines show in neck hair.

HALF EAGLES

	Quan. Minted	Fine	V. Fine	Unc.
1839	118,143	$ 40.00	$ 55.00	$ 95.00
1839C	23,467	95.00	150.00	250.00
1839D	18,939	100.00	155.00	260.00
1840	137,382	40.00	50.00	80.00
1840C	19,028	85.00	130.00	225.00
1840D	22,896	85.00	130.00	225.00
1840O	30,400	52.50	80.00	120.00
1841	15,833	40.00	60.00	125.00
1841C	21,511	72.50	110.00	160.00
1841D	30,495	72.50	110.00	160.00
1841O (2 Known)	8,350	—	—	—

Small Letters   Large Letters

	Quan. Minted	Fine	Unc.
1842 Small letters - All Kinds	27,578	85.00	175.00
1842 Large letters		60.00	125.00
1842C Small date - All Kinds	27,480	100.00	175.00
1842C Large date		110.00	185.00
1842D Small date - All Kinds	59,608	100.00	175.00
1842D Large date		110.00	185.00
1842O	16,400	90.00	135.00
1843	611,205	40.00	65.00
1843C	44,353	80.00	125.00
1843D	98,452	85.00	135.00
1843O Small letters - All Kinds	101,075	60.00	90.00
1843O Large letters		60.00	90.00
1844	340,330	40.00	70.00
1844C	23,631	95.00	165.00
1844D	88,982	75.00	135.00
1844O	364,600	45.00	85.00
1845	417,099	40.00	65.00
1845D	90,629	85.00	150.00
1845O	41,000	55.00	95.00
1846	395,942	40.00	60.00
1846C	12,995	110.00	175.00
1846D	80,294	90.00	150.00
1846O	58,000	55.00	105.00
1847	915,981	37.50	55.00
1847C	84,151	75.00	125.00
1847D	64,405	100.00	175.00
1847O	12,000	90.00	130.00
1848	260,775	40.00	65.00
1848C	64,472	100.00	160.00
1848D	47,465	95.00	150.00
1849	133,070	40.00	55.00

HALF EAGLES

	Quan. Minted	V. Fine	Unc.	Proof
1849C	64,823	$ 85.00	$150.00	
1849D	39,036	90.00	160.00	
1850	64,491	40.00	60.00	
1850C	63,591	90.00	150.00	
1850D	43,950	90.00	150.00	
1851	377,505	35.00	57.50	
1851C	49,176	95.00	155.00	
1851D	62,710	95.00	155.00	
1851O	41,000	55.00	100.00	
1852	573,901	32.50	57.50	
1852C	72,574	95.00	145.00	
1852D	91,452	95.00	145.00	
1853	305,770	35.00	52.50	
1853C	65,571	95.00	140.00	
1853D	89,678	95.00	140.00	
1854	160,675	35.00	52.50	
1854C	39,291	95.00	150.00	
1854D	56,413	95.00	150.00	
1854O	46,000	60.00	115.00	
1854S Wolfson Sale E. Fine $16,500	268	—	—	
1855	117,098	32.50	50.00	$2,200.00
1855C	39,788	100.00	150.00	
1855D	22,432	115.00	175.00	
1855O	11,100	90.00	150.00	
1855S	61,000	40.00	100.00	
1856	197,990	32.50	60.00	2,200.00
1856C	28,457	85.00	125.00	
1856D	19,786	115.00	150.00	
1856O	10,000	85.00	130.00	
1856S	105,100	35.00	60.00	
1857	98,188	40.00	60.00	2,200.00
1857C	31,360	95.00	160.00	
1857D	17,046	100.00	155.00	
1857O	13,000	75.00	120.00	
1857S	87,000	40.00	60.00	
1858	15,136	85.00	125.00	1,300.00
1858C	38,856	90.00	140.00	
1858D	15,362	125.00	175.00	
1858S	18,600	75.00	120.00	
1859	16,814	80.00	120.00	1,000.00
1859C	31,847	95.00	135.00	
1859D	10,366	110.00	190.00	
1859S	13,220	80.00	125.00	
1860	19,825	75.00	115.00	600.00
1860C	14,813	90.00	150.00	
1860D	14,635	85.00	140.00	
1860S	21,200	55.00	80.00	
1861	639,950	40.00	55.00	550.00
1861C	6,879	250.00	450.00	
1861D	1,597	650.00	900.00	
1861S	18,000	60.00	90.00	
1862	4,465	150.00	250.00	550.00
1862S	9,500	100.00	150.00	

HALF EAGLES

	Quan. Minted	V. Fine	Unc.	Proof
1863	2,472	$150.00	$400.00	$650.00
1863S	17,000	55.00	150.00	
1864	4,220	150.00	250.00	650.00
1864S	3,888	175.00	250.00	
1865	(25) 1,295	300.00	450.00	650.00
1865S	27,612	50.00	75.00	
1866S - All Kinds	43,920	95.00	200.00	

MOTTO OVER EAGLE

V. Fine — *Half of hairlines above coronet missing. Hair curls under ear evident, but worn. Motto and its ribbon sharp.*

	Quan. Minted	V. Fine	Unc.	Proof
1866	(30) 6,720	200.00	325.00	550.00
1866S		185.00	250.00	
1867	(50) 6,920	100.00	200.00	475.00
1867S	29,000	85.00	150.00	
1868	(25) 5,725	120.00	190.00	600.00
1868S	52,000	70.00	110.00	
1869	(25) 1,785	175.00	425.00	1,000.00
1869S	31,000	70.00	100.00	
1870	(35) 4,035	80.00	130.00	750.00
1870CC	7,675	275.00	400.00	
1870S	17,000	70.00	150.00	
1871	(30) 3,230	130.00	225.00	800.00
1871CC	20,770	125.00	200.00	
1871S	25,000	85.00	130.00	
1872	(30) 1,690	175.00	300.00	850.00
1872CC	16,980	75.00	180.00	
1872S	36,400	55.00	85.00	
1873 Closed 3 - All Kinds	(25) 112,505	60.00	90.00	600.00
1873 Open 3		32.50	45.00	
1873CC	7,416	135.00	225.00	
1873S	31,000	60.00	80.00	
1874	(20) 3,508	175.00	250.00	700.00
1874CC	21,198	120.00	200.00	
1874S	16,000	50.00	80.00	
1875	(20) 220	650.00	1,700.00	2,200.00
1875CC	11,828	120.00	200.00	
1875S	9,000	105.00	150.00	
1876	(45) 1,477	225.00	400.00	700.00
1876CC	6,887	160.00	300.00	
1876S	4,000	75.00	125.00	
1877	(20) 1,152	300.00	500.00	1,100.00
1877CC	8,680	150.00	250.00	
1877S	26,700	45.00	100.00	
1878	(20) 131,740	30.00	40.00	900.00

HALF EAGLES

	Quan. Minted	V. Fine	Unc.	Proof
1878CC	9,054	$200.00	$325.00	
1878S	144,700	35.00	42.50	
1879	(30) 301,950	30.00	40.00	$450.00
1879CC	17,281	90.00	150.00	
1879S	426,200	30.00	40.00	
1880	(36) 3,166,436	25.00	35.00	400.00
1880CC	51,017	65.00	95.00	
1880S	1,348,900	25.00	35.00	
1881	(40) 5,708,800	25.00	35.00	350.00
1881CC	13,886	70.00	115.00	
1881S	969,000	25.00	32.50	
1882	(40) 2,514,560	25.00	32.50	400.00
1882CC	82,817	60.00	90.00	
1882S	969,000	25.00	32.50	
1883	(40) 233,440	25.00	32.50	400.00
1883CC	12,958	80.00	125.00	
1883S	83,200	25.00	32.50	
1884	(18) 191,048	25.00	32.50	600.00
1884CC	16,402	60.00	95.00	
1884S	177,000	25.00	32.50	
1885	(66) 601,506	25.00	32.50	375.00
1885S	1,211,500	25.00	32.50	
1886	(72) 388,432	25.00	32.50	375.00
1886S	3,268,000	25.00	32.50	
1887 Proofs only	(87) 87			1,700.00
1887S	1,912,000	25.00	32.50	
1888	(94) 18,296	45.00	80.00	500.00
1888S	293,900	25.00	32.50	
1889	(45) 7,565	150.00	300.00	550.00
1890	(88) 4,328	200.00	375.00	550.00
1890CC	53,800	42.00	70.00	
1891	(53) 61,413	35.00	55.00	400.00
1891CC	208,000	30.00	55.00	
1892	(92) 753,572	25.00	40.00	375.00
1892CC	82,968	35.00	60.00	
1892O	10,000	200.00	400.00	
1892S	298,400	27.50	45.00	
1893	(77) 1,528,197	25.00	32.50	350.00
1893CC	60,000	50.00	80.00	
1893O	110,000	50.00	75.00	
1893S	224,000	27.50	37.50	
1894	(75) 957,957	25.00	35.00	400.00
1894O	16,600	50.00	85.00	
1894S	55,900	32.50	45.00	
1895	(81) 1,345,936	27.50	37.50	350.00
1895S	112,000	27.50	37.50	
1896	(103) 59,063	27.50	40.00	350.00
1896S	155,400	27.50	37.50	
1897	(83) 867,883	25.00	32.50	350.00
1897S	354,000	25.00	32.50	
1898	(75) 633,495	25.00	32.50	360.00
1898S	1,397,400	25.00	32.50	
1899	(99) 1,710,729	25.00	32.50	350.00
1899S	1,545,000	25.00	32.50	

HALF EAGLES

	Quan. Minted	V. Fine	Unc.	Proof
1900 ....(230)	1,405,730	$25.00	$32.50	$350.00
1900S...........................	329,000	25.00	32.50	
1901 ....(140)	616,040	25.00	32.50	350.00
1901S...........................	3,648,000	25.00	32.50	
1902 ....(162)	172,562	25.00	32.50	350.00
1902S...........................	939,000	25.00	32.50	
1903 ....(154)	227,024	25.00	32.50	350.00
1903S...........................	1,855,000	25.00	32.50	
1904 ....(136)	392,136	25.00	32.50	350.00
1904S...........................	97,000	47.50	75.00	
1905 ....(108)	302,308	25.00	32.50	350.00
1905S...........................	880,700	25.00	32.50	
1906 ....(85)	348,820	25.00	32.50	350.00
1906D...........................	320,000	25.00	32.50	
1906S...........................	598,000	25.00	32.50	
1907 ....(92)	626,192	25.00	32.50	350.00
1907D...........................	888,000	25.00	32.50	
1908	421,874	25.00	32.50	

INDIAN HEAD TYPE

This type conforms with the quarter eagle of the same date. The incuse designs and lettering make this a unique series, along with the quarter eagle, in our United States coinage.

The scarcer mint marks, when well struck command higher prices.

V. Fine — Noticeable wear on large middle feathers and tip of eagle's wing.

	Quan. Minted	V. Fine	Unc.	Matte Proof
1908 ....(167)	578,012	25.00	35.00	650.00
1908D...........................	148,000	27.50	37.50	
1908S...........................	82,000	110.00	260.00	
1909 ....(78)	627,138	27.50	37.50	650.00
1909D...........................	3,423,560	27.50	35.00	
*1909O..........................	34,200	275.00	400.00	
1909S...........................	297,200	32.50	55.00	
1910 ....(250)	604,250	27.50	35.00	650.00
1910D...........................	193,600	27.50	40.00	
1910S...........................	770,200	29.00	42.50	
1911 ....(139)	915,139	27.50	35.00	650.00
1911D...........................	72,500	110.00	210.00	

*Beware spurious "O" mint mark.

HALF EAGLES

	Quan. Minted	V. Fine	Unc.	Matte Proof
1911S	1,416,000	$ 33.00	$ 47.50	
1912	(144) 790,144	25.00	35.00	$650.00
1912S	392,000	30.00	52.50	
1913	(99) 916,099	26.00	37.50	650.00
1913S	408,000	33.00	60.00	
1914	(125) 247,125	32.50	40.00	700.00
1914D	247,000	32.50	45.00	
1914S	263,000	35.00	55.00	
1915*	(75) 588,075	27.50	37.50	700.00
1915S	164,000	32.50	60.00	
1916S	240,000	32.50	60.00	
1929	662,000	650.00	1,100.00	

*Pieces dated 1915D are counterfeit.

EAGLES ($10.00 Gold Pieces)

Coinage authority including specified weights and fineness of the eagle conforms with that of the half-eagle. The small eagle reverse was used until 1797 when the large, heraldic eagle replaced it. The early dates have variations in the number of stars, the rarest date being 1798. No eagles were struck from 1805 to 1837. Proofs prior to 1855 are known to exist of some dates, and all are rare.

Fine—Details on turban and head obliterated.

V.F.—Neck hairlines and details under turban and over forehead are worn, but distinguishable.

	Quan. Minted	Fine	V. Fine	Unc.
1795 Small Eagle	2,795	625.00	825.00	1,500.00
1796 Small Eagle	6,080	550.00	775.00	1,400.00
1797 Small Eagle - All Kinds	9,177	550.00	750.00	1,450.00

		Fine	V. Fine	Unc.
1797 Large Eagle		425.00	550.00	825.00

EAGLES

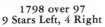

1798 over 97	1798 over 97	1799
9 Stars Left, 4 Right	7 Stars Left, 6 Right	

	Quan. Minted	Fine	V. Fine	Unc.
1798 over 97 9 Stars Left, 4 Right				
All Kinds	7,974	$ 900.00	$1,150.00	$1,600.00
1798 over 97 7 Stars Left, 6 Right		1,950.00	2,700.00	5,000.00
1799	17,483	350.00	500.00	750.00
1800	25,965	350.00	460.00	725.00
1801	29,254	350.00	460.00	725.00
1803	8,979	350.00	500.00	775.00
1804	9,795	425.00	550.00	1,000.00

CORONET TYPE — Reduced Size

In 1838 the weight and diameter of the eagle were reduced and the obverse and reverse were redesigned. Liberty now faces left and the word LIBERTY is placed on the coronet. A more natural appearing eagle is used on the reverse. The value, TEN D., is shown for the first time on this denomination.

Fine—LIBERTY readable but may be slightly worn.

V. Fine—Hairlines above coronet partly worn. Curls under ear worn but defined.

		Fine	V. Fine	Unc.
1838	7,200	300.00	400.00	600.00
1839 Large letters - All Kinds	38,248	250.00	350.00	550.00
1839 Small letters		250.00	350.00	650.00
1840	47,338		60.00	150.00
1841	63,131		57.50	110.00
1841O	2,500		225.00	450.00
1842 Small date - All Kinds	81,507		55.00	110.00
1842 Large date			55.00	110.00
1842O	27,400		57.50	115.00
1843	75,462		50.00	70.00

EAGLES

	Quan. Minted	V. Fine	Unc.	Proof
1843O	175,162	$ 47.50	$ 75.00	
1844	6,361	110.00	225.00	
1844O	118,700	47.50	80.00	
1845	26,153	55.00	110.00	
1845O	47,500	45.00	80.00	
1846	20,095	55.00	110.00	
1846O	81,780	47.50	80.00	
1847	862,258	40.00	75.00	
1847O	571,500	40.00	75.00	
1848	145,484	40.00	75.00	
1848O	35,850	45.00	85.00	
1849	653,618	40.00	75.00	
1849O	23,900	45.00	100.00	
1850	291,451	40.00	75.00	
1850O	57,500	42.50	85.00	
1851	176,328	40.00	75.00	
1851O	263,000	42.50	75.00	
1852	263,106	40.00	75.00	
1852O	18,000	55.00	110.00	
1853	201,253	40.00	75.00	
1853O	51,000	45.00	85.00	
1854	54,250	45.00	80.00	
1854O	52,500	42.50	80.00	
1854S	123,826	42.50	80.00	
1855	121,701	42.50	80.00	$4,000.00
1855O	18,000	60.00	115.00	
1855S	9,000	115.00	225.00	
1856	60,490	45.00	95.00	2,000.00
1856O	14,500	60.00	125.00	
1856S	68,000	45.00	80.00	
1857	16,606	55.00	130.00	2,000.00
1857O	5,500	150.00	260.00	
1857S	26,000	60.00	125.00	
*1858	2,521	3,000.00	6,000.00	———
1858O	20,000	70.00	105.00	
1858S	11,800	80.00	125.00	
1859	16,093	55.00	110.00	1,100.00
1859O	2,300	150.00	300.00	
1859S	7,000	95.00	180.00	
1860	11,783	70.00	135.00	1,100.00
1860O	11,100	70.00	135.00	
1860S	5,000	115.00	250.00	
1861	113,233	42.00	75.00	1,000.00
1861S	15,500	75.00	140.00	
1862	10,995	85.00	170.00	1,000.00
1862S	12,500	80.00	150.00	
1863	1,248	200.00	400.00	1,100.00
1863S	10,000	90.00	150.00	
1864	3,580	150.00	250.00	1,000.00
1864S	2,500	175.00	400.00	
1865	(25) 4,005	125.00	225.00	1,000.00
1865S All Kinds	16,700	70.00	130.00	

*Beware removed mint mark.

EAGLES

	Quan. Minted	V. Fine	Unc.	Proof
1865S over Inverted 186				
1866S All Kinds	20,000	$100.00	$200.00	

MOTTO OVER EAGLE

V. Fine—Half of hairlines over coronet visible. Curls under ear worn but defined. IN GOD WE TRUST and its ribbon are sharp.

		V. Fine	Unc.	Proof
1866	(30) 3,780	130.00	250.00	$ 900.00
1866S		100.00	160.00	
1867	(50) 3,140	135.00	200.00	800.00
1867S	9,000	90.00	175.00	
1868	(25) 10,655	80.00	150.00	850.00
1868S	13,500	65.00	125.00	
1869	(25) 1,855	200.00	300.00	850.00
1869S	6,430	95.00	175.00	
1870	(35) 2,535	155.00	300.00	775.00
1870CC	5,908	150.00	235.00	
1870S	8,000	80.00	150.00	
1871	(30) 1,780	175.00	275.00	800.00
1871CC	7,185	100.00	250.00	
1871S	16,500	65.00	140.00	
1872	(30) 1,650	175.00	300.00	900.00
1872CC	5,500	135.00	250.00	
1872S	17,300	65.00	125.00	
1873	(25) 825	225.00	400.00	1,500.00
1873CC	4,543	150.00	250.00	
1873S	12,000	65.00	140.00	
1874	(20) 53,160	47.50	85.00	1,300.00
1874CC	16,767	85.00	150.00	
1874S	10,000	82.50	145.00	
1875	(20) 120	500.00	1,000.00	2,200.00
1875CC	7,715	90.00	175.00	
1876	(45) 732	250.00	500.00	1,200.00
1876CC	4,696	125.00	220.00	
1876S	5,000	75.00	150.00	
1877	(20) 817	250.00	400.00	1,500.00
1877CC	3,332	160.00	260.00	
1877S	17,000	55.00	105.00	
1878	(20) 73,800	40.00	65.00	1,200.00
1878CC	3,244	155.00	275.00	
1878S	26,100	40.00	65.00	
1879	(30) 384,770	37.50	55.00	800.00
1879CC	1,762	400.00	1,000.00	

EAGLES

	Quan. Minted	V. Fine	Unc.	Proof
1879O	1,500	$425.00	$ 700.00	
1879S	224,000	37.50	52.50	
1880	(36) 1,644,876	35.00	45.00	$800.00
1880CC	11,190	60.00	120.00	
1880O	9,200	65.00	130.00	
1880S	506,250	35.00	45.00	
1881	(40) 3,877,260	35.00	45.00	700.00
1881CC	24,015	55.00	90.00	
1881O	8,350	70.00	140.00	
1881S	970,000	35.00	45.00	
1882	(40) 2,324,480	35.00	45.00	700.00
1882CC	6,764	95.00	135.00	
1882O	10,820	55.00	100.00	
1882S	132,000	35.00	50.00	
1883	(40) 208,740	35.00	50.00	700.00
1883CC	12,000	67.50	110.00	
1883O	800	600.00	1,100.00	
1883S	38,000	42.50	70.00	
1884	(15) 76,905	37.50	60.00	700.00
1884CC	9,925	65.00	120.00	
1884S	124,250	37.50	52.50	
1885	(65) 253,527	35.00	50.00	650.00
1885S	228,000	35.00	50.00	
1886	(60) 236,160	35.00	50.00	650.00
1886S	826,000	35.00	50.00	
1887	(80) 53,680	50.00	70.00	625.00
1887S	817,000	35.00	50.00	
1888	(72) 132,996	35.00	50.00	625.00
1888O	21,335	55.00	100.00	
1888S	648,700	35.00	50.00	
1889	(45) 4,485	110.00	210.00	650.00
1889S	425,400	35.00	50.00	
1890	(63) 58,043	40.00	67.50	625.00
1890CC	17,500	55.00	100.00	
1891	(48) 91,868	35.00	50.00	625.00
1891CC	103,732	42.50	65.00	
1892	(72) 797,552	35.00	47.50	625.00
1892CC	40,000	50.00	80.00	
1892O	28,688	50.00	80.00	
1892S	115,500	45.00	60.00	
1893	(55) 1,840,895	35.00	47.50	625.00
1893CC	14,000	65.00	125.00	
1893O	17,000	55.00	90.00	
1893S	141,350	35.00	50.00	
1894	(43) 2,470,778	35.00	47.50	650.00
1894O	107,500	45.00	70.00	
1894S	25,000	60.00	110.00	
1895	(56) 567,826	35.00	47.50	625.00
1895O	98,000	42.50	70.00	
1895S	49,000	40.00	65.00	
1896	(78) 76,348	35.00	50.00	600.00
1896S	123,750	35.00	50.00	

EAGLES

	Quan. Minted	V. Fine	Unc.	Proof
1897........................(69)	1,000,159	$32.50	$45.00	$600.00
1897O...........................42,500		45.00	70.00	
1897S..........................234,750		32.50	50.00	
1898........................(67)	812,197	32.50	50.00	600.00
1898S..........................473,600		32.50	50.00	
1899........................(86)	1,262,305	32.50	50.00	575.00
1899O...........................37,047		50.00	80.00	
1899S..........................841,000		32.50	50.00	
1900........................(120)	293,960	32.50	80.00	575.00
1900S...........................81,000		35.00	50.00	
1901........................(85)	1,718,825	32.50	47.50	575.00
1901O...........................72,041		40.00	70.00	
1901S.........................2,812,750		32.50	50.00	
1902........................(113)	82,513	40.00	55.00	575.00
1902S..........................469,500		32.50	47.50	
1903........................(96)	125,926	32.50	47.50	575.00
1903O..........................112,771		32.50	55.00	
1903S..........................538,000		32.50	47.50	
1904........................(108)	162,038	40.00	50.00	575.00
1904O..........................108,950		32.50	65.00	
1905........................(86)	201,078	32.50	47.50	575.00
1905S..........................369,250		32.50	47.50	
1906........................(77)	165,497	32.50	47.50	575.00
1906D..........................981,000		32.50	47.50	
1906O...........................86,895		40.00	60.00	
1906S..........................457,000		32.50	60.00	
1907 All Kinds..............(74)	1,203,973	32.50	60.00	600.00
1907D.........................1,030,000		32.50	60.00	
1907S..........................210,500		32.50	60.00	

INDIAN HEAD TYPE

Augustus Saint-Gaudens, considered by many the greatest of modern sculptors, introduced a new high standard of art in United States coins evidenced by his eagle and double-eagle types of 1907. The obverse of the eagle shows the head of Liberty crowned with an Indian war bonnet while an impressively majestic eagle dominates the reverse side. A departure from older standards is found on the edge of the piece where 46 raised stars are arranged signifying the states of the Union, instead of a lettered or reeded edge. (48 stars 1912 and later.)

The first eagles struck had no motto IN GOD WE TRUST as did the later issues starting in 1908. President Theodore Roosevelt personally objected to the use of the Deity's name on coins. The motto was restored to the coins by Act of Congress in 1908.

V. Fine—Bonnet feathers worn near band. Hair high points show wear.

EAGLES

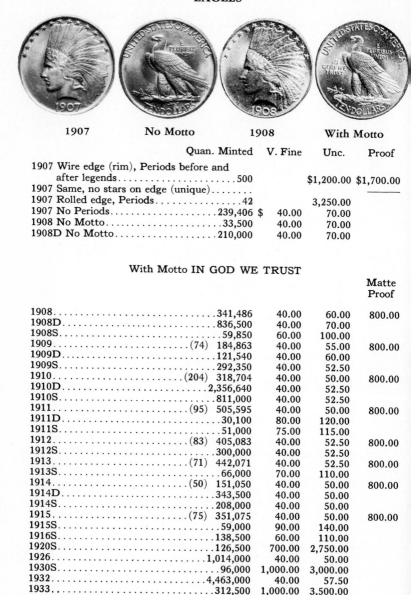

| 1907 | No Motto | 1908 | With Motto |

	Quan. Minted	V. Fine	Unc.	Proof
1907 Wire edge (rim), Periods before and after legends	500		$1,200.00	$1,700.00
1907 Same, no stars on edge (unique)				
1907 Rolled edge, Periods	42		3,250.00	
1907 No Periods	239,406	$ 40.00	70.00	
1908 No Motto	33,500	40.00	70.00	
1908D No Motto	210,000	40.00	70.00	

With Motto IN GOD WE TRUST

	Quan. Minted	V. Fine	Unc.	Matte Proof
1908	341,486	40.00	60.00	800.00
1908D	836,500	40.00	70.00	
1908S	59,850	60.00	100.00	
1909	(74) 184,863	40.00	55.00	800.00
1909D	121,540	40.00	60.00	
1909S	292,350	40.00	52.50	
1910	(204) 318,704	40.00	50.00	800.00
1910D	2,356,640	40.00	52.50	
1910S	811,000	40.00	52.50	
1911	(95) 505,595	40.00	50.00	800.00
1911D	30,100	80.00	120.00	
1911S	51,000	75.00	115.00	
1912	(83) 405,083	40.00	52.50	800.00
1912S	300,000	40.00	52.50	
1913	(71) 442,071	40.00	52.50	800.00
1913S	66,000	70.00	110.00	
1914	(50) 151,050	40.00	50.00	800.00
1914D	343,500	40.00	50.00	
1914S	208,000	40.00	50.00	
1915	(75) 351,075	40.00	50.00	800.00
1915S	59,000	90.00	140.00	
1916S	138,500	60.00	110.00	
1920S	126,500	700.00	2,750.00	
1926	1,014,000	40.00	50.00	
1930S	96,000	1,000.00	3,000.00	
1932	4,463,000	40.00	57.50	
1933	312,500	1,000.00	3,500.00	

DOUBLE EAGLES ($20.00 Gold Pieces) — 1849-1933

This largest of all regular United States issues was authorized to be coined by the Act of March 3, 1849. Its weight was 516 grains, .900 fine. The 1849 double-eagle is a unique pattern and reposes in the Mint collection. The rarest date obtainable is 1883. The 1861S reverse design by Paquet was withdrawn soon after striking. Very few specimens are known.

V. Fine — LIBERTY is bold. Jewels on crown defined. Lower half worn flat. Hair worn about ear.

1861S Paquet Reverse

	Quan. Minted	V. Fine	Unc.	Proof
1849 Unique — U.S. Mint Collection				
1850	1,170,261	$100.00	$ 275.00	
1850O	141,000	125.00	250.00	
1851	2,087,155	80.00	150.00	
1851O	315,000	125.00	200.00	
1852	2,053,026	75.00	150.00	
1852O	190,000	115.00	225.00	
1853	1,261,326	75.00	125.00	
1853O	71,000	115.00	230.00	
1854	757,899	75.00	140.00	
1854O	3,250	575.00	950.00	
1854S	141,468	130.00	230.00	
1855	364,666	75.00	145.00	
1855O	8,000	170.00	325.00	
1855S	879,675	80.00	135.00	
1856	329,878	80.00	135.00	
1856O	2,250	775.00	1,225.00	
1856S	1,189,750	80.00	130.00	
1857	439,375	85.00	135.00	
1857O	30,000	175.00	285.00	
1857S	970,500	80.00	130.00	
1858	211,714	80.00	150.00	$2,700.00
1858O	35,250	175.00	265.00	
1858S	846,710	80.00	120.00	
1859	43,597	147.50	285.00	2,200.00
1859O	9,100	215.00	315.00	
1859S	636,445	85.00	150.00	
1860	577,670	75.00	125.00	1,900.00
1860O	6,600	350.00	650.00	
1860S	544,950	80.00	135.00	
1861	2,976,453	80.00	130.00	1,900.00

DOUBLE EAGLES

	Quan. Minted	V. Fine	Unc.	Proof
1861O	5,000	$400.00	$625.00	
1861S	768,000	80.00	130.00	
1861—A.C. Paquet Rev	(Ex. Rare)			
1861S—A.C. Paquet Rev. (Tall Letters)	(Ex. Rare)			
1862	92,133	110.00	175.00	$1,900.00
1862S	854,173	87.50	145.00	
1863	142,790	95.00	145.00	1,900.00
1863S	966,570	85.00	150.00	
1864	204,285	100.00	175.00	1,900.00
1864S	793,660	85.00	140.00	
1865	(25) 351,200	100.00	175.00	1,900.00
1865S	1,042,500	80.00	130.00	
1866S		375.00	725.00	

MOTTO ABOVE EAGLE

		V. Fine	Unc.	Proof
1866	(30) 698,775	85.00	140.00	1,850.00
1866S	842,500	85.00	140.00	
1867	(50) 251,065	87.50	140.00	1,850.00
1867S	920,750	85.00	130.00	
1868	(25) 98,600	92.50	155.00	1,950.00
1868S	837,500	75.00	115.00	
1869	(25) 175,155	85.00	150.00	1,850.00
1869S	686,750	77.50	110.00	
1870	(35) 155,185	95.00	155.00	1,850.00
1870CC	3,789	3,000.00	6,000.00	
1870S	982,000	70.00	110.00	
1871	(30) 80,150	110.00	180.00	1,850.00
1871CC	14,687	190.00	350.00	
1871S	928,000	67.50	110.00	
1872	(30) 251,880	90.00	140.00	1,850.00
1872CC	29,650	130.00	280.00	
1872S	780,000	65.00	115.00	
1873 (Closed 3) All Kinds	(25) 1,709,825	115.00	500.00	1,950.00
1873 (Open 3)		65.00	95.00	
1873CC (Closed 3)	22,410	155.00	260.00	
1873S	1,040,600	67.50	95.00	
1874	(20) 366,800	75.00	100.00	1,850.00
1874CC	115,085	100.00	150.00	
1874S	1,214,000	65.00	100.00	
1875	(20) 295,740	75.00	115.00	1,450.00

DOUBLE EAGLES

	Quan. Minted	V. Fine	Unc.	Proof
1875CC	111,151	$ 90.00	$150.00	
1875S	1,230,000	65.00	105.00	
1876	(45) 583,905	65.00	95.00	$1,800.00
1876CC	138,441	85.00	135.00	
1876S	1,597,000	65.00	110.00	

TWENTY DOLLARS

	Quan. Minted	V. Fine	Unc.	Proof
1877	(20) 397,670	62.50	100.00	1,900.00
1877CC	42,565	95.00	170.00	
1877S	1,735,000	65.00	95.00	
1878	(20) 543,645	65.00	95.00	1,850.00
1878CC	13,180	115.00	225.00	
1878S	1,739,000	65.00	95.00	
1879	(30) 207,630	75.00	125.00	1,850.00
1879CC	10,708	135.00	265.00	
1879O	2,325	300.00	600.00	
1879S	1,223,800	62.50	95.00	
1880	(36) 51,456	80.00	125.00	1,850.00
1880S	836,000	60.00	95.00	
1881	(40) 2,260	275.00	500.00	1,950.00
1881S	727,000	60.00	95.00	
1882	(40) 630	400.00	1,000.00	1,975.00
1882CC	39,140	90.00	160.00	
1882S	1,125,000	57.50	90.00	
1883 Proofs Only	(40) 40			5,500.00
1883CC	59,962	82.50	150.00	
1883S	1,189,000	55.00	95.00	
1884 Proofs Only	(71) 71			5,000.00
1884CC	81,139	85.00	155.00	
1884S	916,000	60.00	90.00	
1885	(77) 828	400.00	800.00	2,500.00
1885CC	9,450	145.00	250.00	
1885S	683,500	55.00	85.00	
1886	(106) 1,106	350.00	750.00	2,500.00
1887 Proofs Only	(121) 121			3,500.00
1887S	283,000	57.50	95.00	
1888	(102) 226,266	57.50	95.00	2,500.00
1888S	859,600	57.50	85.00	
1889	(41) 44,111	85.00	130.00	2,200.00
1889CC	30,945	95.00	175.00	
1889S	774,700	55.00	80.00	
1890	(55) 75,995	70.00	130.00	2,200.00

DOUBLE EAGLES

	Quan. Minted	V. Fine	Unc.	Proof
1890CC	91,209	$ 85.00	$150.00	
1890S	802,750	55.00	85.00	
1891	(52) 1,442	200.00	400.00	$2,000.00
1891CC	5,000	150.00	300.00	
1891S	1,288,125	55.00	85.00	
1892	(93) 4,523	150.00	275.00	1,900.00
1892CC	27,265	105.00	175.00	
1892S	930,150	55.00	85.00	
1893	(59) 344,339	80.00	115.00	1,700.00
1893CC	18,402	115.00	200.00	
1893S	996,175	55.00	85.00	
1894	(50) 1,368,990	55.00	85.00	1,800.00
1894S	1,048,550	55.00	85.00	
1895	(51) 1,114,656	55.00	90.00	1,800.00
1895S	1,143,500	55.00	85.00	
1896	(128) 792,663	55.00	85.00	1,500.00
1896S	1,403,925	55.00	85.00	
1897	(76) 1,383,261	55.00	85.00	1,500.00
1897S	1,470,250	55.00	85.00	
1898	(75) 170,470	65.00	110.00	1,500.00
1898S	2,575,175	55.00	85.00	
1899	(84) 1,669,384	55.00	85.00	1,600.00
1899S	2,010,300	55.00	85.00	
1900	(124) 1,874,584	55.00	85.00	1,600.00
1900S	2,459,500	55.00	85.00	
1901	(96) 111,526	80.00	125.00	1,500.00
1901S	1,596,000	55.00	85.00	
1902	(114) 31,254	115.00	180.00	1,500.00
1902S	1,753,625	55.00	85.00	
1903	(158) 287,428	72.50	105.00	1,600.00
1903S	954,000	55.00	85.00	
1904	(98) 6,256,797	55.00	85.00	1,600.00
1904S	5,134,175	55.00	85.00	
1905	(92) 59,011	77.50	130.00	1,800.00
1905S	1,813,000	55.00	85.00	
1906	(94) 69,690	77.50	125.00	1,800.00
1906D	620,250	60.00	95.00	
1906S	2,065,750	60.00	95.00	
1907	(78) 1,451,864	55.00	85.00	1,800.00
1907D	842,250	55.00	85.00	
1907S	2,165,800	55.00	85.00	

SAINT-GAUDENS TYPE

A few experimental pieces were struck having an extremely high relief. They are easily distinguished from the ones issued later for general circulation, which also have a very high relief.

The field of the rare experimental pieces is excessively concave and connects directly with the edge without any border, giving it a sharp knife-like appearance; Liberty's skirt shows two folds on the side of her right leg; the Capitol building in the background at left is very small; the sun, on the reverse side, has 14 rays as opposed to the regular high relief coins that have only 13 rays extending from the sun.

11,250 high relief pieces were struck for general circulation. The relief is somewhat lower but both have the date 1907 in Roman numerals. Flat-relief double eagles were issued later in 1907 with Arabic numerals.

DOUBLE EAGLES

	Quan. Minted	Ex. Fine	Unc.	Proof
1907 Ex. High Relief plain edge (Unique)........................				———
1907 Ex. High Relief Lettered Edge — New York Sale, 1961..................................			$18,250.00	

Ex. Fine — Drapery lines on chest visible. Wear on right breast, knee and below. Eagle's feathers on breast and right wing are bold.

	Quan. Minted	Ex. Fine	Unc.	Proof
1907 High Relief Roman Numerals (MCMVII) Wire Rim - All Kinds.	11,250	$550.00	$850.00	$2,500.00
1907 Same High Relief Flat Rim...........		550.00	850.00	2,500.00

Arabic
Numerals

No
Motto

	Quan. Minted	Ex. Fine	Unc.	Proof
1907 Large Letters on Edge (Proof only) Unique...............				———
1907 Small Letters on Edge All Kinds....................361,667		87.50	115.00	
1908............................4,271,551		67.50	87.50	
1908D............................663,750		67.50	92.50	

With
Motto
IN GOD
WE TRUST

←⟞⟞

Matte
Proof

	Quan. Minted	Ex. Fine	Unc.	Proof
1908.......................(101) 156,359		67.50	87.50	1,600.00

[187]

DOUBLE EAGLES

	Quan. Minted	Ex. Fine	Unc.	Matte Proof
1908D	349,500	$ 70.00	$ 90.00	
1908S	22,000	140.00	250.00	
1909 over 8		115.00	165.00	
1909 All Kinds	(67) 161,282	85.00	125.00	$2,000.00
1909D	52,500	95.00	140.00	
1909S	2,774,925	70.00	85.00	
1910	(167) 482,167	65.00	82.50	1,900.00
1910D	429,000	70.00	90.00	
1910S	2,128,250	65.00	80.00	
1911	(100) 197,350	75.00	85.00	1,900.00
1911D	846,500	70.00	80.00	
1911S	775,750	67.50	90.00	
1912	(74) 149,824	82.50	100.00	1,900.00
1913	(58) 168,838	70.00	87.50	1,900.00
1913D	393,500	70.00	90.00	
1913S	34,000	110.00	180.00	
1914	(70) 95,320	80.00	110.00	1,900.00
1914D	453,000	77.50	90.00	
1914S	1,498,000	75.00	95.00	
1915	(50) 152,050	75.00	95.00	1,900.00
1915S	567,500	75.00	95.00	
1916S	796,000	100.00	130.00	
1920	228,250	70.00	85.00	
1920S	558,000	325.00	700.00	
1921	528,500	750.00	1,000.00	
1922	1,375,500	65.00	85.00	
1922S	2,658,000	150.00	225.00	
1923	566,000	65.00	85.00	
1923D	1,702,000	65.00	80.00	
1924	4,323,500	65.00	80.00	
1924D	3,049,500	115.00	140.00	
1924S	2,927,500	225.00	310.00	
1925	2,831,750	65.00	80.00	
1925D	2,938,500	210.00	450.00	
1925S	3,776,500	155.00	235.00	
1926	816,750	65.00	80.00	
1926D	481,000	325.00	500.00	
1926S	2,041,500	250.00	375.00	
1927	2,946,750	65.00	85.00	
1927D	180,000	1,250.00	2,500.00	
1927S	3,107,000	375.00	700.00	
1928	8,816,000	60.00	80.00	
1929	1,779,750	400.00	800.00	
1930S	74,000	575.00	1,300.00	
1931	2,938,250	625.00	1,300.00	
1931D	106,500	700.00	1,400.00	
1932	1,101,750	575.00	1,300.00	

1933 None in circulation.

COMMEMORATIVE
COINS

Commemorative coins have been popular since the days of the Greeks and Romans. In the beginning they served to record and honor important events and in the absence of newspapers they proved highly useful in passing along news of the day.

Many modern nations have issued commemorative coins and such pieces are highly esteemed by collectors. Yet no nation has surpassed our own country when it comes to commemorative coins and in this we have reason to be proud.

The unique position occupied by commemoratives in United States coinage is largely due to the fact that with few exceptions they are the only coins that have a real historical significance. The progress and advance of people in the New World are presented in an interesting and instructive manner on the commemorative issues. Such a record of facts artistically presented on our gold and silver memorial issues appeals strongly to the collector who favors the historical side of numismatics. It is the historical features of the commemoratives, in fact, which create interest among many people who would otherwise have little interest in coins.

Commemorative issues are considered for coinage by two committees of Congress — The Committee on Banking and Currency of the Senate, and the Committee on Coinage, Weights and Measures of the House. Congress is guided to a great extent by the reports of these committees when passing upon bills authorizing commemorative coins.

These special coins are usually issued either to commemorate events or to help pay for monuments or celebrations that commemorate historical persons, places or things. The commemorative coins are offered in most instances by a commission in charge of the event to be commemorated, and sold at a price in advance of the face value of the piece.

During a half century over fifty different types of commemorative coins have been issued in the United States. A complete type set of commemorative half dollars consists of forty-eight pieces. The addition of mint mark varieties makes a total of 142 coins in the series.

No commemorative coins were struck from 1940 to 1945, and none since 1954.

Unless otherwise stated, the coinage figures given represent the total outstanding coinage. In many cases, larger quantities were minted but were not all sold. The unsold coins were usually returned to the mint and melted, although some were placed in circulation at face value.

Note: The Commemorative section following is arranged alphabetically.

ISABELLA QUARTER DOLLAR

In 1893 the Board of Lady Managers of the Columbian Exposition petitioned for a souvenir quarter-dollar. Authority was granted March 3, 1893. The coin known as the Isabella quarter was designed by C. E. Barber. These souvenir quarters were sold for $1.00. The obverse has the crowned bust of Queen Isabella of Spain. The kneeling female on the reverse with distaff and spindle is emblematic of woman's industry.

		Quan. Minted	Ex. Fine	Unc.
1893	Columbian Exposition, Chicago	24,214	$45.00	$75.00

LAFAYETTE DOLLAR

The heads of Washington and Lafayette appear on this commemorative issue, which was the first commemorative coin of one dollar denomination, and the first authorized United States coin to bear a portrait of one of our presidents. The dies were prepared by C. E. Barber. The statue on the reverse is similar to the monument of General Lafayette which was erected in Paris as a gift of the American people. The coins were sold by the Lafayette Memorial Commission for $2.00 each.

1900	Lafayette Dollar	36,026	55.00	100.00

ALABAMA CENTENNIAL

The Alabama half dollars were authorized in 1920 for the centennial which was celebrated in 1919, but they were not struck until 1921. The coins, designed by Laura Gardin Fraser, were offered first during President Harding's visit to Birmingham, October 26, 1921. The St. Andrews cross, an emblem on the state flag, appears on a part of the issue between the figures 22 indicating the twenty-second state of the Union. The obverse has busts of W. W. Bibb, first governor of Alabama, and T. E. Kilby, governor at the time of the centennial. This is the first instance of the use of a living person's portrait on a United States coin.

2x2 in field

		Quan. Minted	Ex. Fine	Unc.
1921	Alabama Centennial, with 2 x 2 in field of obverse	6,006	$40.00	$70.00
1921	Alabama Centennial, no 2 x 2	59,038	35.00	50.00

ALBANY, NEW YORK CHARTER

The two hundred and fiftieth anniversary of the granting of a charter to the city of Albany was the occasion for a commemorative half dollar. The reverse design shows Governor Dongan, Peter Schuyler and Robert Livingston. The obverse has a beaver which is gnawing on a maple branch. Gertrude K. Lathrop of Albany was the designer.

1936	Albany, New York	17,671	25.00	50.00

BATTLE OF ANTIETAM

A souvenir half dollar was designed by William Marks Simpson and struck in 1937 to commemorate the seventy-fifth anniversary of the famous Civil War battle over possession of Burnside Bridge. The opposing generals McClellan and Lee are featured on the obverse while the Burnside Bridge is shown on the reverse. The Battle of Antietam was one of the bloodiest single-day battles of the war. Approximately 25,000 men were killed during the fighting which occurred September 17, 1862.

1937	Battle of Antietam 1862-1937	18,028	30.00	90.00

ARKANSAS CENTENNIAL

This souvenir issue marked the one hundredth anniversary of the admission of Arkansas into the Union. Edward Everett Burr designed the piece and models were prepared by Emily Bates of Arkansas. Although 1936 was the centennial year the first of several issues was brought out in 1935 from all three mints. During 1936 a new design was authorized by Congress. The late Senator Joseph T. Robinson consented to have his portrait placed on the obverse side of the coins which were struck in January 1937 at the Philadelphia Mint. The 1937 and 1938 issues were the same as those of 1935 except for the dates. They were sold by the distributors at $8.75 per set of three coins. The obverse shows accolated heads of an Indian chief of 1836 and an American girl of 1936.

		Quan. Minted		Unc.
1935	Arkansas Centennial	13,012		$ 9.00
1935D	Same type D mint	5,505		10.00
1935S	Same type S mint	5,506		10.00
1936	Arkansas Centennial, same as 1935 — date 1936 on rev	9,660		
1936D	Same type D mint	9,660	Set	35.00
1936S	Same type S mint	9,662		
1937	Arkansas Centennial (same as 1935)	5,505		
1937D	Same type D mint	5,505	Set	37.50
1937S	Same type S mint	5,506		
1938	Arkansas Centennial (same as 1935)	3,156		
1938D	Same type D mint	3,155	Set	67.50
1938S	Same type S mint	3,156		
1939	Arkansas Centennial (same as 1935)	2,104		
1939D	Same type D mint	2,104	Set	315.00
1939S	Same type S mint	2,105		

BAY BRIDGE SAN FRANCISCO-OAKLAND

The opening of the Oakland Bay Bridge was the occasion for a special souvenir fifty-cent piece. The designs were the work of Jacques Schnier, a San Francisco artist. A California grizzly bear dominates the obverse. The famous bridge is shown on the reverse. The coins were struck at the San Francisco Mint in November 1936. The bear depicted was Monarch II.

		Quan. Minted	Ex. Fine	Unc.
1936	San Francisco-Oakland Bay Bridge S mint	71,424	11.00	32.50

COMMEMORATIVE SILVER — Boone

DANIEL BOONE
BICENTENNIAL

This coin, issues for which covered several dates, was struck to commemorate the two hundredth anniversary of the famous frontiersman's birth. The commemorative date, 1934, was removed after the first issue. The change of date to 1935 for the next year's coinage brought about the addition of 1934 above the words PIONEER YEAR. Coinage covered several years similar to the schedule for the Texas issues. The models for this coin were prepared by Augustus Lukeman. The obverse bears a portrait of Daniel Boone. The reverse shows Boone with Chief Black Fish.

		Quan. Minted		Unc.
1934	Daniel Boone Bicentennial	10,007		$13.50
1935	Same type	10,010		12.50
1935D	Same type D mint	5,005		13.50
1935S	Same type S mint	5,005		13.50

1935	Daniel Boone Bicentennial same as 1934 but small 1934 added on reverse	10,008		12.50
1935D	Same type D mint	2,003	Pair	325.00
1935S	Same type S mint	2,004		
1936	Daniel Boone Bicentennial (same as 1934)	12,012		12.50
1936D	Same type D mint	5,005		13.50
1936S	Same type S mint	5,006		13.50
1937	Daniel Boone Bicentennial (same as 1934)	9,810		11.00
1937D	Same type D mint	2,506	Pair	250.00
1937S	Same type S mint	2,506		
1938	Daniel Boone Bicentennial (same as 1934)	2,100		
1938D	Same type D mint	2,100	Set	350.00
1938S	Same type S mint	2,100		

BRIDGEPORT, CONNECTICUT CENTENNIAL

In commemoration of the one hundredth anniversary of the incorporation of the city of Bridgeport a special fifty-cent piece was authorized May 15, 1936. Henry Kreiss designed this coin which somewhat resembles the Connecticut Tercentenary issue. The head of P. T. Barnum, who was Bridgeport's best known citizen, occupies the obverse. An ultra-modernistic eagle dominates the reverse.

	Quan. Minted	Ex. Fine	Unc.
1936 Bridgeport, Conn., Centennial	25,015	$15.00	$35.00

CALIFORNIA DIAMOND JUBILEE

The California half dollar was designed by Jo Mora, a noted California sculptor. The obverse bears a kneeling figure of a forty-niner. The reverse shows a walking grizzly bear, the state emblem. The celebration for which these coins were struck marked the seventy-fifth anniversary of the admission of California into the Union. The jubilee was held in 1925.

	Quan. Minted	Ex. Fine	Unc.
1925S California Diamond Jubilee	86,594	$12.50	$30.00

CINCINNATI MUSICAL CENTER

Although the head of Stephen Foster, "America's Troubadour," dominates the obverse of this special issue the anniversary celebrated bears no relation to him. The coins, designed by Constance Ortmayer of Washington, D. C., were struck to commemorate the fiftieth anniversary in 1936 of Cincinnati as a center of music. The coins were struck at the three mints and were sold only in sets at $7.75, the highest initial cost of a new type.

1936 Cincinnati Musical Center	5,005	
1936D Same type D	5,005 } Set	$275.00
1936S Same type S	5,006	
Single, type coin		100.00

COMM. SILVER — Cleveland, Columbia, S. C., Columbian

CLEVELAND GREAT LAKES EXPOSITION

A special coinage of fifty-cent pieces was authorized in commemoration of the centennial celebration of Cleveland, Ohio on the occasion of the Great Lakes Exposition held there in 1936. The designs were prepared by Brenda Putnam. Although half the coinage was struck in 1937 all were dated 1936. The obverse has a bust of Moses Cleaveland and the reverse displays a map of the Great Lakes region with a compass pointed at Cleveland. Nine Great Lakes cities are marked by stars.

		Quan. Minted	Ex. Fine	Unc.
1936	Cleveland, Great Lakes Exposition	50,030	$5.00	$12.50

COLUMBIA, SOUTH CAROLINA SESQUICENTENNIAL

Souvenir half dollars were authorized to help finance the extensive celebrations marking the sesquicentennial of the founding of Columbia in 1786. A. Wolfe Davidson designed the coin which was struck at all three mints and sold only in sets. The obverse bears the figure of Justice with sword and scales. At the left is the Capitol of 1786 and at the right the Capitol of 1936. A palmetto tree, the state emblem, is the reverse device.

1936	Columbia, S. C., Sesquicentennial	9,007		
1936D	Same type D mint	8,009	Set	85.00
1936S	Same type S mint	8,007		
	Single, type coin			30.00

COLUMBIAN EXPOSITION HALF DOLLAR

The first United States commemorative coin was the Columbian half dollar. C. E. Barber designed the obverse showing the bust of Columbus; and G. T. Morgan designed the reverse having a representation of Columbus' flagship the Santa Maria above two hemispheres. The coins were sold for $1.00 each at the World's Columbian Exposition in Chicago during 1893. A great many remained unsold and a substantial quantity was later released for circulation at face value.

1892	Columbian Exposition, Chicago	950,000	2.75	6.00
1893	Same type	1,550,405	1.50	3.50

CONNECTICUT TERCENTENARY

In commemoration of the three hundredth anniversary of the founding of the Colony of Connecticut a souvenir half dollar was struck. Henry Kreiss designed the coin. The famous "Charter Oak" is the main device on the obverse. According to tradition the Royal Charter was secreted in the tree during the reign of James II who wished to revoke it. The Charter was produced after the king's overthrow in 1688 and the Colony continued under its protection.

	Quan. Minted	Ex. Fine	Unc.
1935 Connecticut Tercentenary	25,018	$27.50	$52.50

DELAWARE TERCENTENARY

The three hundredth anniversary of the landing of the Swedes in Delaware was the occasion for a souvenir issue of half dollars. The colonists landed on a spot which is now Wilmington and established a church which is the oldest Protestant church still used for worship. Their ship "Kalmar Nyckel" is shown on the obverse of the coin and the old Swedes church is on the reverse. Designs were chosen from a competition which was won by Carl L. Schmitz. This coin was authorized in 1936, struck in 1937 and dated 1938 on the obverse and 1936 on the reverse. The anniversary was celebrated in 1938 both in Sweden and America. A two kroner coin was issued in Sweden to commemorate the same event.

1936 Delaware Tercentenary	20,993	22.50	47.50

ELGIN, ILLINOIS CENTENNIAL

The one hundredth anniversary of the founding of Elgin was marked by a special issue of half dollars in 1936. The proceeds were devoted to financing a Pioneer Memorial statue, which is depicted on the reverse of the coin. The year 1673 bears no relation to the event but refers to the year in which Joliet and Marquette entered Illinois Territory. The designs were prepared by Trygve Rovelstad who also designed the Memorial.

1936 Elgin, Illinois, Centennial	20,015	16.00	40.00

COMMEMORATIVE SILVER — Gettysburg, Grant, Hawaiian

BATTLE OF GETTYSBURG

On June 16, 1936 Congress authorized a coinage of fifty-cent pieces in commemoration of the Battle of Gettysburg. The models were prepared by Frank Vittor, a Philadelphia sculptor. Portraits of a Union and a Confederate veteran are shown on the obverse. Two shields representing the Union and Confederate armies separated by a double-bladed fasces are on the reverse.

	Quan. Minted	Ex. Fine	Unc.
1936 Battle of Gettysburg 1863-1938	26,928	$22.50	$50.00

GRANT MEMORIAL

This coin was struck during 1922 as a centenary souvenir of Ulysses S. Grant's birth. A star which appeared on the first issues was later removed, creating a second variety. The star has no particular significance. Laura Gardin Fraser designed both the Grant half dollar and gold dollar. The reverse shows a log cabin in Point Pleasant, Ohio, where Grant lived as a boy.

(Fake stars have flattened spot on reverse.)

		Quan. Minted	Ex. Fine	Unc.
1922	Grant Memorial. Star in obverse field	4,256	75.00	130.00
1922	Same, no star	67,405	9.50	22.50

HAWAIIAN SESQUICENTENNIAL

This small issue was struck to commemorate the 150th anniversary of the rediscovery of the Hawaiian Islands by Captain James Cook in 1778. The design was sketched by Juliette May Fraser of Honolulu and executed by Chester Beach. Captain Cook is shown on the obverse and a native chief on the reverse. The coins were distributed in 1928 and sold for $2.00 each, the highest initial sale price up to that time.

1928 Hawaiian Sesquicentennial	10,008	225.00	425.00
1928 Hawaiian Sesquicentennial — Sandblast Proof Presentation Piece — 50 struck			900.00

HUDSON, NEW YORK SESQUICENTENNIAL

This souvenir half dollar marked the one hundred and fiftieth anniversary of the founding of Hudson, New York, which was named after the explorer Hendrik Hudson. The designs by Chester Beach show Hudson's flagship the "Half Moon" on the obverse and the seal of the City of Hudson on the reverse. Details of the seal include representations of Neptune with trident on a spouting whale and a mermaid blowing a conch shell.

	Quan. Minted	Ex. Fine	Unc.
1935 Hudson, N. Y. Sesquicentennial	10,008	$125.00	$235.00

HUGUENOT-WALLOON TERCENTENARY

Settling of the Huguenots and Walloons in the New World was the occasion commemorated by this issue. New Netherlands, now New York, was founded in 1624 by a group of Dutch colonists. The persons represented on the obverse were not directly concerned with the occasion, however. They are Admiral Coligny and William the Silent. The reverse shows the vessel "Nieu Nederland." G. T. Morgan prepared the models for this coin.

1924 Huguenot-Walloon Tercentenary	142,080	12.50	26.50

IOWA CENTENNIAL

This half dollar, commemorating the one hundredth anniversary of Iowa's statehood, was designed by Adam Pietz of Philadelphia. The obverse shows the Iowa state seal and the reverse has the first stone capitol building at Iowa City. This issue was sold

first to the residents of Iowa and only a small remainder to others. The entire issue was disposed of in a few weeks.

1946 Iowa Centennial	100,057	9.00	18.50

LEXINGTON-CONCORD SESQUICENTENNIAL

The two famous battles fought in 1775 are commemorated on this coin. A statue of the familiar Minute Man is depicted on the obverse, and the old Belfry at Lexington is the reverse device. Chester Beach designed the coin. The famous statue by Daniel Chester French located in Concord was used for the design.

		Quan. Minted	Ex. Fine	Unc.
1925	Lexington-Concord Sesquicentennial	162,013	$6.00	$12.50

LINCOLN-ILLINOIS CENTENNIAL

The obverse was designed by G. T. Morgan and the reverse by J. R. Sinnock. The obverse shows the head of Lincoln taken from the statue by Andrew O'Connor in Springfield, Illinois. The reverse is based on the Illinois State Seal. This coin was authorized to commemorate the one hundredth anniversary of the admission of Illinois into the Union, the first souvenir piece for such an event.

1918	Illinois Centennial	100,058	11.50	22.50

LONG ISLAND TERCENTENARY

This souvenir issue was authorized to commemorate the three hundredth anniversary of the first white settlement on Long Island which was at Jamaica Bay by Dutch colonists. The design was prepared by Howard Kenneth Weinman, son of the sculptor A. A. Weinman, who designed the regular Liberty standing type half dollar. Accolated heads depicting a Dutch settler and an Indian are shown on the obverse, while a Dutch sailing vessel is the reverse device. This was the first issue for which a date was specified (1936) irrespective of the year minted or issued.

1936	Long Island Tercentenary	81,826	8.00	17.50

COMMEMORATIVE SILVER — Lynchburg, Maine, Maryland

LYNCHBURG, VIRGINIA SESQUICENTENNIAL

The issuance of a charter to the city of Lynchburg in 1786 was commemorated in 1936 by a special coinage of half dollars. The models for the coin were prepared by Charles Keck. The obverse bears a portrait of Senator Carter Glass, a native of Lynchburg and former Secretary of the Treasury, who objected to the idea of using portraits of living men on coins. Despite his protests his likeness was incorporated on the coin. The reverse shows Liberty standing, with the old Lynchburg courthouse in the background.

	Quan. Minted	Ex. Fine	Unc.
1936 Lynchburg, Va., Sesquicentennial	20,013	$15.00	$37.50

MAINE CENTENNIAL

Congress authorized the Maine Centennial half dollar May 10, 1920, to be sold at the Centennial celebration at Portland. They were received too late for this event and were sold by the state Treasurer until all were sold. Anthony de Francisci modeled this coin according to specifications furnished him. The latin word DIRIGO means: I direct. The obverse device is the arms of the state of Maine.

1920 Maine Centennial	50,028	12.50	27.50

MARYLAND TERCENTENARY

The three hundredth anniversary of the founding of the Maryland Colony by Cecil Calvert (known as Lord Baltimore) was the occasion for this special coin. The profits from the sale of this issue were used to finance the celebration in Baltimore during 1934. Hans Schuler designed the coin which shows the facing head of Lord Baltimore on the obverse and the arms of Maryland on the reverse, reminiscent of the Maryland colonial pieces.

1934 Maryland Tercentenary	25,015	14.00	35.00

MISSOURI CENTENNIAL

The one hundredth anniversary of the admission of Missouri to the Union was celebrated at Sedalia during August, 1921. To mark the occasion Congress authorized the coinage of a fifty-cent piece. Robert Aitken designed the piece which shows the bust of a frontiersman on the obverse, and another frontiersman and Indian on the reverse. The first coins struck show 2★4 incused, indicating that Missouri was the twenty-fourth star in the flag. The type without the star was struck later, but was the first to be sold.

2★4 in field

		Quan. Minted	Ex. Fine	Unc.
1921	Missouri Centennial 2★4 in field of obverse	5,000	$80.00	$125.00
1921	Missouri Centennial, no 2★4	15,428	75.00	100.00

MONROE DOCTRINE CENTENNIAL

The motion picture industry promoted this issue in conjunction with a motion picture exposition in June 1923. The obverse shows the heads of James Monroe and John Quincy Adams who were identified with the Monroe Doctrine. The Western Hemisphere is portrayed on the reverse by two female figures. Chester Beach prepared the models for this coin.

1923S Monroe Doctrine Centennial	274,077	7.50	15.00

NEW ROCHELLE, NEW YORK

To observe the founding of New Rochelle in 1688 by French Huguenots, a special half dollar was issued in 1938. The title to the land which the Huguenots purchased from John Pell provided that a fattened calf be given away every year on June 20th. This will explain the appearance of the

COMMEMORATIVE SILVER — Norfolk, Oregon

calf and figure representing John Pell on the obverse of the coin. The fleur-de-lis which is shown on the reverse is adopted from the Seal of the city. Both sides of the coin were designed by Gertrude K. Lathrop.

		Quan. Minted	Ex. Fine	Unc.
1938	New Rochelle, N. Y. 1688-1938	15,266	$30.00	$67.50

NORFOLK, VIRGINIA BICENTENNIAL

To provide funds for the celebration of Norfolk's anniversary of its growth from a township in 1682 to a royal borough in 1736, Congress first passed a law for the striking of medals. The proponents, however, being dissatisfied finally succeeded in winning authority for commemorative half dollars. William Marks Simpson and his wife Marjorie Emory Simpson designed the piece. The obverse shows the Seal of the City of Norfolk with a three-masted ship as the central device. The reverse features the Royal Mace of Norfolk which had been presented by Lieutenant Governor Dinwiddie in 1753.

1936	Norfolk, Va., Bicentennial	16,936	27.50	57.50

OREGON TRAIL MEMORIAL

This memorial coin was struck in commemoration of the Oregon trail and in memory of the pioneers many of whom lie buried along the famous 2,000 mile highway of history. James Earle Fraser and his wife, Laura Gardin Fraser, prepared the designs. The original issue was struck at Philadelphia and San Francisco in 1926. The coin was reissued in 1928 (released in 1933), 1933, 1934, 1936, and 1938. The 1933 half dollar was the first commemorative coin struck at the Denver Mint.

1926	Oregon Trail Memorial	47,955	3.00	12.50
1926S	Same type, S mint	83,055	3.00	12.50
1928	Oregon Trail Memorial (same as 1926)	6,028		15.00
1933D	Oregon Trail Memorial, same type, D mint	5,008		20.00
1934D	Oregon Trail Memorial, same type, D mint	7,006		12.50
1936	Oregon Trail Memorial, (same as 1926)	10,006		12.50
1936S	Same type S mint	5,006		15.00
1937D	Oregon Trail Memorial, D mint (same as 1926)	12,008		12.50
1938	Oregon Trail Memorial (same as 1926)	6,006		
1938D	Same type D mint	6,005	Set	37.50
1938S	Same type S mint	6,006		
1939	Oregon Trail (same as 1926)	3,004		
1939D	Same type D mint	3,004	Set	100.00
1939S	Same type S mint	3,005		

PANAMA-PACIFIC EXPOSITION

This half dollar was designed by C. E. Barber. The exposition held in San Francisco in 1915 celebrated the opening of the Panama Canal. The coins were struck at the San Francisco Mint and were sold at $1.00 each during the exposition. The Panama-Pacific coins have the distinction of being the first commemorative coins to carry the motto. IN GOD WE TRUST appears above the eagle. A representation of Columbia with the golden gate in the background is the principal feature of the obverse.

	Quan. Minted	Ex. Fine	Unc.
1915S Panama-Pacific Exposition	27,134	$45.00	$80.00

PILGRIM TERCENTENARY

To commemorate the landing of the Pilgrims at Plymouth, Massachusetts in 1620, Congress authorized a special half dollar May 12, 1920. Cyrus E. Dallin, a Boston sculptor, executed the designs furnished him by the Commission. The obverse has a portrait of Governor Bradford. The reverse shows the "Mayflower." The first issue had no date on the obverse. The coins struck in 1921 show that date in addition to 1620-1920. There was a large coinage of both issues and not all were sold. A total of 148,000 were returned to the mint and melted.

1920 Pilgrim Tercentenary	152,112	4.50	10.00

1921 Same type	20,053	9.00	20.00

RHODE ISLAND, TERCENTENARY PROVIDENCE

The three hundredth anniversary of Roger Williams' founding of Providence was the occasion for this special half dollar in 1935. The designs were the work of Arthur Graham Carey and John Howard Benson. The obverse shows Roger Williams in a canoe being welcomed by an Indian. The reverse has the anchor of Hope with a shield and mantling in the background. Although the founding of Providence was being celebrated, no mention of the city is to be found on the coin.

		Quan. Minted	Ex. Fine	Unc.
1936	Rhode Island Tercentenary	20,013		
1936D	Same type D mint	15,010 } Set		$47.50
1936S	Same type S mint	15,011		
	Single, Type Coin		$7.00	17.00

ROANOKE ISLAND, NORTH CAROLINA

A celebration was held in Old Fort Raleigh in 1937 to commemorate the three hundred and fiftieth anniversary of Sir Walter Raleigh's "Lost Colony" and the birth of Virginia Dare, the first white child born on the American Continent. A special half dollar was minted for the occasion which was designed by William Marks Simpson of Baltimore. The obverse bears a portrait of Sir Walter Raleigh and the reverse has a figure representing Eleanor Dare holding the child Virginia Dare.

1937	Roanoke Island, N. C., 1587-1937	29,030	10.00	27.50

ROBINSON-ARKANSAS CENTENNIAL

A new obverse design for the Arkansas Centennial coin was authorized by the Act of June 26, 1936. Senator Joseph T. Robinson is the subject for the new issue designed by Henry Kreiss. The reverse, designed by Everett Burr, was unchanged. The law specified a change in the reverse, because of the fact that the obverse side is that which bears the date. From a numismatic viewpoint, however, the side which has the portrait is usually considered the obverse. Thus in this instance, the side with the eagle device is considered the reverse.

1936	Arkansas Centennial (Robinson)	25,265	12.50	25.00

COMM. SILVER — San Diego, Sesqui-Centennial, Spanish Trail

SAN DIEGO-CALIFORNIA-PACIFIC EXPOSITION

Congress approved the coinage of souvenir half dollars for the exposition May 3, 1935. Robert Aitken designed the coin which was struck at the San Francisco Mint. The same type with date 1936 was struck at the Denver Mint, under authority of the special Recoinage Act of May 6, 1936, which specified that 180,000 pieces could be recoined with the date 1936 irrespective of the year of issue. The obverse displays a seated female with spear and a bear in the left background. The reverse shows the observation tower and the State of California building at the Exposition.

	Quan. Minted	Ex. Fine	Unc.
1935S San Diego, California-Pacific Exp. S mint...	70,132	$7.00	$17.50
1936D San Diego, California-Pacific Exposition D mint (same as 1935).................	30,092	8.00	20.00

SESQUICENTENNIAL OF AMERICAN INDEPENDENCE

The one hundred and fiftieth anniversary of the signing of the Declaration of Independence was the occasion for an International Fair held in Philadelphia in 1926. To help raise funds for financing the fair special issues of half dollars and quarter-eagles were authorized by Congress. For the first time a portrait of a president appeared on a coin struck during his lifetime. President Coolidge and Washington are depicted on the obverse of the half-dollar. The reverse bears an accurate model of the Liberty Bell. John R. Sinnock, Chief Engraver of the United States mint, designed the sesquicentennial coins. The dies were in very low relief causing much loss of detail in the coin.

	Quan. Minted	Ex. Fine	Unc.
1926 Sesquicentennial of American Independence........................	141,120	7.50	20.00

OLD SPANISH TRAIL

This coin commemorated the four hundredth anniversary of the overland trek of the Cabeza de Vaca Expedition through the gulf states in 1535. L. W. Hoffecker designed the coin models which were prepared by

COMMEMORATIVE SILVER — Stone Mountain, Texas

Edmund J. Senn. The explorer's name literally translated means "head of a cow," therefore this device was chosen for the obverse. The reverse bears a yucca tree and a map showing the Old Spanish Trail.

		Quan. Minted	Ex. Fine	Unc.
1935	Old Spanish Trail 1535-1935	10,008	$100.00	$210.00

STONE MOUNTAIN MEMORIAL

The models for this coin were prepared by Gutzon Borglum. The first coins were struck at Philadelphia January 21, 1925, General Thomas "Stonewall" Jackson's birthday. General Robert E. Lee and Jackson, mounted, are shown on the obverse. The reverse has an eagle and the words MEMORIAL TO THE VALOR OF THE SOLDIER OF THE SOUTH. The funds received from the sale of this large issue of half dollars were devoted to the expense of carving figures of Confederate leaders and soldiers on Stone Mountain in Georgia. The work was never completed.

1925	Stone Mountain Memorial	1,314,709	3.50	6.50

TEXAS CENTENNIAL

This issue commemorated the independence of Texas. The first of several dates was offered in 1934. The later dates were struck at all three mints. The models were prepared by Pompeo Coppini. The reverse shows the kneeling figure of winged Victory, and on each side, medallions with portraits of General Sam Houston and Stephen Austin, founders of the Republic and State of Texas. The large five-pointed star behind the eagle on the obverse carries out the "Lone star" tradition.

1934	Texas Centennial	61,350		14.00
1935	Texas Centennial (same as 1934)	9,994		
1935D	Same type D mint	10,007	Set	35.00
1935S	Same type S mint	10,008		
1936	Texas Centennial (same as 1934)	8,911		
1936D	Same type D mint	9,039	Set	40.00
1936S	Same type S mint	9,064		
1937	Texas Centennial (same as 1934)	6,571		
1937D	Same type D mint	6,605	Set	37.50
1937S	Same type S mint	6,637		
1938	Texas Centennial (same as 1934)	3,780		
1938D	Same type D mint	3,775	Set	82.50
1938S	Same type S mint	3,816		

FORT VANCOUVER CENTENNIAL

Dr. John McLaughlin shown on the obverse of this coin, built Fort Vancouver, on the Columbia River in 1825. The sale of the coins at $1.00 each helped to finance the pageant staged for the celebration. Laura Gardin Fraser prepared the models for this coin, which was minted in San Francisco. The S Mint mark was omitted. The reverse has a pioneer settler in buckskin suit with a musket in his hands. Fort Vancouver is in the background.

	Quan. Minted	Ex. Fine	Unc.
1925 Fort Vancouver Centennial	14,994	$52.50	$95.00

VERMONT SESQUICENTENNIAL

This souvenir issue commemorates the 150th Anniversary of the Battle of Bennington and the Independence of Vermont. Authorized in 1925 it was not coined until 1927. The models were prepared by Charles Keck. The obverse shows the head of Ira Allen, founder of Vermont. The reverse bears a catamount on a pedestal.

1927 Vermont Sesquicentennial (Bennington)	28,142	25.00	50.00

BOOKER T. WASHINGTON MEMORIAL

The great Negro educator was memorialized in this half dollar. Issued from all mints, it received wide distribution from the start. The reverse has the legend FROM SLAVE CABIN TO HALL OF FAME. His log cabin birthplace is shown beneath. Designed by Isaac Scott Hathaway, as was the Washington-Carver half dollar issued under the same authority.

COMM. SILVER — Washington-Carver

		Quan. Minted	Ex. Fine	Unc.
1946	Booker T. Washington	*1,000,546		$ 2.50
1946D	Same type D mint	200,113		3.00
1946S	Same type S mint	500,279		3.00
1947	Same type as 1946	100,017		
1947D	Same type D mint	100,017	Set	15.00
1947S	Same type S mint	100,017		
1948	Same type as 1946	8,005		
1948D	Same type D mint	8,005	Set	25.00
1948S	Same type S mint	8,005		
1949	Same type as 1946	6,004		
1949D	Same type D mint	6,004	Set	27.50
1949S	Same type S mint	6,004		
1950	Same type as 1946	6,004		
1950D	Same type D mint	6,004	Set	27.50
1950S	Same type S mint	512,091		
1951	Same type as 1946	510,082		
1951D	Same type D mint	7,004	Set	25.00
1951S	Same type S mint	7,004		

*Minted; quantity melted unknown.

WASHINGTON-CARVER

Designed by Isaac Scott Hathaway.

1951	Washington-Carver	110,018		
1951D	Same type D mint	10,004	Set	17.50
1951S	Same type S mint	10,004		
1952	Same type as 1951	2,006,292		
1952D	Same type D mint	8,006	Set	27.50
1952S	Same type S mint	8,006		
1953	Same type as 1951	8,003		
1953D	Same type D mint	8,003	Set	27.50
1953S	Same type S mint	108,020		
1954	Same type as 1951	12,006		
1954D	Same type D mint	12,006	Set	20.00
1954S	Same type S mint	122,024		
	Single, Type Coin			2.00

WISCONSIN TERRITORIAL CENTENNIAL

The one hundredth anniversary of the Wisconsin Territorial government was the occasion for a special half dollar issue. The original design was made by David Parsons, a University of Wisconsin student. Benjamin Hawkins, a New York artist, made changes to conform with technical requirements. The obverse has the Territorial Seal, which includes a forearm holding a pickaxe over a mound of lead ore, and the inscription 4th DAY OF JULY ANNO DOMINI 1836. The reverse shows a badger on a log typifying the early fur trade, and the state emblem.

		Quan. Minted	Ex. Fine	Unc.
1936	Wisconsin Centennial...................	25,015	$12.50	$30.00

YORK COUNTY, MAINE TERCENTENARY

A souvenir half dollar was authorized by Congress upon the three hundredth anniversary of the founding of York County, Maine. Brown's Garrison on the Saco River was the site of a town which was settled in 1636. The designs were made by Walter H. Rich of Portland. The reverse design shows a stockade and the obverse has an adaptation of the York County seal. The oversize border inscriptions have been the basis for much adverse criticism.

1936	York County, Maine Centennial..........	25,015	12.00	21.00

COMMEMORATIVE GOLD —
Grant, Lewis & Clark, Louisiana Purchase

GRANT MEMORIAL GOLD DOLLARS

Like the half-dollar commemorative coins the gold dollars were issued first with a star which was removed for the later issues. The designs by Laura Gardin Fraser are the same as for the half-dollar coinage.

		Quan. Minted	Ex. Fine	Unc.
1922	Grant Memorial Dollar with star	5,016	$170.00	$315.00
1922	Grant Memorial Dollar without star	5,000	180.00	350.00

LEWIS AND CLARK EXPOSITION

The Lewis and Clark Centennial Exposition was held in Portland, Oregon in 1905. A souvenir issue of gold dollars was struck to mark the event with the dates 1904 and 1905. The two famous explorers are represented on each side of the coin which was designed by C. E. Barber. A bronze memorial of the Indian guide, Sacagawea, who assisted in the famous expedition was erected in Portland, Oregon and financed by the sale of these coins.

1904	Lewis and Clark Exposition Dollar	10,025	195.00	380.00
1905	Lewis and Clark Exposition Dollar	10,041	195.00	380.00

LOUISIANA PURCHASE EXPOSITION

The first souvenir gold coins were authorized for the Louisiana Purchase Exposition held in St. Louis in 1904. There are two varieties of gold dollars — one with the head of Jefferson who was president when the Louisiana Territory was purchased from France; and the other President William McKinley who sanctioned the Exposition. The reverse is the same for each variety. The designs were by C. E. Barber.

*1903	Louisiana Purchase Jefferson Dollar	17,500	45.00	100.00
*1903	Louisiana Purchase McKinley Dollar	17,500	45.00	100.00

*Proofs exist of each type.

COMMEMORATIVE GOLD — McKinley, Panama-Pacific

McKINLEY MEMORIAL GOLD DOLLARS

The sale of the McKinley dollars aided in paying for a memorial building at Niles, Ohio, the martyred president's birthplace. The obverse showing a profile of McKinley was designed by C. E. Barber and the reverse with the memorial building designed by G. T. Morgan.

		Quan. Minted	Ex. Fine	Unc.
1916	McKinley Memorial Dollar	9,977	$ 45.00	$110.00
1917	McKinley Memorial Dollar	10,000	65.00	180.00

PANAMA-PACIFIC EXPOSITION

Charles Keck designed the gold dollar the obverse of which has the head of a man representing a Panama Canal laborer. Two dolphins encircle **ONE DOLLAR** on the reverse.

1915S	Panama-Pacific Exposition Dollar	15,000	40.00	75.00

The quarter-eagle was the work of Charles E. Barber and George T. Morgan. It was the first commemorative coin of this denomination. The obverse shows Columbia with a caduceus in her left hand seated on a hippocampus typifying the use of the Panama Canal. An American eagle with raised wings is shown on the reverse.

1915S	Panama-Pacific Exposition $2.50	6,749	195.00	350.00

The fifty-dollar gold piece was designed by Robert Aitken and was issued in round and octagonal form. The obverse bears the helmeted head of Minerva; the owl, symbol of wisdom, is on the reverse. The octagonal issue has eight dolphins in the angles on both sides. The devices are smaller on the octagonal variety.

	Quan. Minted	Ex. Fine	Unc.
1915S Panama-Pacific $50 Round.................483			$5,000.00
1915S Panama-Pacific $50 Octagonal..............645			4,000.00

PHILADELPHIA SESQUICENTENNIAL—QUARTER EAGLES

The obverse of this special gold issue has a standing female figure symbolic of Liberty, holding in one hand a scroll representing the Declaration of Independence and in the other the Torch of Freedom. The reverse bears a representation of Independence Hall in Philadelphia. The coin was designed by J. R. Sinnock.

1926   Philadelphia Sesquicentennial $2.50........46,019   40.00   70.00

BIBLIOGRAPHY

Bullowa, David M., The Commemorative Coinage of the U. S., 1938.
Mosher, Stuart, U. S. Commemorative Coins (1892-1939), 1940.
Slabaugh, Arlie., United States Commemorative Coins, 1962.

PRIVATE OR TERRITORIAL GOLD COINS

The words "Private Gold," used with reference to coins struck outside of the United States Mint, are a general term. In the sense that no state or territory had authority to coin money, private gold simply refers to those interesting necessity pieces of various shapes, denominations and degrees of intrinsic worth which were circulated in isolated areas of our country by individuals, assayers, bankers, etc. Some will use the words "Territorial" and "State" to cover certain issues because they were coined and circulated in a Territory or State. While the state of California properly sanctioned the ingots stamped by F. D. Kohler as state assayer, in no instance were any of the gold pieces struck by authority of any of the territorial governments.

The stamped ingots put out by Augustus Humbert, the United States assayer of gold, were not recognized at the United States Mint as an official issue of coins, but simply as ingots, though Humbert placed the value and fineness on the pieces as an official agent of the federal government.

Private coins were circulated in most instances because of a shortage of regular coinage. In the western states particularly, money became so scarce that the very commodity which the pioneers had come so far to acquire was converted into a local medium of exchange.

Ephraim Brasher's New York doubloon of 1787 described on page 40 also falls into this class.

BIBLIOGRAPHY — Private Gold Coinage

Adams, Edgar H., Private Gold Coinage of California.................1913
Adams, Edgar H., Official Premium Lists, Private Territorial Gold.....1909
Griffin, Clarence, The Bechtlers and Bechtler Coinage and Gold
   Mining in North Carolina (1814-1830)............................1929
Lee, Ed. M., California Gold Quarters, Halves and Dollars............1932
Renz, Dr. Russell H., Private Gold Coinage of The United States......1938

TEMPLETON REID
Georgia 1830

Gold pieces were struck by Templeton Reid, a goldsmith and assayer, in Lumpkin County, Georgia, in 1830. The designs and denominations of these coins were well known, but almost nothing has been learned about Templeton Reid. Denominations struck were $2.50, $5.00 and $10.00.

	Fine
1830 $2.50..	
1830 $5.00..	

TEMPLETON REID — GEORGIA

Fine

1830 TEN DOLLARS.................................... ——

(No Date) TEN DOLLARS.............................. ——

TEMPLETON REID
San Francisco, California 1849

The later Templeton Reid issues were made in California in 1849. It is supposed that he moved his coining equipment to California when gold was discovered there. The California issues were in denominations of ten and twenty-five dollars. The twenty-five-dollar issue is unique in design and denomination.

1849 TEN DOLLAR GOLD (Mint Collection Unique)............ ——
1849 TWENTY-FIVE DOLLARS GOLD...................... ——

The only specimen known of this piece was stolen from the Cabinet of the U. S. Mint on August 16, 1858. It was never recovered.

THE BECHTLERS
Rutherford County, N. C. 1830-1852

Two skilled German metallurgists, Christopher Bechtler and his son, August Bechtler, and later Christopher Bechtler, Junior, a nephew of Christopher the elder, operated a "private" mint at Rutherfordton, North Carolina. Rutherford county in which Rutherfordton is located was the principal source of the nation's gold supply from 1790 to 1840. At first only $2.50 and five-dollar pieces were struck. The dollar was first coined in 1832.

The coins minted by the Bechtlers were of only three denominations, but they cover a wide variety of weights and sizes. These variations are due to the fact that some gold contained foreign metals, and to conform exactly with the gold standard, such coins were made heavier.

The one-dollar coins are divided into three sets: 27 grains, 28 grains and 30 grains. The thirty-grain dollar was believed to have been the first struck. The Bechtlers have the distinction of producing the first gold dollar in the United States. The government mint did not release the first regular series until 1849. Christopher Bechtler's books showed that from 1831 to 1840 $2,241,850.50 was coined.

The inscription "Aug. 1, 1834" on one variety of the five-dollar piece has a special significance. The law reducing the weight and value of gold was passed in 1834. The Secretary of the Treasury recommended to the Director of the Mint that the gold coins of the reduced weight bear the date "Aug. 1, 1834." Instead of this, however, a new U. S. Gold design was used (the motto was omitted). Christopher Bechtler evidently acted on the official recommendation to avoid any difficulty with Treasury authorities.

CHRISTOPHER BECHTLER

	Fine	Unc.
ONE DOLLAR CAROLINA, 28 gr. N reversed	$50.00	$100.00

	Fine	Unc.
$2.50 CAROLINA, 67 gr. 21 carats	$200.00	$325.00

ONE DOLLAR N. CAROLINA,
28 gr., without star.....225.00   600.00
ONE DOLLAR N. CAROLINA,
28 gr., with star... 95.00   185.00

$2.50 CAROLINA,
70 gr. 20 carats...225.00   450.00

ONE DOLLAR N. CAROLINA,
30 gr.............100.00   200.00

$2.50 GEORGIA,
64 gr. 22 carats....175.00   375.00
$2.50 GEORGIA, 64 gr.
22 carats—even 22.450.00   900.00

THE BECHTLERS

Fine   Unc.

$2.50 NORTH CAROLINA,
75 gr. 20 carats. RUTHER-
FORD in a circle . $550.00 $950.00
$2.50 NORTH CAROLINA,
without 75 G 420.00   750.00

$2.50 NORTH CAROLINA, 20 carats
on obv. 75 gr. on rev 1,150.00

5 DOLLARS CAROLINA,
RUTHERFORD, 140 gr. 20 carats.
Date August 1, 1834. 200.00   400.00

5 DOLLARS CAROLINA,
134 gr. 21 carats . . . 180.00   360.00

Fine   Unc.

5 DOLLARS GEORGIA,
128 gr. 22 carats,
RUTHERFORD . $185.00 $375.00
5 DOLLARS GEORGIA,
128 gr. 22 carats,
RUTHERF 175.00   350.00

5 DOLLARS, Obv. C. Bechtler,
Rev. A. Bechtler (Unique)
(A.N.A. 1956 Sale E.F.) $5,000.00

5 DOLLARS CAROLINA,
RUTHERF. 140 gr. 20 carats. Date
August 1, 1834 . . . . 190.00   385.00

Without
150 G

5 DOLLARS NORTH CAROLINA, 150 gr. 20 carats . .   500.00   1000.00
5 DOLLARS. Same as last variety without 150 G 1400.00   2000.00

[216]

THE BECHTLERS
AUGUST BECHTLER
1842-1852

	Fine	Unc.
1 DOLLAR CAROLINA,		
27 gr. 21 carats	$60.00	$125.00

	Fine	Unc.
5 DOLLARS CAROLINA,		
128 gr. 22 carats	$140.00	$300.00

5 DOLLARS CAROLINA,		
134 gr. 21 carats	215.00	525.00

5 DOLLARS CAROLINA,		
141 gr. 20 carats	215.00	525.00

CALIFORNIA GOLD
ANONYMOUS GOLD INGOT
Probably the first such piece struck in California

Fine

TEN DOLLARS
San Francisco 1849
(Unique) . . . . _____

NORRIS, GRIEG & NORRIS
San Francisco 1849

Edgar H. Adams considered this piece the first of the California private gold coins. A newspaper account dated May 31, 1849, described a five-dollar gold coin, struck at Benicia City, though with the imprint San Francisco. It mentioned the private stamp of Norris, Grieg and Norris. The initials N. G. and N. were not identified until 1902 when the coins of Augustus Humbert were sold. An uncirculated gold piece of this type was found wrapped in a sheet of paper with the words "From my friends, Norris, Grigg and Norris." The second name was evidently misspelled by Humbert as newspaper accounts had spelled the name Grieg.

NORRIS, GRIEG & NORRIS

1849 HALF EAGLE—Plain Edge
Fine....$325.00   Unc....$900.00
1849 HALF EAGLE—Reeded Edge
Fine....$325.00   Unc..$825.00

A recently discovered specimen is dated 1850, with STOCKTON beneath date.
1850 HALF EAGLE (Unique)
. . . . ———

MEYERS & COMPANY

The exact location of this firm is presently unknown, as is the date of issue. Except for the rounded corners, this ingot appears almost identical to the Moffat issues.

$18.00 Ingot (Unique). . . . . ———

MOFFAT & CO.
San Francisco 1849-1853

The firm of Moffat and Company was perhaps the most important of the California private coiners. Operating for a longer period than any of the others, its issues were never questioned. The assay office they conducted was semi-official in character. The successors to this firm, Curtis, Perry and Ward, later established the United States Branch mint of San Francisco.

In June or July, 1849, Moffat & Co. began to issue small rectangular pieces of gold owing to lack of coin in the locality, in values from $9.43 to $264. The $9.43, $14.25 and $16.00 varieties are the only types known today.

$14.25 Ingot 1849

MOFFAT & CO.

The only specimen known of the $9.43 ingot is in the National Coin Collection. The illustration of the $16.00 ingot is reproduced from a photograph furnished by courtesy of the Smithsonian Institution.

	Fine	Unc.
$9.43 Ingot (Unique)...................................		
$14.25 Ingot (Unique) A.N.A. 1956 sale (Very Fine)......		$9250.00
$16.00 Ingot..	$1200.00	2250.00

The dies for the $10 piece were cut by a Bavarian, Albert Kuner. The words **MOFFAT & CO.** appear on the coronet of Liberty instead of the word **LIBERTY** as in regular United States issues.

	Fine	Unc.
1849 **TEN DOL**	400.00	1,000.00
1849 **TEN D**...	400.00	1,000.00
1849 **FIVE DOL**	160.00	350.00

	Fine	Unc.
1850 **FIVE DOL**	$175.00	$350.00

United States Assay Office
AUGUST HUMBERT
U. S. Assayer 1851

Augustus Humbert, a New York watch-case maker, was appointed United States Assayer, and he placed his name and the government stamp on the ingots of gold issued by Moffat & Co. The assay office was a temporary expedient to accomodate the Californians until the establishment of a permanent branch mint.

The fifty-dollar piece was at first gratefully received by the Californians as they badly needed a medium which would be accepted at the Custom House where gold dust and private gold coins were refused. It was accepted as legal tender on a par with standard U. S. gold coins and was known variously as a slug, quintuple eagle or five-eagle piece. It was officially termed an ingot.

LETTERED EDGE VARIETIES

Fine   Unc.

1851 50 D C 880 THOUS. No 50 on Reverse. Sunk in Edge:
AUGUSTUS HUMBERT UNITED STATES
ASSAYER OF GOLD CALIFORNIA 1851......$1750.00 $5000.00

1851 50 D C Similar to last variety,
   but 50 on Reverse..$1800.00 $5000.00
1851 Similar to last variety,
   but 887 THOUS...$1800.00 $5000.00
1851 50 D C 887 THOUS.
   No 50 on Reverse..$1750.00 $4500.00

Fine   Unc.

1851 50 D C 880 THOUS.
   Rev. Rays from central star.
   (Unique).......... ——— ———

MOFFAT — HUMBERT

REEDED EDGE VARIETIES

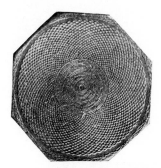

	Fine	Unc.
1851 FIFTY DOLLS 880 THOUS. "Target" Reverse...	$1200.00	$3200.00
1851 FIFTY DOLLS 887 THOUS. "Target" Reverse...	1200.00	3000.00
1852 FIFTY DOLLS. 887 THOUS...................	1150.00	3300.00

The withdrawal of the discredited private coins of $5, $10 and $20 denomination as a result of the new U. S. Assay operations, caused a new turn of affairs for Californians. The new $50 slug was too large a denomination for ordinary transactions.

The fractional currency coins of almost every nation were pressed into service by the Californians, but the supply was too small to help to any extent.

The local businessmen and bankers, however, had so urgently requested Moffat & Co. to relieve the currency situation that the company proceeded in January, 1852, to issue a new ten-dollar piece bearing the stamp **MOFFAT & CO.** to the amount of $300,000.

1852 TEN D. MOFFAT & CO.......................$200.00 $400.00

Government authority for issue of ingots in values of $10 and $20 was finally received at the United States Assay Office early in February, 1852.

The twenty-dollar piece was the first put out by the U. S. Assay Office. The date is struck 1852 over 51.

[221]

MOFFAT — HUMBERT

	Fine	Unc.
1852 TWENTY DOLS. 1852 over 1 . . . . $1500.00		$3500.00

1852 TEN DOLS. 1852 over 1	225.00	450.00
1852 TEN DOLS	175.00	340.00

UNITED STATES ASSAY OFFICE OF GOLD

1852

The firm of Moffat & Co. dissolved and a new reorganized company known as the United States Assay Office of Gold, composed of Curtis, Perry and Ward took over the contract.

1852 FIFTY DOLLS. 887 THOUS	1200.00	3250.00
1852 FIFTY DOLLS. 900 THOUS	1150.00	3150.00

[222]

UNITED STATES ASSAY OFFICE

	Fine	Unc.
1852 TEN DOLS 884 THOUS......................	$200.00	$375.00

| 1853 TEN D. 884 THOUS......................... | 200.00 | 375.00 |

| 1853 TEN D. 900 THOUS......................... | 185.00 | 365.00 |

| 1853 TWENTY D. 884 THOUS..................... | 300.00 | 500.00 |

MASSACHUSETTS AND CALIFORNIA COMPANY
San Francisco 1849

The history of this firm is very obscure. Edgar H. Adams in his book on California private gold coinage mentions an old newspaper article printed in Massachusetts in May, 1849. This article stated that a party had "gone from Northampton, Mass., taking with them a mint, or, rather, all the implements necessary for coining gold and silver, and a competent assayer." They intended to establish a private mint, buy gold and coin it. The plant was to have had a capacity of $10,000 a day, and curiously it was "said to have the sanction of the government."

Henry Chapman, cataloger of the A. C. Nygren collection of pioneer gold coins April 29, 1924, has this to say of the Massachusetts and California Company five-dollar piece of 1849, "organized at Northhampton, Mass., with a capital of $6,000 increased it to $50,000. Josiah Hayden was President; S. S. Wells, Miles G. Moies and others, Directors. It sent Rev. F. P. Tracy and W. Hayden to California, accompanied by coining Machinery." A very fine specimen in silver sold in this sale for $510.00, rated excessively rare.

A San Francisco paper contained an article which mentioned that a five-dollar piece of the Massachusetts and California Company was understood to have been struck in the East. This is very likely as the piece contained copper, while native gold, with a percentage of silver but no copper, was used for nearly all other California private gold coins. There were several patterns prepared, suggesting that an extensive coinage was contemplated. These were struck in silver and copper, including one for a $10.00 coin. The only variety in gold known to Adams is described by him as follows:

Five Dollars 1849

"Obverse, a shield bearing a mounted vaquero in the act of throwing a lasso. Supporters, on the right a stag, and on the left a bear, both rampant. On a ribbon scroll directly underneath, ALTA (upper). Crest, an arm, with the hand holding an arrow. Around the border of the field are thirteen stars, the whole forming a very handsome design. Reverse, in the field a wreath enclosing in two lines, FIVE D. Around the border is the legend, MASSA-CHUSETTS & CALIFORNIA CO. Below is the date, 1849." They are all struck in a low grade gold.

	Fine	Unc.
1849 FIVE D.	$4000.00	——
1849 TEN D (Brass)	——	——

MINERS' BANK
San Francisco 1849

The institution of Wright & Co. exchange brokers located in Portsmouth Square, San Francisco, was known as the Miners' Bank. On August 7, 1849,

MINERS' BANK

they asked state authorities for permission to issue gold coins of $5 and $10 denomination. They wanted to make the coins available for payment of duties, and to afford a circulating medium for business transactions in the area. The request was rejected.

A ten-dollar piece was issued in the autumn of 1849, but the coins were not readily accepted because they were worth less than face value. The firm dissolved January 14, 1850. Unlike most issues, the gold in these coins was alloyed with copper.

	Fine	Unc.
(1849) TEN. D.	$1400.00	$3000.00

J. S. ORMSBY
Sacramento 1849

The initials J. S. O. which appear on certain issues of California privately coined gold pieces represent the firm of J. S. Ormsby & Co. They struck both five- and ten-dollar denominations, and are undated.

There are 31 stars on the $10 piece which coincide with the number of states in the Union upon the admission of California in 1850. This fact would indicate that the coins were minted in 1850 although some authorities state all of them were minted in 1849.

The firm Ormsby & Co. was composed of Dr. J. S. and Major William M. Ormsby. They operated an assay office and mint on K Street in Sacramento. Dr. Ormsby was a member of the California legislature in 1858. Major Ormsby was a Nevada pioneer having once owned a house in Eagle Valley where Carson City is now situated. Ormsby County in Nevada was named for him. He was killed during a fight with Indians near Pyramid Lake in 1860.

	Fine	Unc.
(1849) 5 DOLLS.	———	———

	Fine	Unc.
(1849) 10 DOLLS.	———	———

PACIFIC COMPANY
San Francisco 1849

The origin of the Pacific Co. is very uncertain. All data regarding the firm is based on conjecture.

There was a Virginia firm called the "Pacific Mining and Trading Co." organized in 1849 with 115 members. They sailed, according to a newspaper account, April 7, 1849, from Richmond and it was said to be the first expedition from that state. This may have been the company which produced the gold coins, now very rare, of one-dollar, $2.50, five- and ten-dollar denominations, all dated 1849.

There is also a record of a company of 30 members known as "The Pacific Company," which organized in Boston, Mass., and sailed for California February 20, 1849.

There is no proof that either of these groups was responsible for the gold pieces bearing the title "The Pacific Company."

Edgar H. Adams wrote that he believed that the coins bearing the stamp of the Pacific Company were produced by the coining firm of Broderick and Kohler. The coins were probably handstruck, with the aid of a sledgehammer.

	Fine	Unc.
1849 1 DOLLAR (known in silver and tin).............	———	———
1849 2½ DOLLARS (known in silver only).............	———	$575.00

1849 5 DOLLARS .. ——— ———

1849 10 DOLLARS ——— ———

Fine   Unc.

[228]

F. D. KOHLER
California State Assayer 1850

The State Assay Office was the outgrowth of a meeting of citizens in San Francisco July 22, 1848. A resolution, addressed to Military Governor Richard B. Mason, called for assayers to test the quality of mined gold, and that such gold be converted into ingots and be stamped with the weight and fineness and the name of the person furnishing the gold.

No legislative action was taken, however, until April 12, 1850, when a law was passed providing for an office of State Assayer, melter and refiner of gold.

Section nine of the act reads in part "The state assayer shall regularly number and stamp upon the ingots or bars thus made a true value in dollars and cents, and the correct weight and carat fineness thereof — also the letters 'CAL.,' the date, and his own initials —."

Other provisions of the act specified that the bars were to be accepted in payment of all state and county dues, taxes and assessments, at the value expressed thereon; that when the United States government established a branch mint within the state, the office of State Assayer was to be abolished.

Governor Burnett appointed O. P. Sutton as Director and Frederick D. Kohler as Assayer for the state. Upon accepting this office Mr. Kohler sold his private assaying business to Baldwin and Company.

A branch office was soon established in Sacramento June 28, 1850. John Bigler, afterward governor of California, was appointed as director. Kohler was named assayer at this office also.

The ingots issued ranged from $36.55 to $150. They were also known as "slugs." They were actually worth more than U. S. gold.

The State Assay Office was discontinued at the time the United States Assay Office was established February 1, 1851.

The State Assay Office ingots are excessively rare. The $45.34 ingot of 1850 illustrated herewith is typical.

	Fine
36.55 Sacramento..........	———
40.07 San Francisco........	———
37.31 San Francisco........	———
45.34 San Francisco........	———
50.00 San Francisco........	———
54.09 San Francisco........	———

BLAKE & AGNELL, ASSAYERS
Sacramento 1855

Gorham Blake and —— Agnell conducted an assaying and gold-smelting plant at 52 J Street in Sacramento, in and after 1854. Mr. Agnell died a few days after Christmas in 1855.

1855 $25.00 Ingot
(Unique) ———

BLAKE & AGNELL, ASSAYERS

1855 $23.30 Ingot
(Unique) ———

BLAKE & COMPANY
Sacramento 1855

The twenty-dollar piece shown herewith was undoubtedly made during the last days of December, 1855. The piece illustrated is by far the finer of only two known specimens. There are also known, in copper or brass, trial pieces for a conventional appearing double eagle dated 1856, and bearing the legend "Blake & Co."

1855 $20.00 . . . . ———

DUBOSQ & COMPANY
San Francisco 1850

Theodore Dubosq, senior member of the firm, was a jeweler in Philadelphia. According to a news item in the Philadelphia Evening Bulletin of January 18, 1849, the names of Theodore Dubosq, Sr., Theodore Dubosq, Jr., and Henry A. Dubosq appear on the passenger list of the *Gray Eagle*. The account goes on to say that "Mr. Theodore Dubosq, jeweler, North Second Street, we understand takes out with him the machinery for melting and coining gold, and stamping it with a private mark, so as to establish a currency which will afford the greater convenience and facility for dealing in the raw material."

On May 31, 1849, an item in the "Alta California" published in San Francisco reads, "We learn that Mr. Theodore Dubosq, a jeweler from Philadelphia, who recently arrived in the 'Gray Eagle,' has brought with him the necessary machinery for striking private coins."

Although the five- and ten-dollar gold pieces were circulated generally they are very rare. Dies for trial pieces with T. DUBOSQ 1849 on the obverse were supposedly engraved before going west. These are known to exist only in copper of $2.50 and five-dollar denominations.

DUBOSQ & COMPANY

1849 2½ DOL. Trial Piece (copper).. ———

Fine   Unc.

1849 FIVE DOL. Trial
piece (copper)..... ——— ———

	Fine	Unc.
1850 TEN D.	———	———
1850 FIVE D Similar to TEN D....	———	———

BALDWIN & COMPANY
San Francisco 1850

George C. Baldwin and Thomas S. Holman were in the jewelry business in San Francisco and were known as Baldwin & Co. They were the successors to F. D. Kohler & Co., taking over their machinery and other equipment in May, 1850.

The output of this firm was very large, even exceeding that of the U. S. Assay Office in the first three months of 1851. Baldwin & Co. struck $590,000 worth of gold coins during that period.

The quality of these coins, however, left much to be desired. An assay of specimens conducted by August Humbert disclosed the fact that all of the Baldwin coins had an intrinsic value below their face value.

The *Pacific News* printed an editorial April 9, 1851, headed "The Gold Coin Swindle." The article suggested that the public refuse to accept the coin since Baldwin's establishment imposed a penalty of 5% on a citizen who had presented two Baldwin $20 pieces for redemption in silver.

On April 17 the same newspaper reported that the manufacturers of the Baldwin coin had left in the steamer *Panama* for the Atlantic states.

Two denominations, Five and Ten Dollars, were issued in 1850. The dies were cut by Albert Kuner.

Horseman Type	Fine	Unc.		Fine	Unc.
1850 TEN DOLLARS..$1650.	———		1850 FIVE DOL..$385.00	$750.00

BALDWIN & COMPANY

	Fine	Unc.
1851 TEN D.	$2500.00	$4750.00

The Baldwin & Co. $20 piece was the first of that denomination issued in California.

Baldwin coins were believed to have contained about twenty-thousandths copper alloy.

	Fine	Unc.
1851 TWENTY D..................................	$2650.00	$5250.00

JAMES KING OF WILLIAM & COMPANY
San Francisco 1851

James King of William was one of the first California pioneers. After finding out that he was not physically able to work in the gold fields, he made his way to Sacramento. In the fall of 1849 he went to San Francisco and opened an "Exchange and Deposit Office" in partnership with Jacob R. Snyder. In 1851, the firm's name was changed to James King of William & Company. Three years later, King sold out to Adams & Co., which organization failed in 1855. Later that year, he became editor and publisher of a San Francisco newspaper, and immediately crusaded against the baser elements in the city. For his pains, he was shot down on May 14, 1856, by James Casey, a local politician.

It is believed that the twenty-dollar piece illustrated below was struck in 1851. This specimen is presently the only one known, having been discovered in 1955.

(1851) 20 DOLLARS................................(Unique) ———

SCHULTZ & COMPANY
San Francisco 1851

The firm located in back of Baldwins' establishment conducted a brass foundry beginning in 1851. Judge G. W. Schultz and William T. Garratt were partners in the enterprise.

According to a biographical sketch of Mr. Garratt in "Builders of a Great City," published in San Francisco in 1891, this firm made all the dies for private coinage in San Francisco except those of Moffat & Co. Albert Kuner did the engraving of these dies. Besides the actual manufacture of the dies the firm also coined five-dollar pieces. Machinery was made for coining both five- and ten-dollar pieces but only five-dollar coins are known. The company discontinued operations when the state legislature passed a law placing private coiners on a banking basis.

FIVE DOLLARS 1851

Obverse: Head of Liberty facing left surrounded by thirteen stars. SHULTS & CO. (Misspelled by the engraver with an S instead of Z.) Date 1851 below.

Reverse: Eagle with outstretched wings and shield on its breast, holding arrows and olive branch in its talons. Above, PURE CALIFORNIA GOLD; below, FIVE D.

	Fine	Unc.
1851 FIVE D	$1650.00	$2750.00

DUNBAR & COMPANY
San Francisco 1851

Edward E. Dunbar conducted the California Bank in San Francisco. At the time when Baldwin & Co. coins were being refused, a Dunbar advertisement appeared offering to redeem the coins. Baldwin & Co. ceased to strike coins at about this time and Dunbar supposedly took over the machinery from the former firm. Five dollars was the only denomination issued.

Mr. Dunbar later returned to New York and organized the famous Continental Bank Note Co.

1851 FIVE D	2500.00	5000.00

WASS, MOLITOR & COMPANY
San Francisco 1852-1855

The gold smelting and assaying plant of Wass, Molitor & Co. was composed of two Hungarian patriots Count S. C. Wass and A. P. Molitor. They maintained an excellent laboratory and complete apparatus for analysis and coinage of gold.

The firm at first did not undertake to strike coins, but offered to pay over the proceeds in any coin that was current at the banks.

During the latter part of 1851 the only coins struck in that area were the Augustus Humbert octagonal fifty-dollar pieces, and gold pieces of small denomination were hoarded for custom house payments on foreign shipments. As stated in the history of Moffat & Co. the businessmen of San Francisco petitioned for gold coins of smaller size. Wass, Molitor took the initiative by bringing out on January 8, 1852, their first gold coin, a five-dollar piece.

	Fine	Unc.
1852 FIVE DOLLARS..............................	$215.00	$425.00

The company struck five-, ten-, twenty- and fifty-dollar coins. In 1852 in addition to the five-dollar piece illustrated above they produced a ten-dollar piece similar in design to the five-dollar denomination. The difference is in the reverse legend which reads: SMV (Standard Mint Value) CALIFORNIA GOLD TEN D.

| 1852 TEN D. Large Head............................ | 375.00 | 675.00 |

| 1852 TEN D. Small Head............................ | 900.00 | 1600.00 |

WASS, MOLITOR & COMPANY

No pieces were coined in 1853 or 1854, but they brought out the twenty-dollar and fifty-dollar pieces in 1855. A considerable number of the fifty-dollar coins were made. At one time they were produced at the rate of $38,000 a day. There was a ten-dollar piece issued in 1855 also, with a somewhat different design of the Liberty head.

	Fine	Unc.
1855 TEN D..	$ 275.00	$ 500.00

| 1855 TWENTY DOL. Large Head.................. | 2200.00 | 4100.00 |

| 1855 TWENTY DOL. Small Head.................. | 750.00 | 1400.00 |

WASS, MOLITOR & COMPANY

	Fine	Unc.
1855 50 DOLLARS	$2450.00	$8000.00

KELLOGG & COMPANY
San Francisco 1854-1855

John G. Kellogg came to San Francisco October 12, 1849, from Auburn, New York. At first he was employed by Moffat and Company, and remained with that organization when control passed to Curtis, Perry and Ward. When the United States Assay Office was discontinued December 14, 1853, Mr. Kellogg became associated with G. F. Richter who had been an assayer in the government assay office. These two set up business as Kellogg & Richter December 19, 1853.

When the U. S. Assay Office ceased operations a period ensued during which no private firm was striking gold. The new San Francisco branch mint did not produce coins for some months after Curtis & Perry took the contract for the government. The lack of coin was again keenly felt by business men who petitioned Kellogg & Richter to "supply the vacuum" by issuing private coin.

Their plea was soon answered, for on February 9, 1854, Kellogg & Co. placed their first twenty-dollar piece in circulation.

1854 TWENTY D.	250.00	515.00

The 1855 twenty-dollar piece is similar to that dated 1854. The letters on the reverse side are larger and the arrows longer on one 1854 variety. There are several die varieties of both issues.

KELLOGG & COMPANY

	Fine	Unc.
1855 TWENTY D................................. $	260.00	$550.00

Although the branch mint began operations shortly thereafter, production was very slow. The responsibility for supplying coins therefore fell upon Kellogg & Richter, a job which the publication "Prices Current" characterized as "important . . . in preventing any disarrangement of our financial matters."

The firm dissolved late in 1854 and reorganized as Kellogg & Humbert. The latter partner was Augustus Humbert, for some time identified as U. S. Assayer.

Regardless of the fact that the branch mint was then producing coins, Kellogg & Humbert issued coins in 1855 in a quantity greater than before.

FIFTY DOLLARS 1855

Obverse: Head of Liberty surrounded by thirteen stars. KELLOGG & CO. on the coronet. 1855 beneath. In small letters F. GRUNER at truncation of bust of Liberty. (Ferdinand Gruner.)

Reverse: An eagle similar to that on Octagonal $50 piece, U. S. shield and arrows in left talon. Beak holds a ribbon, 1309 GRS 887 THOUS. inscribed on flowing ribbon. Around border, SAN FRANCISCO CALIFORNIA FIFTY DOLLS. Reeded edge.

1855 FIFTY DOLLS............................... 6500.00   ————

KELLOGG & COMPANY

Edgar H. Adams believed that the above type and denomination designed by Ferdinand Gruner was never issued in quantity for he could find no records of any but the Wass, Molitor & Co. issued during the period referred to. Thirteen specimens are known to exist. The dies are still in existence.

E. R. Kellogg, a son of the pioneer coiner, stated in a letter to Frank Doughty May 6, 1891, that about 60,000 were struck of the $50 Kellogg piece. The letter came to light many years later and was printed in the February 1921 *Numismatist.* Mr. Kellogg, the elder, died April 21, 1886, having dissolved partnership with Augustus Humbert in 1860.

CALIFORNIA SMALL DENOMINATION GOLD PIECES

California Gold quarters, halves and dollars were struck from 1852 to 1882, when the U. S. Government passed a law forbidding private coinage. The impetus of the gold rush created a shortage of "small change," and private companies supplied these coins for the 30-year period in direct proportion to the need.

Shapes were both octagonal and round, and the genuine coins bear one of the following — "cents," "Dol," "Doll" or "Dollar" on the reverse. Obverses are of three main types — Liberty Head, Indian Head and Washington Head. The reverses are also of three main types — Wreath, Beaded Circle and Eagle. Coins with the word "cents" or the Washington Head or the Eagle Reverse are more scarce and command premium prices of about twice regular values.

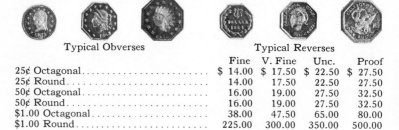

Typical Obverses · · · · · · · · Typical Reverses

	Fine	V. Fine	Unc.	Proof
25¢ Octagonal	$ 14.00	$ 17.50	$ 22.50	$ 27.50
25¢ Round	14.00	17.50	22.50	27.50
50¢ Octagonal	16.00	19.00	27.50	32.50
50¢ Round	16.00	19.00	27.50	32.50
$1.00 Octagonal	38.00	47.50	65.00	80.00
$1.00 Round	225.00	300.00	350.00	500.00

OREGON EXCHANGE COMPANY
Oregon City, 1849
THE BEAVER COINS OF OREGON

The early settlers of the Oregon Territory took over a wild and uninhabited country without the aid or protection of any government. There industries were chiefly agriculture, lumbering and trapping. The beaver was the principal fur-bearing animal and the pelts were used widely in the earliest days as a medium of exchange. Wheat also was of standard value and used for swapping of commodities.

The provisional territory government passed an act December 10, 1845, providing that "treasury drafts, approved orders on solvent merchants and good merchantable wheat at the market value . . . shall be lawful tender for payment of taxes and judgments rendered in the courts. . . ."

Upon the discovery of gold in California there was a great exodus of settlers who joined in the hunt for the precious metal. Soon returning gold seekers offered their gold dust, which became the accepted medium of exchange.

OREGON EXCHANGE COMPANY

As in other western areas of that time the uncertain qualities of the gold and weighing devices tended to irk the tradespeople and petitions were made to the legislature for a standard gold coin issue.

On February 16, 1849, the legislature passed an act providing for a mint and specified five- and ten-dollar gold coins without alloy. Oregon City, the largest city in the territory with a population of about 1000, was designated as the location for the mint. At the time this act was passed Oregon had been brought into the United States as a territory by act of Congress. When the new governor arrived March second, he declared the coinage act unconstitutional.

The public-spirited people, however, continued to work for a convenient medium of exchange and soon took matters into their own hands by starting a private mint. Eight men of affairs whose names were Kilborne, Magruder, Taylor, Abernethy, Willson, Rector, Campbell and Smith set up the Oregon Exchange Company.

Hamilton Campbell was employed to engrave the five-dollar dies. Thomas Powell, a blacksmith, forged the machinery which was said to have been made from old wagon tires and the like. The coins struck were of virgin gold as specified in the original act. Ten-dollar dies were made later, and were of finer design and workmanship.

FIVE DOLLARS 1849

Obverse: Initials of the members of the Oregon Exchange Co. KMTAWRGS· The initial G was an error and was supposed to have been a C for Campbell. Center, a beaver facing right on a log. Below, T. O.—another error which should have read O. T. (Oregon Territory). Date at bottom, 1849.

Reverse: OREGON EXCHANGE CO. In the center, 130 G NATIVE GOLD, 5D.

	Fine	Unc.
1849 5 D	$1500.00	$3300.00

TEN DOLLARS 1849

The ten-dollar dies were engraved by Victor Wallace and were similar to the five-dollar denomination. Errors mentioned in the above description were corrected, but the initials for Abernethy and Willson were eliminated for reasons unknown.

Since the coins contained about eight per cent more gold than was necessary, they were bought up and remelted, causing a great scarcity of these issues. These interesting coins are known as the "Beaver Coins of Oregon."

OREGON EXCHANGE COMPANY

	Fine	Unc.
1849 TEN D......................................	$4500.00	$8000.00

MORMON GOLD PIECES
Salt Lake City, Utah 1849-1860

The first name given to the organized Mormon Territory was the "State of Deseret," the latter word meaning "honey bee." The beehive, which is shown on the reverse of the five-dollar 1860 piece, was a favorite device of the followers of Joseph Smith and Brigham Young. The clasped hands appear on most Mormon coins and exemplify strength in unity. "Holiness to the Lord" was an inscription frequently used.

Brigham Young was the instigator of the coinage system and personally supervised the mint which was housed in a little adobe building in Salt Lake City.

The mint was inaugurated late in 1849 as a public convenience. As in other gold mining sections there was much trouble in payment of small sums in the form of gold dust.

Obverse: Eye of Providence and bishop's mitre. Legend around border, HOLINESS TO THE LORD.

Reverse: Clasped hands in center, 1849 beneath. In circle G.S.L.C.P.G. (Great Salt Lake City Pure Gold.)

1849 TWO AND HALF DO.........................	400.00	825.00

1849 FIVE DOLLARS..............................	325.00	625.00

MORMON GOLD PIECES

	Fine	Unc.
1849 TEN DOLLARS............................	$3000.00	$5500.00

| 1849 TWENTY DOLLARS......................... | 1500.00 | 2250.00 |

The Mormon twenty-dollar piece was the first of that denomination to be coined in this country.

1850 FIVE DOLLARS. 345.00   700.00

FIVE DOLLARS 1860

Obverse: Lion facing left, surrounded by legend in the Mormon alphabet. HOLINESS TO THE LORD. 1860 beneath.

Reverse: Beehive with eagle holding a laurel branch and arrows in its talons. Around border, DESERET ASSAY OFFICE PURE GOLD. Below is 5D.

	Fine	Unc.
1860 5D.........	$700.00	$1500.00

COLORADO GOLD PIECES
Clark Gruber & Co. — Denver 1860-1861

Clark, Gruber and Co. was a well-known private minting firm in Denver, Colo., in the early sixties.

Austin M. and Milton E. Clark, brothers, and E. H. Gruber composed the firm, which organized a banking business in Leavenworth, Kansas, in 1858. As gold dust and nuggets were coming in from the Denver country they decided to establish a bank in Denver also. They had made heavy purchases of gold dust and were obliged to ship it to the states to have it coined into money. This procedure took from three weeks to three months as only stage coaches and pony express were available for transportation. High insurance and shipping rates added greatly to the cost so the idea for establishing a mint in connection with the bank was not long in becoming a reality.

The bank and mint were established in July, 1860. The dies and presses were purchased in Boston and were delivered overland to Denver by ox or mule team from Missouri River points, heavily guarded from Indian attacks.

CLARK & CO. 1860

	Fine	Unc.
1860 2½ D	$ 120.00	$ 275.00
1860 5D	120.00	300.00

CLARK GRUBER & CO. 1860

1860 TEN D	600.00	1500.00

1860 TWENTY D	2250.00	4250.00

CLARK GRUBER & COMPANY

The $2.50 and five-dollar pieces of 1861 follow closely the designs of the 1860 issues. The main difference is found in the legends. The reverse side now has CLARK GRUBER & CO. DENVER, PIKES PEAK is on the coronet of Liberty.

	Fine	Unc.
1861 2½D	$220.00	$ 530.00
1861 FIVE D	110.00	235.00
1861 TEN D	250.00	425.00

	Fine	Unc.
1861 TWENTY D	1450.00	3250.00

JOHN PARSONS & COMPANY
Tarryall Mines — Colorado 1861

Very little is known regarding the mint of John Parsons and Co., although it is reasonably certain that it operated in the South Park of Colorado, near Tarryall, in the summer of 1861.

The coins are undated, but the *Weekly News* of Denver, and the *Miner's Record* issued at Tarryall carried news items in 1861 concerning the J. Parsons and Co. gold coinage.

Although the spelling of the name is correct with the final "s," the omission on the coins was probably owing to a mistake by the engraver.

1860 20 DOLS. Gold Ingot....................................... ———

JOHN PARSONS & COMPANY

Obverse: Quartz stamp mill device in the center, J. PARSON & CO. above ORO below.

Reverse: An eagle with wings outstretched and a shield on its breast. A laurel wreath is held in the left talon, three arrows in the other. PIKES PEAK GOLD in circle above, 2½ D or Five D, below.

	Fine	Unc.
(1861) Undated 2½ D............................	$2850.00	$4000.00
(1861) Undated FIVE D...........................	4500.00	8000.00

J. J. CONWAY & COMPANY
Georgia Gulch — Colorado, 1861

Records show that the Conway Mint operated for a short while in 1861. As in all gold mining areas the value of gold dust caused disagreement among the merchants and the miners. The firm of J. J. Conway & Co. solved this difficulty by bringing out their gold pieces in August, 1861.

A news item about this company appeared in the *Rocky Mountain News*, August 21, 1861, as follows: "There is a mint in Georgia Gulch, conducted by J. J. Conway & Co., jewelers and bankers. Their machinery seems to be as fine as that of Clark, Gruber & Co., and their five- and ten-dollar gold pieces look as nice and rich as Uncle Sam himself could get up."

	Fine	Unc.
(1861) Undated 2½ DOLL'S.......................	2000.00	3750.00
(1861) Undated FIVE DOLLARS...................	2000.00	4250.00
(1861) Undated FIVE DOLLARS, Similar.		
Variety without numeral 5 on reverse...........	———	———

(1861) Undated TEN
DOLLARS... ———

LESHER REFERENDUM DOLLARS

Coined by Joseph Lesher in 1900 and 1901 at Victor, Colorado. Used in trade to some extent, and stocked by various merchants who redeemed them in goods. Coins were numbered and a blank space left at bottom of 1901 issues, in which were stamped names of businessmen who bought them. All are quite rare, many varieties extremely rare.

| | 1900 | 1901 |

	V. Fine	Unc.
1900 First Type, no business name....................	$190.00	$275.00
1900 A.B. Bumstead, with scrolls.......................	175.00	250.00
1900 A.B. Bumstead, no scrolls........................	125.00	225.00
1900 Bank Type (5 known)..............................	400.00	750.00
1901 Imprint Type, no name...........................	175.00	275.00
1901 J. M. Slusher, Cripple Creek, Colo................	160.00	240.00
1901 Sam Cohen, Victor, Colo..........................	285.00	500.00
1901 D. W. Klein & Co., Pueblo, Colo.................	450.00	725.00
1901 George Mullen, Victor, Colo......................	285.00	475.00
1901 Boyd Park, Denver, Colo..........................	180.00	270.00
1901 W. C. Alexander, Salida, Colo....................	340.00	500.00
1901 Goodspeeds & Co., Pikes Peak Ave. (3 known)......	500.00	——
1901 W. F. White, Grand Junction, Colo...............	450.00	——
1901 J.E. Nelson & Co., Holdredge, Nebr. (Only 3 known).	500.00	——

HARD TIME
TOKENS
1834-1844

In addition to the coins issued by the United States government, numismatists include in their collections the Hard Times and Civil War tokens which circulated as money during two periods in this country's history when nearly all the minor coin was hoarded.

The Hard Times tokens were issued in the period 1834-1844 and are the size of the large U. S. cent. They were generally struck in copper and are of two general groups: political tokens whose theme centered around President Jackson's fight against the United States Bank, and those issued by merchants (tradesman's cards). Many different varieties exist. The most common pieces are generally valued at $1.00 good to $4.50 Unc.

CIVIL WAR TOKENS — 1861-1864

Civil War Tokens are generally divided into two groups; tradesmen's tokens, and anonymously issued pieces with political or patriotic themes. They came into existence only because of the scarcity of government coins and disappeared as soon as the bronze coins of 1864 met the public demand for small copper change.

From the outset of the Civil War, government cents were insufficient in number, widely hoarded and worth a premium over all other currencies. As a result of this scarcity of cent pieces, private copper coins were issued by many individuals. Their wide circulation was made possible by the scarcity of copper-nickel cents and the public dislike of fractional paper money.

The tradesmen's tokens were issued by various firms to provide change and advertise the dealers' wares. They usually bore an implied or an explicit promise of redemption in goods or money. The second type were simply unauthorized substitutes for government coins, produced at a profit by private manufacturers and put into general circulation through various agencies.

These tokens are of great variety in composition and design. A number were more or less faithful imitations of the copper-nickel cent. A few of this type have the word "NOT" in very small letters above the words "ONE CENT."

Many pieces, especially of the tradesmen token type, were individual in device and size, representing any caprice of design or slogan that appealed to the maker. Some were political or patriotic in character, carrying the likeness of some military leader such as McClellan or bearing such inscriptions as "Millions for contractors, not one cent for the widows." An estimated 50,000,000 or more of these pieces were issued. Approximately 10,000 different varieties have been recorded.

The legal status of the Civil War Tokens was uncertain. Mint Director Pollock thought they were illegal; however, there was no law prohibiting the issue of tradesmen's tokens or of private coins not in imitation of United States coins. A law was passed on April 22, 1864 prohibiting the issue of any one or two-cent coins, tokens, or devices for use as money, and on June 8 another law was passed which abolished private coinage of every kind.

	Fine	V. Fine	Unc.
Copper or Brass Tokens	$1.25	$ 2.50	$ 4.00
Nickel or German Silver Tokens	2.50	5.00	9.00
White Metal Tokens	3.00	6.00	11.00
Copper-Nickel Tokens	2.50	5.00	9.00
Silver Tokens	7.00	11.00	20.00

CONFEDERATE STATES OF AMERICA
Confederate 1861 Half Dollar

The half dollar struck by the Confederacy was unknown to collectors until 1879. A specimen of the coin and both dies were found in the possession of Dr. B. F. Taylor of New Orleans. Mr. E. Mason, Jr., of Philadelphia purchased Dr. Taylor's specimen and the reverse die and later sold them to J. W. Scott and Company of New York.

CONFEDERATE STATES OF AMERICA — 1861

Five hundred genuine 1861 half dollars from the New Orleans mint were acquired by J. W. Scott and Company. The reverses were planed off and then restamped with the Confederate die. These are known as restrikes. The restrikes have flattened obverses.

According to records only four originals were struck. These were made on a hand press. Original silver half dollar planchets were used, as well as the original obverse die. One of the coins was given to the Secretary of the Confederacy Memminger who passed it on to President Jefferson Davis for his approval. Another was given to Prof. Biddle of the University of Louisiana. Dr. E. Ames of New Orleans received a third specimen, the last being kept by Chief Coiner Taylor, who sold it later as mentioned above.

Lack of bullion prevented the Confederate government from proceeding with any coinage plans that might have been made.

J. W. Scott struck some tokens in white metal using the Confederate reverse die and a special die bearing the inscription
4 ORIGINALS STRUCK BY ORDER OF C. S. A. IN NEW ORLEANS 1861 ******* REV. SAME AS U. S. (FROM ORIGINAL DIE SCOTT)

Confederate Reverse   Scott Obverse

	V. Fine	Unc.
1861 HALF DOL. (Ex. Rare)		
1861 HALF DOL. Restrike	$375.00	$650.00
1861 Scott Token, obverse. Confederate reverse	60.00	100.00

THE CONFEDERATE CENT

An order to make cents for the Confederacy was placed with Mr. Robert Lovett Jr., an engraver and die-sinker of Philadelphia, through a jewelry firm of that city. Fearing arrest by the United States government for giving assistance to the enemy, Mr. Lovett decided against delivering the coins to the Confederate government and hid the coins and dies in his cellar.

The original dies were later purchased by Capt. John W. Haseltine who made restrikes from the dies.

	Proof
1861 Cent Original (copper-nickel) 12 struck	1,500.00
1861 Cent Restrike (copper) 55 struck	800.00
1861 Cent Restrike (gold) 7 struck	2,500.00
1861 Cent Restrike (silver) 12 struck	1,000.00

COINS AND TOKENS OF HAWAII

The first official coins of Hawaii were the copper cents of 1847 issued by King Kamehameha III. The five cent piece of 1881 and the eighth dollar piece of 1883 are patterns. In 1883 Kalakaua I issued silver dimes, quarters, halves and dollars bearing his bust and showing the Hawaiian coat of arms on the reverse. The plantation tokens listed here were all used as small change on the Islands.

Ten Cents 1883

One Cent — 1847

	Quan. Minted	Fine	V. Fine	Ex. Fine	Unc.	Proof
1847 Cent	1,000,000	$ 45.00	$ 65.00	$ 85.00	$130.00	———
1881 Five Cents		———	———	———	550.00	$850.00
1883 Ten Cents	250,000	12.50	17.50	25.00	55.00	200.00
1883 Eighth Dollar (12½¢)		100.00	125.00	200.00	400.00	700.00
1883 Quarter Dollar	500,000	10.00	15.00	20.00	27.50	200.00
1883 Half Dollar	700,000	25.00	35.00	50.00	80.00	200.00
1883 Dollar	500,000	60.00	85.00	110.00	240.00	325.00

HAWAIIAN TOKENS

Thomas Hobron Token —1879   Haiku Plantation — 1882

Wailuku Plantation — 1871   Wailuku Plantation — 1880

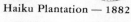

	Fine	Ex. Fine
Waterhouse Token 1862. Bust of Kamehameha IV	$300.00	$500.00
Wailuku Plantation Token 1871	80.00	135.00
Wailuku Plantation Token 1880	100.00	150.00
Thomas Hobron Token 1879	80.00	135.00
Haiku Plantation Token	55.00	85.00
Grove Ranch Plantation Token 1886	125.00	175.00

ALASKA RURAL REHABILITATION CORPORATION
TOKENS OF 1935

These tokens were issued by the U. S. Government for the use of the colonists of the Matanuska Valley Colonization Project to supply them with much needed Federal aid. They were redeemable only at the ARRC stores. The "Bingles", as they were called, were in use only about six months during 1935-1936 after which they were redeemed for regular U. S. money and destroyed. They were issued on a basis of family dependents. Each token is the size of the corresponding U. S. coin with the exception of the one cent piece which is octagonal. The design is the same on both sides of each denomination.

	Quan. Minted	V. Fine	Unc.
1¢ Aluminum	5,000	$12.00	$17.50
5¢ Aluminum	5,000	12.00	17.50
10¢ Aluminum	5,000	12.00	17.50
25¢ Aluminum	3,000	16.00	22.50
50¢ Aluminum	2,500	17.50	35.00
$1.00 Aluminum	2,500	30.00	50.00
$5.00 Brass	1,000	45.00	65.00
$10.00 Brass	1,000	60.00	75.00

PHILIPPINES UNDER SOVEREIGNTY OF THE U.S.

The 1903-19 issues were struck at Philadelphia and San Francisco. 1920 and after were struck at Manila. Because of World War II the 1944-45 coins were minted at Philadelphia, Denver and San Francisco.

Bronze

	Unc.
½ Centavo 1903-08	$ 1.75
1 Centavo 1903-36	1.75

Copper-Nickel

5 Centavos 1903-28	2.00
5 Centavos 1918 Rev. of 20 Centavos (Mule)	60.00

Reduced Size

5 Centavos 1930-35	2.25

Silver

10 Centavos 1903-06	3.00
20 Centavos 1903-06	5.50
50 Centavos 1903-06	9.00
1 Peso 1903-06	15.00

Size Reduced

	Unc.
10 Centavos 1907-35	$ 3.25
20 Centavos 1907-29	4.75
20 Centavos 1928 Rev. of 5 Centavos (Mule)	40.00
50 Centavos 1907-21	8.00
1 Peso 1907-12	13.00

Bronze

1 Centavo 1937-44	.30

Copper-Nickel

5 Centavos 1937-41	1.50

Nickel-Silver

Same Type as Cop.-Nic.

5 Centavos 1944-45	.40

Silver

10 Centavos 1937-45	.20
20 Centavos 1937-45	.75
50 Centavos 1944-45	1.00

PHILIPPINES UNDER SOVEREIGNTY OF THE U. S.

Silver Coins Commemorating the Establishment of the Commonwealth of the Philippines, 1935

Murphy and Quezon Facing Each Other

Unc.

50 Centavos 1936. . . . .$12.50

Gov. Gen. Murphy and Quezon   Roosevelt and Quezon

	Unc.		Unc.
1 Peso 1936. . . . .$25.00.		1 Peso 1936. . . . .$27.50	

PUERTO RICO

The farthest island east of the Greater Antilles in the Atlantic Ocean. Ceded to the United States after the Spanish-American war, it is a self-governing Commonwealth of the United States. Major industry: sugar cultivation and processing. Capital: *San Juan*. Area: 3,435 square miles. Population: 2,210,703.

UNDER SPAIN
ALFONSO XIII
1886-1898

	Quantity Minted	Good	Fine	V F.	Unc.
5 Centavos 1896.	600,000	1.50	3.50	5.00	7.50
10 Centavos 1896.	700,000	9.00	17.00	27.50	35.00
20 Centavos 1895.	967,364	6.00	9.00	15.00	25.00
20 Centavos 1896.	2,382,642	(Very Scarce)			
40 Centavos 1896.	725,002	15.00	25.00	45.00	60.00
1 Peso 1895.	8,500,021	25.00	45.00	60.00	75.00

INDEX

[252]

INDEX — *Continued*

INDEX — *Continued*

INDEX — *Continued*

The following numismatic magazines are obtainable by subscription. They are published monthly or as indicated below:

The Numismatist
Published by the American
Numismatic Association
3520 No. 7th Street
Phoenix 14, Ariz.
(Single Copy 50¢)

Coins Magazine
Iola, Wisconsin
(Single Copy 35¢)

Numismatic News (Every other week)
Iola, Wisconsin
(Single Copy 20¢)

Coin World (Weekly)
Sidney News Building
Sidney, Ohio
(Single Copy 25¢)

Hobbies Magazine
1006 S. Michigan Ave.
Chicago, Ill.
(Has a coin section, Single copy 35¢)

Numismatic Scrapbook Magazine
7320 N. Milwaukee Ave.
Chicago 48, Ill.
(Single Copy 50¢)

COIN FOLDERS

**A Convenient Method
for Housing Your Collection**

Made in two tones of blue . . . printed in black and silver, giving a brilliant "Jewel Case" effect to your coin collection.

Made by WHITMAN   Size Folded 5¾" x 7½"

COMPLETE LIST OF STYLES
UNITED STATES

Large Cent — 1793 to 1825
Large Cent — 1826 to 1857
Indian-Eagle Cents — 1856 to 1909
Lincoln Head Cent — 1909 to 1940
Lincoln Head Cent — Starting 1941
Lincoln Memorial Cent — Starting 1959
Cents — Plain, no printing

Half Dime — 1794 to 1873
Shield Type Nickel — 1866 to 1883
Liberty Head Nickel — 1883 to 1913
Buffalo Nickel — 1913 to 1938
Jefferson Nickel — 1938 to 1961
Jefferson Nickel — Starting 1962
Nickels — Plain, no printing

Bust Type Dime — 1796 to 1837
Liberty Seated Dime — 1837 to 1862
Liberty Seated Dime — 1863 to 1891
Barber Dime — 1892 to 1916
Mercury Head Dime — 1916 to 1945
Roosevelt Dime — Starting 1946
Dimes — Plain, no printing

Liberty Seated Quarter — 1838 to 1865
Liberty Seated Quarter — 1866 to 1891
Barber Quarter — 1892 to 1905
Barber Quarter — 1906 to 1916
Lib. Standing Quarter — 1916 to 1930
Wash. Head Quarter — 1932 to 1945
Wash. Head Quarter — 1946 to 1959
Wash. Head Quarter — Starting 1960
Quarters — Plain, no printing

Lib. Seated Half Dollar — 1839 to 1850
Lib. Seated Half Dollar — 1851 to 1862
Lib. Seated Half Dollar — 1863 to 1873
Lib. Seated Half Dollar — 1873 to 1891
Barber Half Dollar — 1892 to 1903
Barber Half Dollar — 1904 to 1915
Lib. Standing Half Dollar—1916 to 1936
Lib. Standing Half Dollar—1937 to 1947
Ben. Franklin Half Dollar—Starting 1948
Halves — Plain, no printing

Morgan Dollar — 1878 to 1883
Morgan Dollar — 1884 to 1890
Morgan Dollar — 1891 to 1897
Morgan Dollar — 1898 to 1921
Peace Dollar — 1921 to 1935
Dollars — Plain, no printing

MISCELLANEOUS

Half Cent — 1793 to 1857
Silver Three Cent — 1851 to 1873
Two Cent — Nickel Three Cent — 1864 to 1889
Type Coins, Small Denominations
Type Coins, Large Denominations
20th Century Type Coins

CANADA

Large Cents — 1858 to 1920
Small Cents — Starting 1920
Silver Five Cents — 1858 to 1921
Nickels — 1922-1960
Nickels — Starting 1961
Dimes — 1858 to 1936
Dimes — Starting 1937
Quarters — 1858 to 1910
Quarters — 1911 to 1952
Quarters — Starting 1953
Halves — 1870 to 1910
Halves — 1911 to 1936
Halves — 1937-1960
Halves — Starting 1961
Silver Dollars — 1935 to 1957
Silver Dollars — Starting 1958
Quarters — Plain, no printing
Halves — Plain, no printing
Canada Coin Type Collection
Dollars — Plain, no printing

NEWFOUNDLAND

Cents & Half Cents — Newfoundland, New Brunswick, Nova Scotia and Prince Edward Island
Newfoundland 5¢ — 1865 to 1947
N. Brunswick 5-10-20¢ — 1862 to 1864
Newfoundland 10¢ — 1865 to 1947
Newfoundland 20-25¢ — 1865 to 1919
Newfoundland 50¢ — 1870 to 1919
Newfoundland Coin Type Collection

GREAT BRITAIN

Farthings — 1860 to 1901
Farthings — 1902 to 1936
Farthings — 1937 to 1956
Halfpennies — 1860 to 1901
Halfpennies — 1902 to 1936
Halfpennies — Starting 1937
Pennies — 1860 to 1880
Pennies — 1881 to 1901
Pennies — 1902 to 1929
Pennies — Starting 1930
Threepence Silver — 1838 to 1901
Threepence Silver — 1902 to 1945
Threepence Brass — Starting 1937
Sixpence — 1902 to 1936
Sixpence — Starting 1937
Shillings — 1902 to 1936
Shillings — 1937 to 1951
Shillings — Starting 1953

MEXICO

One Centavo — Starting 1905
Five Centavos — 1905 to 1955
Five Centavos — Starting 1954